It's Me: Jesus

David J. Aston

SCAN ME!

Onwards and Upwards Publishers,
Berkeley House,
11 Nightingale Crescent,
West Horsley,
Surrey,
KT24 6PD

www.onwardsandupwards.org

First published in the UK by Onwards and Upwards Publishers (2015).

ISBN: 978-1-910197-25-7

Printed in the UK
by 4edge Limited, Essex

Acknowledgements

Heartfelt thanks to all who have supported and encouraged me:

- Mum and Dad for their support throughout, and with them, friends at church who read and commented on early chapters or full copies – Ian, Tony, Robert, Anna, Matt, Alison, and any others I hope I haven't forgotten. Of these, particularly Matt and Alison, whose comments helped shape the book I presented to the publisher.
- Andy Hawthorne OBE and Fiona Bruce MP, who made time in their busy schedules to read and endorse my book.
- Robin Croxon, who, as literary agent, took me on as an unknowing unknown!
- Luke Jeffery and all at Onwards and Upwards Publishers – ditto, and for their guidance; knowledgeable, sensitive and meticulous editing; and fantastic cover design. They have put so much into this book to make it what it is.

About the Author

David Aston grew up in Lichfield, Staffordshire. He and his brother were taught amongst others by both parents at King Edward VI School. His father was ordained while still a teacher, and later became a prison chaplain.

Having studied Computing Science with German, David moved to Congleton, Cheshire, in 1988 after two spells living in Germany. A third followed from 1992 to 1995, in Bubenreuth near Erlangen, Bavaria. He has helped with, and run, mainly church youth groups in both places for much of this time.

In 1999, after four years as a freelance software engineer and in his free time helping to rig World Wide Message Tribe concerts, David had the opportunity to join the events team of the Message Trust[1] full-time. This Manchester-based Christian charity has expanded to do schools, prison, mobile and fixed-location youth and social work all over the city and beyond.

The Operations team gave him plenty of scope to build stage-sets, operate stage camera and learn live vision mixing. For the final three years, he looked after Fleet & Facilities, with various building projects (and still some stage-set) satisfying his creative streak. Where possible, he wrote programs to do his paperwork! Working on cars, however, he preferred his own fleet of A-Series-powered Austin-Rovers...

Mid-2010 David felt it was time to leave the Message, but didn't get the youth worker job at his church as hoped (though a year later became its parish administrator, a role he loves). Instead, God unexpectedly gave him a completely new area of creativity: this book!

---

[1] See www.message.org.uk

Preface

It is a somewhat daunting undertaking to write any book about Jesus, especially for a first-time author with just a few poems and songs to his name, and those written long ago. Writing such a book in the first person – effectively attempting an autobiography – might be considered by some to be presumptuous in the extreme; how could I possibly know how Jesus feels?

25.07.2010 04:10

> Woke up during another night of fitful sleep with an impulse so strong that I got up to jot it down: "Write a book with Jesus in the first person."

Later that day, I noted down a few ideas and then started writing in as much earnest as it's possible to muster when trying to finish multiple jobs around the house whilst preparing to go on holiday.

This book is the result of that initial prompting, which I can only believe came from God, and of many hours since, poring amongst other things over the NIV Study Bible presented to me by my Buglawton church early in 1992 when I was heading for another life-chapter in Germany. The late Rev John Mowll wrote in it the verse Isaiah 41:10: "...I will strengthen you and help you..." This edition of the Holy Scriptures has been the main source of my book, and is referred to in notes mostly as "NIV". Its various time charts, tables and maps have been a helpful source of information.

Of course, trying to amalgamate the contents of all four gospels into one narrative is a 'best guess' of the order of events, given inconsistencies in their narration. I have, for example, used John's account of Jesus' first disciples (1:35-50) as portraying an "initial meeting" with them, with the invitation to "Come and ... see." The narratives of Matthew (4:18-22), Mark (1:16-20) and Luke (5:1-11) are taken as describing their later, permanent calling. Notes at the end of the book discuss such considerations at more length than individual footnotes allow.

Various books and particularly the internet have provided useful commentaries, ideas and background information. It is hard as a non-academic to verify many of these, but the overwhelming majority themselves cite other works. I have sought to quote all sources (Bible references and other) in footnotes throughout the book, with a bibliography at the end. The reader may ignore these or use them for personal study as desired. I personally find footnotes (by definition at the foot of the page containing the text they refer to) easier to use than endnotes, so that's where they are! Footnote references in the text are placed relative to punctuation according to whether the whole or part of a sentence, or a quote, is being referred to.

The Bible is of course our main source of information about God's love for us and his salvation plan through Jesus. I do not seek to answer theological questions such as "Where did God come from?" or "Why does God allow evil?", though the latter is touched upon. Rather, I have tried to do what I believe God told me: to write an account of Jesus' life from his point of view, as imperfect as that attempt will ever be, while staying close to the Bible narrative.

I have woven in as much background information as possible, as well as attempting the presumptuous: adding Jesus' thoughts on His ministry and mission. However, I have aimed throughout to use as little conjecture or poetic licence as possible. To explain why Jesus came in human form at all, you have to recount the initial fall of Adam and Eve and explain the Old Testament system of sacrifices. So, since he was there, Jesus tells the creation story. This, in particular, does not seek to be any more scientific than the Bible is; rather, the purpose is to show the exuberance of creation.

The opening chapter finds Jesus entering Jerusalem on Palm Sunday. It is written in the present tense, as I wanted the action to be immediate, present. I soon relented when starting the creation story, and so the early and middle parts of the book, up to when the narrative catches up with the starting point, are written primarily in the past tense. Various comments by Jesus appear in the present tense, some as if made to the reader now, others describing the ongoing state of events at the point of narration. The reader could perhaps imagine him- or herself walking alongside the donkey as Jesus talks. The latter part of the book remains in the present tense, to bring, I hope, a heightened sense of the events Jesus was going through.

My desire for this book is that you will catch more than a glimpse of God's love for you in Jesus as you read an account of his life, as he might have told it had he written a Gospel himself. I hope, as Jesus invited His first disciples, that you too will want to "come and see".

David J. Aston
Congleton

Foreword

Dave Aston is what can only be described as a legend at The Message Trust, the charity that I set up here in Manchester.

I think it's fair to say he was one of the very first people who caught the vision for the work right back in 1988, when along with my brother Simon, we had the dream of booking the biggest rock venue in Manchester and encouraging churches to re-engage with disenfranchised youth. He was certainly the first person to send us a four figure cheque towards the work. I can well remember nearly falling off my chair when I received it! Dave didn't send the cheque because he was rich but, as I discovered over the next couple of decades as we worked closely together on building the Trust, because a) he is super-generous; b) he gets the vision to reach out to the hardest to reach; and more importantly, c) especially where this book is concerned, Dave is a passionate follower of Jesus.

The Bible says that we are to have "the mind of Christ". Dave seems to have taken this literally with his task of trying to get inside the Mind of the Saviour, and what we have as a result is an exciting and fascinating book that hopefully will draw the reader closer to Jesus and give them a real desire to discover more of him in the Scriptures for themselves.

Dave is one of God's wonderful one-offs, and I know he has put his heart and soul into this project. I'm praying that many will be blessed as a result.

Andy Hawthorne OBE
Founder and Chief Executive,
The Message Trust

FOR

TYG – source of fun and inspiration

My Brother – you work so hard

My Parents – always there for us

Jesus – my Saviour
(You told me to write the book!)

Contents

1

Into Jerusalem

The donkey's grey head is bobbing up and down in time with the rhythmic clip-clop of its hooves on the stone street that we're making our way along. It's a soothing, almost hypnotic beat, in stark contrast with the hubbub around me.

Little more than an alleyway, the street is packed with throngs of visitors, coming to Jerusalem from across the entire region for the annual Passover Feast.[1] I know it well; it leads out to the twisting Jericho road, which exits Jerusalem from the East Gate, set in the wall beneath the towering structure of the temple. The temple... my Father's house.

From there, the road descends into the Kidron Valley before wending its way up to a saddle in the Mount of Olives, and the hamlet of Bethphage, which marks the eastern limits of the city[2]. After reaching the small yet bustling village of Bethany, the road makes its way to the much lower lying city of Jericho, some twenty-five miles east of the mountains here, or a day's walk[3]. Bethany lies a mere two miles along this route and is home to some close friends of mine who have often provided me with a home when I have been in Jerusalem.

We passed through the East Gate just now, on our way into the city from their place. I spent the weekend there, the Sabbath, with Mary

---

1   John 12:1,12
2   Talmud – Pesachim 63b; Menachoth 63a,78b
3   See 'Measurements' note, page 310

and Martha, and my good friend Lazarus, their brother. Did me good, even with Martha fretting as she does, scurrying around making sure everyone has food and something to drink;[4] an oasis of sunshine I could bask in briefly, while the horizon harboured storm clouds drawing ominously closer. Lazarus was in good form. It's been great to see him looking so well again.[5]

There's a young mother with her toddler daughter, standing in a doorway and waving. I smile and wave back. It's a good atmosphere. I sometimes wonder why we chose this way, my Dad and I, so long ago, knowing certainly that in just a few days these same people will have a very different look in their eyes, and words of rejection in their mouths rather than adulation. Most anyway – that mother and child won't be among them, nor will my closest friends, although most of them are going to run away, despite their protestations to the contrary. And one... the poor soul destined to betray me. Better for him that he had never been born. Yet, someone must do it, to set in motion the series of events that will lead to the sacrifice that has to be made.[6]

Here and there, lonely blades of tough grass are forcing themselves upwards between the flagstones that pave this part of the city, stubbornly resisting the multitude of footprints that trample upon them, and the persistent dryness of the dusty streets. If only my friends would remain that strong. *Father, help them in the coming days. They have to continue what you've sent me here to establish.*

I can't stop thinking about what Mary did after dinner last night.[7] Kind of put the seal on everything, really. Raised a few hackles, even amongst my closest friends. But I understood. Any doubts I had... well, not anymore; now it's real. The expensive perfume she poured over my feet was a sign of things to come. Soon. I've known for a long while that it had to be. If only the people throwing down their coats ahead of me and waving palm branches[8] understood fully too.

---

[4] cf. Luke 10:40
[5] following the events of John 11
[6] Matthew 26:24
[7] John 12:3
[8] Luke 19:36; John 12:13

They began their joyful praise as we came over the top of the Mount of Olives from Bethphage and started descending towards Jerusalem,[9] scarcely half an hour ago.

"Blessed is the king who comes in the name of the Lord!"

This line from a Psalm[10] enraged some of the Pharisees travelling in the crowd, and they demanded that I rebuke my disciples.

"I tell you," I replied to them using words from the prophet Habakkuk[11] and pointing across the valley at the temple, "if they keep silent, the stones will shout out." And with that implicit claim, I committed what for the Pharisees is the ultimate blasphemy, for only one is King, and that is God.

Some five hundred years ago, the prophet Zechariah was writing about this very moment. He understood. Even down to the donkey[12], a young colt. A lowly animal of peace, yet a royal mount from the time of King David[13]. Even the patriarch Jacob, later called Israel, had a glimpse of the donkey I'm riding today.[14]

The people are expecting their king to overthrow the Roman occupation and restore the nation to the glory-days of King David. But I'm here to overthrow so much more than that. As another prophet, Isaiah, put it even earlier,[15] I'm here to preach good news to the poor, bind up the broken-hearted, release captives, and comfort those who mourn, bringing beauty in place of ashes, gladness where there is mourning, praise instead of despair; and to proclaim the year of the Lord's favour.

I'm here to overthrow things that have held people hostage for so long: pervasive sin with its ensuing consequences and persistent guilt; wars between nations and even within families; greed and unfairness, some having more than enough, while others have to go hungry; even the empty religious practices that count for worship of a living God, who is desperate to have a close relationship with his created children.

---

9   Luke 19:37
10 Psalm 118:26 (NIV)
11 Habakkuk 2:11 (NIV)
12 John 12:14-15; Zechariah 9:9
13 2 Samuel 16:2; 1 Kings 1:33
14 Genesis 49:10-11
15 Isaiah 61:1-2

The Roman occupation will stay for now; *those* things – they are what I have come to defeat.

However, the way there is going to be necessarily hard. Today is the tenth of our Jewish month Nisan, the day when my people select the sacrificial lambs for the Passover sacrifice, as my Father and I directed our ancestors through Moses[16]. The lambs, or goat kids, are led into the camp and looked after until the afternoon of the fourteenth, when they are sacrificed.

Today is the tenth. Today my people have led me into the city.

"Who is this?" the onlookers keep asking them.

"This is Jesus, the prophet from Nazareth in Galilee,"[17] they reply.

---

[16] Exodus 12:3-6
[17] Matthew 21:10-11 (NIV)

2

Flinging Stars

Matter. Matter everywhere. Dust, gases, molecules of water and a billion other things, floating around aimlessly in an infinitely wide realm of space. We decided to make something out of it all, my Dad and I, something that we could look at and take joy from.

But first we had to create a way of making it all hang together. As I said, to start with, everything just floated around. Everything was random. Nothing held together, and there was no order. So we came up with a phenomenon that English and most Latin-based language speakers would later call 'gravity'. German, Russian and Chinese speakers would term it 'heavy power' or the 'power of weight'. (These different languages came later on, but that's another story.[1])

Gravity meant that everything would hold together instead of floating around without purpose. The friction caused by particles crashing into each other in this swirling ocean of dust gave rise to electrostatic properties that made individual particles stick together. The 'mass' of these larger objects attracted more dust and smaller collections of particles.

We created a wealth of other forces and phenomena, all designed to create order and keep balance, so that matter both joined up and

---

[1] Genesis 11:1-9

separated out into galaxies of suns, stars, planets and other bodies such as moons and comets. You could say we lost count of how many there were, though actually we know. But that's neither here nor there. There was one galaxy we especially turned our attention to, and of that, one planet in particular. It was like, for you, building an intricate model to a plan, poring over tiny details to get it 'just so'.

To start with, all the matter that made up 'Earth' had just gathered into a large, slightly squashed ball. It was pressed together so tightly that the inside of it became molten, just like when you press hard on an ice cube and it melts around the points of pressure. In fact, the inside of this near-spherical earth never did set to this day. But the outside had cooled into a formless, empty landscape, covered in darkness.

Our Spirit hovered over the waters,[2] and I guess we were standing back, imagining what we were planning to do. You know, when you just stand looking at an as yet empty space you want to build something on, or a room you want to redecorate; you simply cast your eye over it for a while, trying to imagine what you could do with it and how it would look. That's what our Spirit was doing: hovering, working out, prompting our imagination to run riot.

Imagine having a blank sheet and being able to design anything you like. Well, that's precisely what we did, and it was thrilling! We spent a whole week coming up with exciting new ideas, each more fantastic than the last, making a whole variety of things as we went along, each planned to sustain the next, and always with a goal in mind, something or someone that would be like us and take over looking after the Earth when we'd finished making it.

You have to remember, incidentally, that when we talk about a week – seven days, that is – we might be talking days as *we* understand them. My friend Peter realised this much later when he wrote[3] that for us a day is like a thousand years, and a thousand years, well, like a day. Another guy, Moses, had also grasped this in one of his prayers[4]. People

---

[2] Genesis 1:2
[3] 2 Peter 3:8
[4] Psalm 90:4

get so caught up discussing the details about these seven days, and it's so *not* the point of the story. Anyway, back to creation...

First, we had to get some light on the subject, and spoke it into being.[5] The Word is one of my names,[6] by the way, and one of my characteristics is being able to speak and command things into – or sometimes out of[7] – existence. The light showed up the surface of the earth, and was separate from the darkness. We looked at that and thought, "This is good." Once we'd done that, there was evening, and then morning, and the first of our days was done.[8]

Then we needed to put a water management system in place. We had decided that water was going to be Earth's lifeblood. However, to achieve that, it couldn't all just stay in one place. There had to be a method of distributing it across the land so that later, for example, crops would grow. (But we'll come to them.) This had to happen repeatedly, and keep on happening in a never-ending cycle. So we created a space to separate the waters that we called 'sky'.[9] Winds would brush water off the surface of the seas and carry it up into the sky where it would form clouds. They would be carried by the winds over the land until they became too cold and heavy to carry the water any more, and so drop it as refreshing and life-giving rain.[10] That was the second, and part of our third, day's work.[11]

Also on the third day, having gathered the waters under the sky into seas, we created the dry ground in between, called land. It too was good. Now we could really get creative! The land produced vegetation: all sorts of seed-bearing plants, and trees that bear fruit with seeds in it, according to their various kinds.[12] So many kinds you couldn't possibly count them all. It was great! The seeds were important. We knew that what we made there and then had to have some way whereby it would be able to recreate itself as time went on. So we made a part of each

---

5 Genesis 1:3
6 John 1:1-14
7 e.g. Exodus 23:27, 1 Samuel 14:20; Mark 9:25-26; John 12:48; cf. Acts 16:18
8 Genesis 1:5
9 Genesis 1:6-7
10 Job 36:27-29; Amos 5:8b
11 Genesis 1:8-10
12 Genesis 1:11 (NIV)

plant, or the fruit of trees, to contain the means by which a new plant would grow. This 'seed' would have to first shrivel up and die, then fall to the ground, where it would take root and burst into life again, growing into a new plant. Remember that, because it's a picture of what would happen to me millennia later...[13]

The light we had created was good. However, we needed to work out how to use it to distinguish day from night and to demarcate seasons and years.[14] So we concentrated all the light near Earth into one place, called the 'Sun'. We made Earth (and several other planets) circle around the Sun, but also spin on its own axis, so that anywhere on Earth, the days we had created were marked out by whether that point was facing the Sun or not. Earth's axis was not quite perpendicular to its orbital plane around the sun, so towards each of its poles, days were longer or shorter, depending on the position around the sun. The sun gave both light and heat to the Earth, warming the ground and helping to create ideal conditions for the plants to grow.

However, the side facing away from the sun wouldn't have any light at all. To improve this, we caused a nearby celestial body called the 'Moon', a smaller collection of matter that had broken off Earth when it was hit by another large object in the chaos of early on and had gradually re-formed,[15] to orbit Earth. That way, it could reflect the light off the sun onto the part of the Earth that was in the dark. We maximised this beneficial effect by angling the moon's orbit such that when the sun – viewed from the earth – rose nearer one pole, the moon would set nearer the other, and vice-versa.[16] The gravity we had created at the beginning kept everything circling round at the right distance and speed from each other, and this gave the earth its rhythm of days, months and seasons, and the rise and fall of the oceans, that you call 'tides'. Oh, this was good! That was our fourth day.[17]

On the fifth day, we really went to town. We had created minerals in the ground and water delivered by clouds from above to feed the

---

[13] John 12:24; 1 Corinthians 15:35-38
[14] Genesis 1:14
[15] BBC; Natural History Museum
[16] Knight & Butler, on "Scissoring of the Moon"
[17] Genesis 1:19

plants and trees, and designed the trees in particular to be an important mechanism for sustaining life, filtering the atmosphere by absorbing carbon dioxide from it and returning oxygen to it. That was great, but what life was it going to support? It was a bit like you in your modern world having the most exciting model railway ever, with points and sidings, bridges and tunnels winding through spectacular scenery, but no trains to bring it to life! So we started making living creatures. The water eventually teemed with them,[18] and ones we called birds flew above the earth and across the sky.

We made huge creatures that lived in the sea, and all sorts of other living and moving things. Some of the animals we created in the seas are like the plants on land; they remain largely in one place, clinging persistently to rocks on the seabed instead of moving about freely. Coral and sea anemones behave like that.

The birds in the sky had muscular yet lightweight, feathered wings that carried them through the air. It was all good. We blessed all these creatures and decreed that they should flourish and multiply to fill the seas and cover the earth.[19]

We started the sixth day in a similar way, by creating all manner of animals that covered the land. Some would be livestock, providing food, some would run, others would crawl along the ground, some would be domesticated, some would be wild. Each according to its kind. We designed all sorts of weird and wacky creatures, just as we had done in the seas and in the sky. And they were good.[20] Some had no legs, some had two, while many had four; others had six or eight legs, and after you would think we had come up with enough variety on the leg front, we had a giggle and created centipedes and millipedes.

Then finally, we were ready to create what we had been working towards all along. Someone in our own image, someone like us: 'mankind', who would rule over the whole earth and everything in it.[21] Someone who would look after everything that we had created, who

---

[18] Genesis 1:20
[19] Genesis 1:22 (NIV)
[20] Genesis 1:25
[21] Genesis 1:26

would till the land and look after the special garden we had formed in the east of the land we called 'Eden'[22]. Someone in whom we could take special pleasure.

We would give them all the vegetation with seeds and fruit as food. To all the beasts of the earth, all the birds of the air, and all the creatures that move on the ground – everything that has the breath of life in it – we gave every green plant for food.[23]

Making the first example of humankind meant putting all of ourselves into the matter we made him out of: dust from the ground. We shaped him, formed him in our own image, and our Spirit breathed life into his nostrils[24] so that he became a living being.

We put the man we had formed into the special garden, and looked for a companion for him, someone to help him look after the garden, and someone with whom he would create new life, sharing in our work of creation. Someone like us.

But there was no-one to be found. We showed the man, named Adam, all of the creatures we had created, but none of them were suitable.[25] So we completed our work by making a modification on the man we had just made. We put him into a deep sleep, took one of his ribs, replacing the gap with flesh, and used what we had taken from him to create someone else: a 'taken-from-man', as the man termed her[26] after he had come round from the anaesthetic; the word in your language is 'woman'. He later gave her the name Eve. In the same way as the woman was taken from the man's flesh, so the two became one flesh again as they joined together to create new life. That is why a man leaves the protective custody of his parents and, with his wife, creates a new family unit.[27]

So that sums up how we made the earth; how we set it all up. We breathed life into everything we had created, and planted within it the ability to produce new life, to 'reproduce'. When we stepped back and

---

[22] Genesis 2:8
[23] Genesis 1:29-30 (NIV)
[24] Genesis 2:7
[25] Genesis 2:19-20
[26] Genesis 2:21-23
[27] Genesis 2:24

looked at it all at the end of the sixth day, we decided that it was all *very* good.[28]

On the seventh day, we rested from all our efforts.[29] What we had created had everything it needed to carry on itself, with our creative work continuing in the processes of reproduction and renewal that we put in place. We decided that mankind should keep the seventh day holy and rest from the work we had given them, just as we rested from ours. They would need this time of rest and relaxation, of restoration, just as we did. It would also be a special opportunity for spending quality time together with us, to strengthen the friendship we would have.

That is why we place so much emphasis on keeping the Sabbath day holy, set apart for friendship and families, for rest and recreation. This is one of the many ways we show our love for you, and it grieves us to see people throwing it away, as if they didn't need it. Our anger is roused when people are treated unfairly, expected to work every day without adequate chance to pause, to draw breath. Our sense of justice is aggrieved when employers threaten to sack workers who do not wish to work when they are told to, even when it is in direct conflict with what we have ordained, and what is good for them. Not, by the way, that we don't realise that in many professions, in the modern world you live in, somebody has to be working on every day of the week. What is important is that everyone has a chance to have his or her Sabbath. That is what we did, and is what you, made in our image, need.

---

[28] Genesis 1:31
[29] Genesis 2:2-3

3

The Trees

When we put the man into the Garden of Eden, we told him he could eat the fruit of any tree in the garden except for the tree of knowledge of good and evil, which stood next to the tree of life in the centre of the garden.[1] We had made people in our image, but they would not cope with all our knowledge.

Sometimes, too much knowledge can be a bad thing. It's good not to know of all the schemes that the devil, the evil one, uses to bring destruction and death with. Sometimes, such things are simply too shocking and awful to contemplate; at other times, they can appear deceptively attractive – easier, better-looking, more exciting – but lead people away from what they know is right, and ultimately to their eternal death.

The tree of life, on the other hand, watered by the river of the water of life that will one day flow from our temple into the Jordan and restore the waters of the Salt Sea (you know it as the Dead Sea),[2] bears its fruit each month,[3] fruit that gives the eater eternal life. Its leaves are for the healing of the nations. It had never been our intention to withhold this fruit from our friends.[4]

---

[1] Genesis 2:9
[2] e.g. Genesis 14:3; Numbers 34:3,12
[3] Revelation 22:1-2; cf. Ezekiel 47:1-12
[4] cf. Genesis 2:9,16-17; Revelation 2:7, 22:14

The man and woman were our friends. We would walk with them through the garden, talk with them; they would show us what they had been working on, and tell us about what fruit had grown that they'd enjoyed eating. We loved being able to relate to them, enjoyed their company, and appreciated the time we spent together. Then one day, as we were walking through the garden in the cool of the morning, we couldn't find them. They didn't come out to meet us when they heard our footsteps approaching, like they always had done. It seemed they didn't want to talk to us anymore. Our special friendship appeared to have evaporated, the relationship jeopardised, their innocence lost.

We called to the man, "Where are you?"

Adam came out and answered, "I heard you approaching, and I was afraid because I was naked; so I hid."[5]

There should have been no reason for him to have known that, and we realised he must have eaten from the tree of knowledge of good and evil. We had told him not to, because we knew that everything would change. Now it had.

Adam told us, "That woman you put here with me – she gave me some fruit from the tree, and I ate it."[6]

As if that excused him for eating it!

The woman said that the serpent had deceived her; she had eaten some of the fruit and given some to the man.[7]

The serpent – one of the guises of the Deceiver, the Evil One. He has always been around, and always seeks to destroy what is good.[8] Always has, always will. Until the end of time anyway.[9]

We rebuked the Deceiver with a warning that enmity would always exist between him and the woman – and between their offspring: hers would crush his head one day.

---

[5] Genesis 3:10 (NIV)
[6] Genesis 3:12 (NIV)
[7] Genesis 3:13
[8] John 8:44; 1 John 3:8
[9] Matthew 25:41; Revelation 20:7-10

The fruit on the tree of knowledge and evil certainly did look good.[10] I can see why the man and the woman were attracted to it. But why did they have to go against what we'd told them?

With the knowledge of evil, particularly, we could no longer allow our friends to eat the fruit of the tree of life, and thus live forever like us.[11] Having eaten of the tree of knowledge and evil, they had become like us, just as the serpent had said[12] they would. But the Deceiver had failed to mention that they had also taken on a 'sin nature' that separated them from us, and that actually made them more like him. Without restraint, their newfound knowledge of evil was too great, too dangerous for them to possess over eternity.

So the question arose: what would we have to do to restore our friendship with humankind?

---

[10] Genesis 3:6
[11] Genesis 3:22
[12] Genesis 3:5

4

Right from Heaven

ight from the start, we gave humanity free will, and – right from the start – they chose to act against the boundaries we set out for their well-being. Like children growing up and rejecting their parents' advice, we too have to look with sadness upon those we have created, our 'children', and watch them cause themselves and others, as well as us, pain.

Were we wrong to give them the right to choose, with all the consequences that brought with it? Would wars have never been fought, lives saved, families stayed together, famine been non-existent, had humankind not had the choice? Without free will mankind would not have been made fully in our image; they are like us because they have the choice. You have to choose: choose to be holy, choose to do good, even when doing so represents a difficult path and not the one that seems easiest.

In addition to a more toilsome life, the consequence of disobedience for Adam and Eve was banishment from our garden. Its entrance lay to the east, and that is where we posted cherubim and a flaming sword to guard the way to the tree of life.[1] Cherubim, or cherubs, are powerful attendants to our divine throne, and are a bit like a flag fluttering on the residence of a head of state in your modern

---

[1] Genesis 3:23-24

world: they signify the presence of the occupant. The garden was our earthly residence, which later became the Tabernacle[2]; the sword of judgement was its cherubim-adorned 'mercy seat'. For now, our residence was out of bounds.

Centuries later, once the Israelites had arrived in the land we had set aside for them, we gave them a set of rules that was to govern their lives with each other and how they should relate to us.[3] We initiated a system of sacrifices, to be made when the people had done wrong and wanted to return to the friendship we previously enjoyed.[4] Right from when we had made clothes from animal skins[5] for the man and the woman to cover their newly-realised nakedness, those sacrifices involved the slaughter of an animal and the shedding of its blood, just as it did at the original Passover; there was no restoration without it.[6]

You see, we are holy and can't stand evil.[7] We simply won't have anything to do with it. You cannot have darkness where there is light. They cannot co-exist. Even a small candle lights up an otherwise dark space, and can be seen a mile away. In order to be right with us, our friends have to remove the darkness from their lives. We thought that making a sacrifice of something that was worth a lot to them was a good way to help our friends come back to us in a manner that showed them (and us) that they were sorry and meant it.

Trouble was, over the generations the system of sacrifices became taken for granted and abused. The original purpose of them became clouded, the idea of giving up something valuable as the cost of restoration of our friendship, gradually forgotten. People thought they could get away with sacrificing an imperfect lamb that had little market value, or a dove with a damaged wing.[8] The sacrifice itself was unimportant to us; it was the thought that counted. Mankind's heart was not in it, that was the problem. You see, we desire mercy, justice

---

2. cf. Exodus 25:18-22, 37:7-9; Numbers 7:89; Psalm 80:1
3. Exodus 20:1-17
4. Pentateuch, esp. Leviticus
5. Genesis 3:21
6. Leviticus 17:11; Hebrews 9:22; Talmud – Yoma 5a
7. Leviticus 19:1; Habakkuk 1:13; 1 Peter 1:14-16
8. Leviticus 22:18-23; Malachi 1:14

and humility, not meaningless sacrifice.[9] No, relying on a human to prepare a sufficient sacrifice that would make him holy enough to enter into our presence again, and to enjoy friendship with us, simply wouldn't work.

To get round this conundrum, we concluded that we ourselves would have to make the sacrifice. After all, it was impossible for something that was not perfect to provide anything that would make itself perfect. We alone were able to offer the perfect and sufficient sacrifice that would make the one seeking forgiveness and restoration good enough to stand before us, holy.

When I thought about how much Dad and I valued our friendship with humankind, and that we needed to provide the sacrifice, I suggested to him – pleaded even – to let me go to Earth and join our friends as a man, born of a woman. I would show them our love for them, and make a sacrifice that would restore our friendship once and for all. I would limit myself to a physical human framework, while still being one with my Father through our Spirit, and able in His power to repel all efforts of the devil to separate us.

The sacrifice of atonement has always meant the taking of a life; the sacrifice I was to make would involve me giving my life, which would be a perfect life without a single imperfection.[10] Only that could bring humanity back into a relationship with us.

Of course, giving my life does also mean the taking of it. Now, as I am riding on the donkey into Jerusalem, I shudder to think of what that will entail. It will be an excruciatingly painful affair, not only physically, but also full of mental anguish. You see, I have never before been separated from my Father. From before time began, we have resided in that indefinable place you call 'heaven'. The galaxies are our home; the stars we flung into space, our solar patio lights; the earth (which we liken to our footstool[11]) the kit we lovingly

---

9   Hosea 6:6; Micah 6:6-8
10 1 Peter 1:19
11 Isaiah 66:1-2; Matthew 5:35; Acts 7:49

put together from individual components, and the ongoing project that we love to lavish care and attention on.

For me, giving my life will not just mean having given up all the glory of heaven while I am here, it will also bring total separation from my Father. At the point of death, I will for a moment in time join the dead, those completely separated from my Father in heaven, taking upon myself everything that can separate us. That's what making the sacrifice for the wrongdoing of our friends will entail, the 'atonement' for their sin. That, and only that, can make them clean again, holy enough to enter our presence, at one with us.

5

Bethlehem

To have a perfect human life without blemish meant that my entire life had to be perfect. To enable this to start off on the right footing, we had to ensure that my birth happened not because of a man's driven will, nor even after the consenting, passionate, shared love of a man and a woman, but without the intervention of imperfect parents. We chose a lowly, godly girl, Mary[1], barely through her teens, who had not been in intimate contact with a man, and our Spirit himself created within her the seed that formed new life – *my* life.

Even this detail we had planned long in advance. The prophet Isaiah had foretold it seven hundred years earlier, talking to Ahaz, King of Judah, at a time when Jerusalem had been attacked by its enemies but prevailed[2]. King Ahaz refused to ask us for a sign, but we gave him one anyway: that one day a virgin would be with child and give birth to a son called 'God with us'[3] ('Emmanuel' in their Hebrew language). Around the same time, the prophet Micah had also foretold[4] that in Bethlehem a ruler would be born, one that had been around from ancient times. Bethlehem was the birthplace of King David, held in high

---

[1] Luke 1:27
[2] Isaiah 7:1-11
[3] Isaiah 7:12-14
[4] Micah 5:2

esteem by the Jewish nation and a man after our own heart[5] – most of the time – of whose line it was expected the Messiah would come.[6]

My mother and my stepfather, Joseph, were each told about this admittedly unusual arrangement by an angel.[7] Angels are, amongst other things, messengers we send to individuals now and again as the need arises. My mother was at the very least puzzled, having not yet had anything to do with a man,[8] not even with my stepfather, to whom she was engaged at the time. He, naturally, finding out that his fiancée was pregnant, was beside himself with worry and an increasing awareness of the shame that this predicament was going to place both of them in, causing huge embarrassment for their respective families – especially his. But his angel messenger assured him that this was within God's plan, and to his credit, he accepted and did not divorce my mother, as he had initially intended[9]. That would have been his right and perfectly normal in our culture, where divorce can apply to an engagement as well as to a marriage.[10]

Now, when Caesar Augustus ordered that a census must be taken of the entire Roman world,[11] it could not have come at a more inconvenient time for my parents. The census meant that every man was required to travel with his family to the town of his ancestral origin. My stepfather Joseph was a descendent of King David, who was born in Bethlehem. So, in fact, was my mother, Mary, through her mother's family.[12] We had to travel the ninety miles from my parents' home in Nazareth, to Bethlehem. I say we; I was still cradled within my mother's womb at that point, but I was expected very soon now, and so the idea of a week-long journey on a donkey was not an appealing one.

When they arrived in the normally sleepy backwater of Bethlehem, my parents found the town to be overflowing with people there for the census, and could not find a room to stay in. After searching all over

---

[5] 1 Samuel 13:14; Acts 13:22
[6] 2 Samuel 7:12,16; Jeremiah 23:5
[7] Matthew 1:18-24; Luke 1:26-38
[8] Luke 1:34
[9] Matthew 1:19
[10] Deuteronomy 22:23-24; Matthew 1:24
[11] Luke 2:1
[12] Matthew 1:1-17; Luke 3:23-38 and NIV Study Bible footnotes

town, they finally came across a sympathetic innkeeper who, while having no spare rooms himself either, offered them the use of the stable at the back of the inn. Other people's beasts were housed there for the night, together with our own donkey. It was not long into the night that my mother started experiencing the painful contractions that culminated in my birth. They wrapped me in some cloths and laid me in one of the mangers, or feeding troughs.[13]

Later that same night, a remarkable event took place.[14] There were many shepherds, working up on the gently rolling hillsides above Bethlehem where their assorted sheep scavenged the best of the meagre supply of grass this arid desert area has to offer. It was, as ever, a busy time for the shepherds. The census had brought a ruck of extra people to Bethlehem, while the population of nearby Jerusalem was also swollen for the same reason. The shepherds supplied the people of both communities with the sacrificial lambs for the various regular festivals held by the devout Jewish believers.[15]

As well as the census, the Feast of the Tabernacles[16] was being held. This was a harvest festival, but the tabernacles in question referred to the 'booths' or temporary dwellings erected by the workers of the harvest on the edges of the fields they were harvesting. All of this was very symbolic of my presence here. As my friend John would say[17], I made my dwelling – pitched my tent – among those I had come to serve and to save.

Our chosen method of saving our friends was to make the sacrifice ourselves, signified by the lambs on the hillsides above Bethlehem, and as the prophet Isaiah had written[18]. The idea of harvest was also one I would come to speak about.[19] It was time for freeing the people from the guilt of their sin, and for 'gathering them in' to our kingdom where such things were banished for good. We intended this for all people, just

---

13 Luke 2:7
14 Luke 2:8ff
15 cf. Genesis 35:19-21; Micah 4:8; Mishnah Shekalim 7.4
16 Exodus 23:16; Leviticus 23:34. See 'Dating Jesus' Birth' note, page 302
17 John 1:14
18 Isaiah 53:6-7
19 Matthew 9:37-38; Luke 10:2

as the Feast of Tabernacles specifically included the Gentiles.[20] Harvest was always a time for celebration, and this one certainly would be!

On the evening of my birth, an angel appeared to the shepherds on the hillside and announced the good news.[21] It was good news of great joy, and it was for all people. The scheme to make all who would accept it right with us once and for all, that we had come up with and announced through the prophets centuries earlier, was underway. It was exhilarating. It was new, revolutionary even. What god made the sacrifices it demanded *itself?* Our messenger told the shepherds exactly what they would find, and that this would be a sign for them that the baby they were about to visit was the awaited Saviour, the Messiah, the One promised of old.

When the angel had reassured the usually imperturbable[22] but in the circumstances understandably terrified shepherds, and delivered his joyous message, a glorious choir of angels appeared with the first, singing praises to God and wishing peace on the earth to all on whom his favour rests. Excited and naturally curious, there was no waiting until morning. The shepherds made their way down into sleepy Bethlehem,[23] found the inn's lowly stable housing my parents and me, and told them about everything that the angel had said, and about the heavenly pop song rendered by a choir of angels. They continued it on their way back up the hills[24] to their probably equally excited sheep.

On the eighth day after my birth, I underwent circumcision, as required by Jewish law, and was formally given the name Jesus, as the angel had instructed my parents.[25] Forty days after my birth, after the traditional time of purification prescribed by the law, we left Bethlehem, and my parents took me to Jerusalem to present me at the temple.

There we were met, first by an old man, Simeon, who served in the temple, and then by an even older prophetess, Anna, who practically lived there. Both spoke moving words of prophecy over me.[26] Simeon

---

20 Deuteronomy 16:14; Zechariah 14:16-19
21 Luke 2:9
22 cf. 1 Samuel 17:34-37
23 Luke 2:16
24 Luke 2:20
25 Luke 2:21
26 Luke 2:25-38

was overjoyed that he had at last seen the salvation plan that God had promised him, before his very eyes. He could now die a happy man. My mother kept all these sayings in her heart, and recounted them to me as I grew up and as I learnt to read the Scriptures.

6

Donkey-ride Home

The crowded, narrow streets are becoming quite difficult for my patient donkey to get through. People all around are waving palm branches, shouting words of greeting and adoration, and singing one of the praise songs we sing at Passover.[1] Oh, if only they understood!

The donkey's gentle swaying movement reminds me of another donkey I rode on, on another journey, way back when I was little. One of my earliest memories. Well, as a young lad anyway...

I must have been approaching three years old. We were riding on donkey-back – my mother, Mary, and I – with my stepfather, Joseph, walking alongside, taking such long strides that the diminutively-statured donkey almost had to trot to keep up with him. So my mum would tell me later on, anyway. I remember sitting in front of her on the back of the donkey, fascinated by its long, furry ears moving backwards and forwards, seemingly independent from each other, and by the black fuzz of mane between them.

My mum told me years later that we had been on our way back from Egypt, where we had had to flee from King Herod. He had wanted to kill me because he thought I was supposed to be the new king. In a

---

[1] Psalm 118:25-26; Matthew 21:9; Mark 11:9; Luke 19:38; John 12:13

sense he was right, but otherwise he had got the wrong end of a very long stick. Anyone said to be a new king was, for him, a threat to his Roman-given authority, and so he had all boys under two years old killed.[2]

The figure of two years was not arbitrary; it had come from some visitors from the East, who had come to see me after I had been born, having followed the path of a bright star for some time. They knew the stars intimately from years of patient study, and rightly interpreted their exciting discovery of a new one as a sign of a significant event, one in which they had a special role to play. When the brightly shining star they had chosen to follow – or was that the other way round? – led them to Jerusalem, they stopped by Herod's palace and asked to see the newborn "King of the Jews".[3] Logical enough, being the Jewish capital, only I wasn't there. Not being where people expect me to be, and vice versa, is still true for you today.

The king consulted the local religious leaders, who told him that the promised ruler would be born in Bethlehem. The prophet Micah had foretold[4] that seven hundred years earlier. At this, Herod asked the visitors when the star had first appeared, and was given to understand that it was two years previously. He told them to call back afterwards so he too could go and worship me.[5] In truth, however, he was already hatching a malicious plot to kill me.

The tragedy was that so many others had to die in the process, just as it had been with a former saviour of the people, many generations earlier. The Israelites had been saved from a famine some twelve hundred years before Micah's prophecy, after a guy called Joseph had been sold into slavery in Egypt[6] and then rose to rule the whole land under the Pharaoh. Joseph's father, Jacob (later called Israel, giving name to the people), and all Joseph's eleven brothers were eventually able to settle in Egypt and so were saved from the famine. My Father and I had planned all this for a long time and used the jealousy of

---

2   Matthew 2:13-23
3   Matthew 2:2
4   Micah 5:2
5   Matthew 2:8
6   Genesis 37:28

Joseph's brothers[7] to move him to where we would be able to both save the people and later bless them with riches as they left.[8]

Long after Joseph had died, and over four hundred years after he was sold into slavery, a new Pharaoh, who knew nothing of him and all he had done to save both his own and the Egyptian people, had taken over the reins in Egypt.[9] He decided that the Israelites had grown too strong, but even the austere work conditions he imposed on them did nothing to weaken them. So the Pharaoh decreed that all boys born to the Israelites should be thrown into the River Nile and killed.[10] Born at exactly this time, Moses was placed in a basket and discovered by the Pharaoh's daughter, of all people. However, she took pity on him and engaged a Hebrew woman – whom we had arranged to be his actual mother! – to look after him for her.[11] He grew up to rescue Israel from slavery in Egypt, and led them towards the Promised Land.[12]

Back to my visitors. The wise men from the East came by the house we stayed in for a while after my birth,[13] bearing three precious gifts that themselves were messengers of what my mission was. Gold, signifying a king; frankincense, representing the priestly duties of prayer and sacrifice; and myrrh, an expensive herb used in burial.[14] These gifts were witness to my identity, and indicators of the sacrifice for all, which was my purpose in coming.

Our Spirit used a dream to warn the visitors not to return home via Herod. He, on hearing that they had disappeared, ordered the killing of all infant boys under two years old, according to the time they had told him that the star had appeared. After Herod's own death a couple of years later[15], it was safe for us to return home. We had fled to Egypt, whose long, ancient river, the Nile, is some two hundred and fifty miles

---

7 Genesis 45:5
8 Exodus 12:35-36
9 Exodus 1:8
10 Exodus 1:22 (1526 BC according to NIV OT Chronology)
11 Exodus 2:8
12 Exodus 3:10, 12:31ff
13 NIV footnote at Matthew 2:11
14 Matthew 2:11
15 4BC, from NIV Study Bible footnote to Matthew 2:19

from Jerusalem, and another hundred miles or so from Nazareth, where we were heading. The journey took around three strenuous weeks.

As a child, I didn't remember much except the donkey's head bobbing along in front of me. Just as the donkey's head is moving up and down in front of me now.

7

In My Father's House

My early childhood in Nazareth was reasonably uneventful. I would often play in my stepfather's modest workshop, which was perpetually covered in a fine layer of sawdust. Even sweeping the room out did not remove this completely, as much of it, once agitated, seemed to settle again on the nearest available surface. I loved helping my stepfather with sweeping the floor, and as I grew, learned from him about the wood that produced all this dust when sawn, how to select timber according to its intended use, to understand the strengths and weaknesses of its grain, and, needless to say, how to cut and shape it in the first place. I had a creative streak after all!

My mother stored up all the events surrounding my birth, details of the visitors we received, and what they had been told by the angels about me, in her heart for a long time.[1] While I was still young, she would recount to me all that had happened, as well as teach me from the law.[2]

When I became old enough – five or six – I started to go with some of my friends to our local synagogue school, the Beit Sefer (which

---

[1] Luke 2:19
[2] Deuteronomy 6:6-9

means, 'House of the Book'[3]). There we began to learn the alphabet[4] and, later, the symbolic meanings of each letter,[5] as well as Moses' books of the law, the Torah, repeating the texts over and over until we knew them by rote.

Once we attended the Beit Talmud (which means, 'House of Learning'), we learnt the other Scriptures, and I discovered many places in the text that talked of the Messiah, or Saviour, of the people, who was to come. I began to wonder whether the stories my mum had told me about my birth tied in with these ancient prophecies. So I started looking for other prophecies about what the Messiah would do. I gradually realised that God must be my Father – but then that must have meant that I was in very nature God![6] It was an impossible thing for a human to be – and yet I could feel it in my very being. When I came across the prophetic writings of Isaiah, I understood with some apprehension that my purpose here as a human representation of God – God incarnate – was not only to make God visible to the world, but to provide the sacrificial lamb that Isaiah wrote about. I was to die what would be a shameful, but sacrificial, human death.[7]

Each year, we would do like all Jewish families in our neighbourhood and travel for several days to our capital city, Jerusalem, for the Passover Feast. This celebrates, to this day, the time just before the Exodus of our people Israel from Egypt, when the angel of death 'passed over' the houses of our people who had painted blood of a sacrificed lamb on their doorposts.[8] It was a visible example of the way that a sacrifice saved the people, and a precursor of the sacrifice I was destined to make in Jerusalem one day.

So, after having come to realise many of these things, I was particularly excited when it was time for the next visit to the temple – my Father's house! I was about twelve at the time,[9] and in another year would reach the age where I would become a bar mitzvah (a 'son of the

---

[3] cf. Talmud – Baba Batra 21a;
[4] cf. Talmud – Avot Ch. 5 Mishnah 21
[5] cf. Talmud – Shabbat 104a; e.g. AICE: "Hebrew"
[6] cf. John 1:1, 14:9, and Philippians 2:6
[7] Isaiah 53
[8] Exodus 12
[9] Luke 2:42. See also NIV footnote.

commandment', obliged to observe the laws given through Moses) and be regarded as an adult[10]. A whole group of my relatives and friends had gone down from Nazareth to Jerusalem. As usual, we stayed in a couple of rooms of a hotel owner we knew, who didn't do as many did and hike the prices for the occasion.

We went to the temple every day, and I soon noticed a particularly interesting-looking group of teachers of the law, discussing the Scriptures and their meaning for us today. Initially I crept in at the back, the child part of me a little shy and unsure whether they would tolerate me hanging around as I was, trying to keep close enough to hear what they were saying. One kindly man noticed my interest and motioned me to come and sit nearer. As the days progressed, I thoroughly enjoyed these debates, and was chuffed that they let me ask awkward questions and join in their heated exchanges.

Whenever we went to the temple, I often wouldn't see much of my family all day, but they would never worry much because we were an extended family group. All the children played together, exploring the temple courts, climbing on some of the large, white[11] stones, and trying not to get told off by some of the grumpier priests. And there was always the building work around the Temple Mount to look at.[12] I liked watching the joiners preparing the timbers for roof sections. But this year I was drawn to the temple courts and the teachers of the law. My parents didn't realise I was here and not playing with the other children.

When the end of the festival was reached, I had forgotten it was time to leave Jerusalem and head back for home, and was busy, as I had been for much of the week, discussing all the different prophecies that I had discovered and which I had become convinced concerned my reason for being here. We looked at prophecies that pointed towards my birth, and at others, which talked about a lamb being led to the slaughter, putting up no argument. That was from the book of Isaiah[13], and written some seven hundred years previously. It was difficult to imagine

---

[10] Discussed by T.R. Rich on www.jewfaq.org
[11] Jospehus (Antiquities of the Jews XV.11.3)
[12] cf. John 2:20; see 'The Temple' note, page 309
[13] Isaiah 53:7

as a boy how that would fit my life. But within me was an ever-growing certainty of my heavenly mission.

Inevitably, at some point my parents missed me.[14] They had already travelled for a whole day, assuming that I was with the wider family group. When they discovered that I was missing, they had to travel for another whole day, back to Jerusalem. My stepfather was not too impressed when they finally found me after a further three days, sat as I had been most of the week in discussion with the teachers of the law.[15]

My mother too was visibly unhappy. "Jesus, why are you treating us like this? We've been beside ourselves looking for you."

They both looked even more askance when I asked them why they had been searching for me. "Didn't you know I had to be in my Father's house?"[16]

I could see the pain on my mother's face, and wondered for a moment how much more pain would be etched in her features before my mission was accomplished.

It was time to go home to Nazareth again and do as well as any twelve-year-old boy could – well, maybe a bit better – at being obedient to my parents[17]. More and more I helped my stepfather in his workshop, as did my brothers as they became older, and learned to make tool handles, rakes, yokes for oxen, and items of furniture. We worked to repair the wooden fishing boats that plied Lake Galilee, whose nearest shores were some fifteen miles away. The nearby town of Zippori provided a lot of general construction carpentry work. It is perched on a hill northwest of Nazareth[18] and got its name from our Hebrew word for 'bird'.[19] Reconstruction is still going on, made necessary after the town's citizens revolted after the death of Herod around the time of my birth. The Roman governor, Varus, captured Zippori and burnt it to the

---

14 Luke 2:44
15 Luke 2:46
16 Luke 2:48-49 (NIV)
17 Luke 2:51
18 e.g. www.welcometohosanna.com (21.6.14)
19 Talmud – Mas. Megilah 6a

ground.[20] Then Herod Antipas later ordered the rebuilding of the town.[21]

I became particularly good at making yokes. Single or double, you have to make these to fit over the broad shoulders of the beasts in such a way as not to rub and cause a sore wound. That's why they tend to be tailor-made for each animal. You have to have a good eye for the undulating contours of an animal's physique, not only when it is standing still but allowing for its ambling movement. The leather straps that hold the wooden yoke in place have to be adjusted just right, to allow for the movement but keep it in place across the animal's shoulders. I would remember all this later on one time when inviting the weary to come and rest in me.[22]

But for now I was known as Jesus, son of Joseph, the carpenter.[23] At some point, my stepfather died, and, as Jewish tradition dictated, I became head of our household. Apart from looking after my mother, there were my younger brothers James, Joseph, Judas and Simon, and our sisters.[24] We did our best to look after each other and generally got on well, though my brothers were sceptical when I made any attempt to look with them at the biblical prophecies I had started to understand spoke of my life here.[25] In that sense I didn't fare much better than Jacob's son Joseph had.[26] There again, one passage, a psalm of King David, prophesies me being "a stranger to my brothers; for zeal for your house consumes me, whoever insults you insults me."[27] In that case, I would never fully get on with my brothers, nor, certainly, with the authorities who had charge of my Father's house.

---

[20] Josephus (Antiquities of the Jews XVII.10.5,9; War II.5.1)
[21] Josephus (Antiquities of the Jews XVIII.2.1)
[22] Matthew 11:29-30
[23] Matthew 14:55; Mark 6:3; Luke 3:23, 4:22; John 1:45, 6:42
[24] Mark 6:3
[25] cf. John 7:5
[26] Genesis 37:8-11
[27] Psalm 69:8-9 (NIV)

8

Cousin John

Six months[1] before the angels appeared to my parents to tell them the news of my impending birth, my mother's cousin, Elizabeth, and her husband, Zechariah, received a similar visit. Both were getting on in years and had never been able to have children.

Zechariah was a priest whose priestly division, that of Abijah, took turns to perform duties in the temple in Jerusalem. On one occasion when he was there burning incense, an angel (our chief messenger Gabriel[2]) told Zechariah that he and Elizabeth would become parents of a son they should call John. John was never to drink wine, and would be filled with our Holy Spirit. He would go before me to prepare people for my arrival. He was also compared with Elijah, and would function like the erstwhile preacher of repentance. The prophet Malachi had foretold[3] his coming to prepare the way for me.

Not surprisingly, Zechariah was rather dubious as to how he and his wife would bear a child, old as they were.[4] The angel told him that because he had doubted our message to him, he would be dumb until John was born. The people outside the temple thought he seemed to be

---

1 Luke 1:26
2 Luke 1:19
3 Malachi 3:1; Matthew 11:10; Luke 1:17
4 Luke 1:18

taking a long time to perform his priestly duties, but were even more surprised when he came back out and couldn't speak!

Months later, after his son's birth, Zechariah wrote the name we had told him to give his son, which was different from the one he would traditionally have been given, and my Father enabled him to speak again[5]. And how he did, as our Spirit opened his eyes to the truth of our redemptive plan, and of the role his newborn son had to play in preparing the way for it[6].

Having had a similarly auspicious pre-start in life to me, it was no surprise to me, growing up, to discover alongside prophecies in the Scriptures about my own life and purpose, passages foretelling Cousin John and his life. Clothed just like Elijah,[7] and preaching in the wilderness to all who would listen, John was to make the way clear for my ministry, challenging people about the imperfect lives they led and leading them into repentance.[8] Whenever we met, as we got old enough to understand them, we would usually end up studying the Scriptures together and trying to work out what they meant for us.

My mother told me she had visited her cousin, Elizabeth, in the hill country of Judea, while both were pregnant with the two of us. When Elizabeth heard my mother's greeting, the as yet unborn baby John leapt in her womb.[9] Filled with my Father God's Spirit, Elizabeth was able to prophesy over us, that my mother, Mary, would be blessed among women for believing the unbelievable news given to her by the angel, and that I, her Lord, would be blessed. Whereupon my mother was inspired to sing a beautiful prayer[10] that echoed the one prayed[11] by Hannah years earlier after her son Samuel had been born. Both songs spoke of the hungry being fed, the humble being lifted up, pain being forgotten, and of God looking after his people. This was our passion, our heartbeat. These were the things that had brought me here. These

---

[5] Luke 1:64
[6] Luke 1:67-79
[7] 2 Kings 1:8; Matthew 3:4; Mark 1:6
[8] Isaiah 40:3; Malachi 4:5; Matthew 11:14; Luke 1:17; John 1:23
[9] Luke 1:39-41
[10] Luke 1:46-55
[11] 1 Samuel 2:1-10

were the things that Isaiah had foretold Cousin John coming to prepare the way for.

As I've said, my mother, Mary, bottled up many events in her heart and doubtless bore a lot of pain and worry. John's mother too had her own set of worries; John did not follow his father, Zechariah, into the traditional role of priest, and Elizabeth had to watch her son grow up into an undeniably odd sort of character, by most measures. There are not many people who hang out in a desert, wearing clothes made from camel hair and held up by an old leather belt, nor whose staple diet consists of locusts and wild honey.[12] Both of these are pretty hard to collect: the locust because of the lightning quick reflexes working its oversized legs to dodge anyone trying to catch it; and the honey because of the industrious bees that produce it, who are more than likely to sting intruders in defence of their supply of food. Fair enough, wouldn't you say?

By the time Pontius Pilate had become the Roman governor of Judea[13] in what calendars will later call AD26, John lived mostly in the Desert of Judea, and went around the desert preaching a message of repentance, urging people to turn from their wicked ways because the kingdom of heaven was near. He was not one to mince his words. Calling people a "brood of vipers"[14] does not endear you to them! He also didn't mind how high-up his audience was, and courted the displeasure of King Herod, tetrarch of Galilee, for his swingeing criticism of him after he had married Herodias, the wife of his brother Philip (who was tetrarch of Ituria and Traconitis)[15].

Yet despite his forthrightness, John's message struck home with many, who, once they got to know about him, would make their way out into the desert to listen to him and a message[16] they were already familiar with. Those who realised that they needed to change and live differently responded to John's words by immersing themselves in the River Jordan. This has long been a symbol for us Jews of the old being

---

12 Matthew 3:4
13 Luke 3:1
14 Luke 3:7
15 Matthew 14:3-4; Mark 6:17-18; Luke 3:1,19; cf. Josephus (Antiquities of the Jews XVIII.5.4)
16 1 Kings 8:33-34; Isaiah 55:6-7

washed away and a person made clean.[17] John knew that this 'baptism' by water was only a precursor of the baptism I would bring in our Spirit.[18] The water was an everyday symbol of cleansing; our Holy Spirit would actually do the work of the cleansing taking place in people's hearts.

There came a point where I knew that my ministry was to start. It had to be public, and publicly acknowledged. The people were waiting for the Messiah promised in Scripture, and they needed to start considering whether the moment in history had arrived when God was stepping in. I was thirty[19] now, the traditional age at which priests began their duties, which we originally prescribed through Moses and Aaron to the Kohathite Levites for looking after the most holy things of the Tent of Meeting[20]. It was also the age at which an earlier saviour of the nation, Joseph, started serving the Egyptian Pharaoh – rising to be his second-in-command – and at which the shepherd boy turned giant-killer, David, became the revered king of Judah[21]. It was time.

And so one day I too made my way down to the River Jordan, which winds its way for nearly two hundred miles (merely sixty miles as the crow flies) from the Sea of Galilee to the Salt Sea, falling over three hundred and fifty cubits[22] as it does so. It is not the wide, navigable current some people imagine, such as the Nile in Egypt[23] or the Oder and Rhine rivers in the northern Roman Empire[24], though it does swell with the spring rains. Rather, with the exception of rapids through a few deep, narrow ravines, it is largely a gently meandering river, struggling to retain its water in the heat of the desert, before reaching Earth's lowest point on land, more than eight hundred cubits below sea level.

---

[17] e.g. Exodus 29:4-5, 30:20; Leviticus 15:13; 2 Kings 5:14
[18] Luke 3:16
[19] Luke 3:23
[20] Numbers 4:3
[21] Genesis 41:46; 2 Samuel 5:4
[22] Approx. 135' or 41m; see 'Measurements' note, page 310
[23] Average 2.8km wide north of Aswan (various internet sources, e.g. Kjeilen)
[24] Part of the E. / W. borders of Germany, both navigable for much of their length

I found John at a bend in the river near Bethany – the one the other side of the Jordan,[25] called Bethabara, where the gentle but persistent current had patiently carved out a pool of sorts from the sandy riverbank. When he saw me, the excitement we had often shared when we were younger, reading the different prophecies on our lives, erupted once again as he announced[26] to the throng of people already present that I was the Lamb of God who would take away the sins of the world. Any Jew listening would understand this as saying that I was the Messiah the Jewish nation had long been waiting for.

Once we had embraced and I had made it clear that I had come for baptism, John became somewhat doubtful. "I ought to be baptised by you," he said, "not the other way round!"

I assured him that he should baptise me, as we had to show that I was thus consecrated to God, my heavenly Father, and that he approved of me.[27] By baptising me and speaking the words he did, John would be announcing the start of my ministry as Messiah. John nodded his agreement, and we went down into the water together. The significance of the moment overwhelmed my thoughts; my ministry among the people, those my heavenly Father and I wanted to draw back into friendship with us, was about to start!

When John had baptised me in the water, and as I was praying, the clouds above us parted as the rays of the sun powered their way through and my Father's Spirit descended on me in the visible form of a dove. This gave tangible confirmation both to John, who had seen his prophetic utterances fulfilled in this moment,[28] and to the people present of who I was and that God was starting to work his purposes out.

It was also a moment when I felt the love of my heavenly Father and his affirmation. As the dove descended, my Father spoke out from heaven: "This is my Son, whom I love; with him I am well pleased."

This was the real start of what we had planned all those years before. Now I was to begin preaching the awesome good news of our

---

[25] John 1:28
[26] John 1:29
[27] Matthew 3:13-15
[28] John 1:29-34

love and redemption to humankind. Now I would prepare people for the sacrifice we intended to make, to enable them to have friendship with us.

Before I could start out on that, though, I had my own demanding time of preparation before me.

9

Testing Times

When you're about to start out on a large project, or an exam, a major speech, a competition, or any sort of new chapter in your life, it is good, necessary even, to have a time of reflection, of gathering one's thoughts, concentrating them towards the goal to be achieved, of drawing strength for the job that lies ahead. This was what I now required, both to prepare myself mentally, and to show that I was able to live up to those things I was here to preach about.

I had to prove myself fit and perfect enough for the sacrifice I was going to make for my heavenly Father, on the people's behalf, a few years down the line. As I mentioned before, a sacrifice must be perfect, but it must also be made with your heart in the right place. I needed to prove myself up to the job. And so my life as the carpenter of Nazareth was over. My brothers had learned the trade with me and were able to provide for the family. My vocation was now to fulfil the purposes for which I had left heaven.

The Judean desert stretches westwards from the Salt Sea up into the Judean Mountains.[1] Bethlehem, the town of my birth, lies at its north-western tip. It is not a constantly shifting sand-dune landscape such as the African Sahara, though there is plenty of sand, but a rugged, mountainous area full of breathtaking views. Various groups of rebels

---

[1] Details here and below from ThinkIsrael.com

and zealots find places of refuge here, such as the fortress at Masada that King Herod (who ordered the slaughter of infants after I was born) had built some sixty years ago. But the desert also offers solitude for monks and hermits, to which group I suppose Cousin John would count himself. Several rivers have carved canyons up to a thousand cubits deep. Some of these carry water all year round, providing green oases of refreshment for the sparse population and those who travel through the otherwise arid and inhospitable terrain.

This was the landscape into which our Spirit now led me. The relative coolness provided by the presence of the water gave way to a blistering heat up in the hills. I wandered from one valley to another, but preferred the ridges and plateau-topped mountains with their peaceful solitude. The valleys provided water to quench the thirst that results from sweating out much moisture with exertion, but up on the mountaintops I could pray and draw close to my heavenly Dad.

At my baptism, my Father in heaven had commissioned and anointed me as the Messiah.[2] Now I had to decide how I was going to be that Messiah. Through our Spirit's promptings, my Father initiated this first test of my resolve.[3] Could I prove myself the perfect sacrifice needed to fulfil the old law? To do that, I could not give in to the temptations of the devil.

Daily, he would try to knock me off course. Just when I thought I was strong, enjoying the view from the top of a ridge, and talking in prayer with my Father, the devil would crash in with a reminder of my hunger, telling me that, surely, God didn't care about me, else why would he put me through such privations, never mind what was to come? There was no way I could make a difference and fulfil my mission!

When you put something through a test, you want it to succeed. It might be that the rabbi wants to see how well you have learnt the Scriptures, or you need to get your camel through its annual 'Mules and Other Transport' health check (desperately hoping it will pass the

---

2   Thoughts based on John & Walley, ch.6
3   Matthew 4:1; Mark 1:12

emissions...)[4] You don't put yourself or whatever it is through the test in order to fail. My Father and I allow you to be tested in life so that you can succeed and grow in your faith and in trusting us.

On the other hand, when the devil tempts you, he is willing you to fail. He knows that if he can persuade you to make the easier, attractive, but wrong choices, he will control you. Give in once, and it's a lot harder to resist the next time.

All of us face such temptations. I have already said that the devil has always made the wrong way appear right – easier, appealing, more attractive. He did it to me again at the end of forty days of wandering in the desert, praying and fasting.

I was hungry. Our Spirit had led me through the desert for what was a significant number of days, reminiscent of Moses' forty days and nights on Mount Sinai, writing the Ten Commandments on the stone tablets[5]; and which also recalled the forty years spent by the people of Israel wandering through the desert after their disobedience[6]. My time in the desert would mark me out as the new saviour of the people, and as a representative of the new Israel, those who are obedient to God.

The devil came and entered straight into my consciousness at my point of need. This is so often how he operates. Pangs of hunger had seemingly torn my stomach apart, but while they had subsided after several days, I was weak now and had lost a lot of weight. Suddenly, out of nowhere, there on the ground in front of me were a couple of smooth, perfectly-rounded stones that you would have mistaken for freshly-baked loaves of bread had you seen them in front of an oven. A feast for the eyes, if an unpleasant surprise for your teeth. (How often does temptation look like that yet bring such consequences when given in to?) I could all but smell them, remembering the scent of freshly baked bread that would permeate the house whenever my mother decided to bake some.

---

4 MOT = Ministry Of Transport; (British) annual vehicle safety test
5 Exodus 34:28
6 e.g. Deuteronomy 2:7, 8:2

"If you are the Son of God, tell these stones to become bread."[7] It was actually a double-pronged approach. Was he sowing seeds of doubt about my identity and thus about the reason for my coming? I was indeed the Son of God, which fact the devil well knew, and he was goading me into proving it by using my divine powers to address my very real physical need of sustenance. But by doing so, he was actually challenging me to act independently of my Father's will and use my powers for my own ends. That would have made me no different from the people we were trying to get back into relationship with us by my being here in the first place, and thus not worthy to make the required sacrifice.

When you are physically weak, it's difficult to think straight and easy to give in to such temptation. I had to dig deep within me to rebuff him, quoting from Scripture. "It is written: 'Man does not live on bread alone, but on every word that comes from the mouth of God.'"[8]

Food is not enough to sustain wellbeing; you need the Word of God too: the written words of Scripture, but also me, the Word, as my friend John will write[9] one day. Whenever the devil comes on the attack, you need to look to God and to His promises. His Word has all you need to rebuff his suggestions and false accusations.

Since he had no answer to the Word of God, the devil changed tack. He led me in a vision to the highest point of the temple in Jerusalem. Herod had the new temple built some fifty years back, extending the original footprint of the Temple Mount but constructing the temple itself on the remaining foundations of the old one. The highest part towers a hundred cubits.[10] There were milling crowds of worshippers in the various courts of the temple.

"If you are the Son of God, throw yourself down."[11] (There he was again, goading me about my identity, and inciting me to prove it.) "For

[7] Matthew 4:3 (NIV); Luke 4:3 (NIV)
[8] Deuteronomy 8:3 (NIV); Matthew 4:4 (NIV); Luke 4:4 (NIV)
[9] John 1:1-2,14
[10] See 'The Temple' note, page 309
[11] Matthew 4:6 (NIV)

it is written: 'He will command his angels to lift you up, so that you will not strike your foot against a stone.'" [12]

The sheer audacity of it! The devil quoting Scripture at me! And misquoting it at that, missing out the bit about guarding me in all my ways. *My* ways, which are *God's* ways; not his ways, the devil's. My way is the way of obedience to my Father, the way of presenting a perfect sacrifice. That doesn't allow for taking shortcuts or the easy way out. The devil also conveniently forgot the following sentence, which talks about me trampling on him!

Oh, it would have been so easy to jump off the top, no safety net, an angelic bungee cord pulling me back up again to safety. What a PR stunt that would have been! The crowds below would have worshipped me instantly. Only, not for the right reasons. I did not come to be hailed in a frenzy of popularity, but to be exalted by my Father because I had obeyed him. This is what we urged Joshua to do, so that he would prosper and be successful. [13] It is the wisdom we showed Isaiah and Jeremiah a glimpse of, when they foretold [14] my coming and what I would do. And it is what we urge you to do when the devil tempts you to take a shortcut. Meditate on our words and draw on your knowledge of our laws to rebut the devil when he tries to trick you into disobeying them.

He was wanting me to test my heavenly Father. So I told him straight, quoting from the laws we gave the Israelites through Moses. "It is also written: 'Do not put the Lord your God to the test.'" [15]

He knew there was no answer to that and again tried another course of action. This time, and in another kind of vision, the devil led me up a high mountain from which all the kingdoms of the world could be seen. [16] In front of us was Herod's small but richly endowed kingdom full of palaces, aqueducts, hilltop fortresses such as Masada, the seaport of Caesarea, and, of course, Jerusalem's enlarged and spectacularly rebuilt temple. Surrounding the entire Mediterranean Sea, the Roman

---

[12] Psalm 91:11-13 (NIV)
[13] Joshua 1:7-8
[14] Isaiah 52:13; Jeremiah 23:5; see also Philippians 2:8-9
[15] Deuteronomy 6:16 (NIV); Matthew 4:7 (NIV); Luke 4:12 (NIV)
[16] Matthew 4:8

Empire stretched as far as Britannia, with Rome at its centre, containing Caesar's palace, the Colosseum and other stadia, mosaic-covered baths, triumphal arches and marble columns. To the North, Germanic tribes formed and broke alliances as they sought to increase their influence and lands. To the East, Chinese dynasties had built great walls spanning thousands of miles to keep invading Mongol tribes from the North, and each other, out of their territories. Far to the West and across the expanse of sea called the Atlantic, the Mayan Empire straddled the thin strip of land between the Americas. Some of its pyramids are covered with a new layer every fifty-two years when the cycles of the Sun and Venus coincide, part of an advanced calendar system.[17]

The devil pointed out the splendour of all these glorious empires, and said he would give me all of them if only I would bow down and worship him. As if they were his to give me! Yes, he rules this world in the sense of holding many captive in sin and guilt, just as he tricked the first man and woman. That is why I came, after all. But who holds power over the nations? Who grants power to their rulers? Certainly not the devil! God alone rules over the nations. No-one has power except that he grants it.[18]

"Away from me, Satan!" I told the devil. "For it is written, 'Worship the Lord your God, and serve him only.'"[19]

At that, the devil left me in peace, for the time being. He would seek out other opportunities later,[20] but for now, he was defeated; this battle was won. As I said, knowing God's word means you can defeat the devil, for it is truth and he can bring nothing against it.

Angels came and attended me. We sometimes use angels, servants[21] from the heavenly realm, at special moments when help is required, or when a special message is to be delivered. They are there to serve us – and you. More often than not, we work through our friends, those who have already learned to trust us. They are quite likely to be viewed as angels by those they have helped!

---

[17] See 'Mayan Pyramids' note, page 310
[18] Psalm 22:28, 47:7-8; John 19:11
[19] Deuteronomy 6:14 (NIV)
[20] Luke 4:13
[21] Hebrews 1:14; Revelation 19:10, 22:9

This particular time of testing was over. My heavenly Father had helped me succeed as I kept my eyes on him and on his Word. The sacrifice would be acceptable, and our saving plan could swing into action. Now it was time for me to go out and start proclaiming this good news. And for that, I needed to recruit a few disciples, close friends who would learn from me and carry on the work after I returned to my Father in heaven.

10

Early Enquirers and Wedding Wine

The next day, buoyed up by having been able to defeat the devil's temptations, bubbling over in the power of our Spirit and invigorated to start telling people about our love for them, I resolved to return to provincial Galilee. I wanted to start preaching about the life-giving freedom we yearned to bring, and to start looking for suitable candidates to be my apprentices.

The first people who proved to be interested in learning more about me and what I was preaching were actually with Cousin John. I was walking past, when John spotted me and proclaimed as he had the day before, "See there, the Lamb of God!" This intrigued two of his followers, who would have understood the sacrifice implied by this expression, and they started out after me. I sensed they were behind, turned to them and asked what they wanted.

"Rabbi," they asked in response, "where are you staying?"[1]

---

1 John 1:38 (NIV)

An odd-sounding question, but one from which I deduced that they wanted to know where I was coming from, what it was that this "Lamb of God" (as their teacher John had labelled me) was about.

"Come with me, and see for yourselves!"

Andrew was one of the two, and after spending the remainder of the day with me he went off and fetched his brother Simon to have a look for himself.

Simon is an ox of a man with a fiery demeanour, but you know where you stand with him. He says things as he sees them, no messing. As I would find, he doesn't always get it right, but I recognised that I could rely on him and build my kingdom with him, and am still confident that I can do so. Straightaway I gave him the nickname Cephas. That means 'rock' in the Aramaic we speak locally; the same name in the Greek, spoken more widely, is 'Peter'.[2]

A little way further on, we came across Philip, who originated from Bethsaida, as did Andrew and Peter.[3] "Follow me," I invited him too, which he accepted straightaway, going off to find his friend Nathanael, who was known as Tolmai's son ('Bar Tolmai' or 'Bartholomew'[4] in the Hebrew language) from Cana[5]. Now Nathanael had been sitting in the shade of a fig tree, having a break from his morning's labours, when Philip found him. I am able to see such things because our Spirit prompts me as needed. This special knowledge was required in Nathanael's case because he didn't believe that anything good could come from Nazareth, my hometown,[6] which lies about three hours' walk from his, Cana. I needed to persuade him.

So when Philip told him that I, Jesus of Nazareth, son of Joseph, was the one Moses wrote[7] about in the law, and that other prophets had written[8] about, he was sceptical to say the least. I surprised him when he arrived by hailing him as a true Israelite in whom nothing is false.

"How do you know me?" he asked in amazement.

---

2 John 1:42
3 John 1:44
4 e.g. MacArthur (pp. 135, 138)
5 John 21:2
6 John 1:46
7 e.g. Deuteronomy 18:15
8 e.g. Isaiah 53; Jeremiah 23:5; Zechariah 9:9, 12:10

"I saw you sitting under the fig tree before Philip spoke to you,"[9] I replied, using that special knowledge.

Knowing people's characters, what is really in their hearts, is another insight the Spirit gives me.[10] Despite his scepticism regarding Nazareth, I knew that Nathanael possessed a heart that longed for the truth. He immediately declared my identity.

"Rabbi, you are the Son of God and King of Israel."[11]

I gently chided him that he had believed because of what I had known about him, and promised him he would see the sort of thing that Jacob could only dream of.[12] "Indeed, you shall see heaven open, and the angels of God ascending and descending on the Son of Man."[13]

Nathanael was dumbfounded.

After making these initial contacts, I headed with my inquisitive band of new followers up to Cana, a three-day journey from Bethabara where John was baptising. We were invited to a friend's wedding celebration,[14] which was going to go on for a week, as such festivities do in these parts. My mother was already there helping with arrangements.

Several days into proceedings she came to me and declared that the wine had run out. This was hugely embarrassing for the bridegroom and his family, and for the master of the banquet, whose task it was to oversee the organisation of the feast for them. For you, running out of burgers at a barbecue would be a little embarrassing, but wouldn't come close. Running out of wine with most of your neighbours and wider circle of friends in attendance would cause a social catastrophe that would blight your reputation for years.

For a moment I wondered why my mother was coming to me about it, then almost simultaneously marvelled at her faith and expectation that now was the opportunity for me to start to demonstrate that I was the Messiah. She knew from all those

---

9 John 1:48 (NIV)
10 John 2:24-25
11 John 1:49 (NIV)
12 Genesis 28:12
13 John 1:51 (NIV)
14 John 2:1-2 (and following)

breathtaking words spoken before and after my birth, and from her own knowledge of Scripture and of the prophecies we would study together as I grew up, that this was my destiny. Perhaps she understood that even better than I did.

However, my destiny as Messiah would be shown later with the sacrifice I would make, and that moment had not yet come.

"Woman," I asked her respectfully,[15] "what is that to you or me?" I was saying to her that this was not part of the plan, but 'leave it to me'.[16] She understood it as such and, in faith that I would do something to address the problem, simply instructed the servants of the bridegroom's household to do whatever I told them.

Outside, there stood six large clay jars of the sort used for ceremonial purification washing. These had a capacity of two or three measures each – ten or fifteen bucketfuls.[17] My fellow Jews feel that they become ceremonially unclean during the normal circumstances of daily life,[18] so a lot of water is required for such festivities involving large numbers, so that people can wash their hands.

I figured the six jars ought to provide enough for the rest of the week (of wine, that is), so had a quiet word with the servants and instructed them to fill the jars with water. After they had filled them right to the brim, I handed one of them a goblet and told him to take some to the master of the banquet; much as you might experience a waiter in a restaurant giving the person at the head of a table a small sample in a glass to give his consent to. Of course, only the servants knew where the contents of the goblet had come from.

You will remember my friend Peter's comparison of time.[19] Well, much of what I did while the servants were approaching the person in charge, was to compress the time it usually takes for a miracle that we cause to happen every year: that is, the time for water (normally drawn up by vines from the ground and into the bunches of grapes that they grow on their branches) to turn (via a wine-press and large clay jars or

---

[15] See 'Addressing Women' note, page 310
[16] St. Ireaneus, Against Heresies III.17.7 (quoted by Hunt, 1998)
[17] 20-30 gallons; 1 measure = 18-27 gallons or 75-115 litres (NIV text note)
[18] NIV Study Bible footnote to John 2:6
[19] See page 18

new wineskins) into that delicately flavoured liquid called wine. To that accelerated process, I added the sugars usually formed by photosynthesis and the flavour-rich tannins that collect in a grape's skin. And because I love to be extravagant when I give to others, well, they just had to be in precisely the right proportions to make it a top-quality one.

The master of the banquet was overwhelmed; he was used to the choicest wine being served early on in festivities when people are, shall we say, a little more discerning of its taste. Later on, when they're not, people generally serve cheaper wine. He couldn't understand the best being saved until so far on into the party.[20]

This whole episode served as a sign – the first sign I performed – of my Father and my kingdom. It caused my new followers to believe in me and in what I had preached thus far.[21] After the wedding festivities were over, my family and friends and I descended from the hill country around Cana to Capernaum, on the shores of Lake Galilee. I stayed there with them for a few days, after which I headed south with my disciples towards Jerusalem, some ninety miles distant.[22]

[20] John 2:10
[21] John 2:11
[22] John 2:12-13,17

11

Water and Spirit

The donkey has stopped now, independently of any signal I might have just given it. It seems to know that we have reached today's destination. We have made our way round the southern end of the temple, passing the steps to the Huldah gates and Gentile entrance. As you come round the south-western corner of the Temple Mount, the covered portico of the Xystus[1] faces you, a smoothly paved Greek exercise area and meeting place. Beyond that, and just behind us now, lies the Hasmonean palace.

I dismount from the donkey and leave him in the hands of one of my followers. All around us, the people that have given me such an enthusiastic welcome are pressing in.

I can see Philip talking with a group of men a few yards away. They appear to be Greeks[2]; they must be here for the Passover celebrations. Gentile believers are tolerated as far as the outer temple court, reserved for them. The sun is getting low now, its rays reaching out under a dotted line of clouds stretching from the horizon to where we are, but it's still pleasantly warm in the spring sunshine.

Philip has just had a word with Andrew, and now both of them are approaching me. "The men over there would like to see you."

---

[1] NIV map at Mark 4; Gottheil & Krauss ("Xystus")
[2] John 12:20-36

I look past Philip and Andrew, and motion the men over, making a point of including them in what I'm about to say.

"The time has come for the Son of Man to be glorified."[3] (The time that hadn't arrived yet when my mother spoke to me at the wedding in Cana; now it is imminent.) "A grain of wheat has to fall into the ground and die, but when it dies, it will come forth and produce many seeds." (Remember what I said when talking about my Dad and me creating the seeds on plants and trees?) I don't have much more time now, just days. These Gentile men, as well as my Jewish compatriots, need to decide to live for me. "Whoever loves his life here too much to serve me, will lose it. Whoever makes room in his life here to serve me, will keep it eternally. Whoever serves me follows me wherever I am, and my Father honours that person." I am feeling troubled by what lies ahead. I voice my fears: "Should I ask my Father to save me from this hour? No, this hour is what I came for." Then I add a short, desperate prayer: "Father, glorify your name!"

I have barely uttered these words when my Father's voice explodes like a thunderclap over us: "I have glorified it, and will glorify it again!"[4] Some of those around me are attributing what they just heard to a simple release of pent-up cumulous energy; others are saying that it was an angel speaking.

"This voice was for your benefit, not mine," I tell my listeners. "Now is the time for judgement on this world, and the prince of this world will be driven out."[5]

I am here to bring people back to my Father, to make the sacrifice that allows them into His presence. However, for Satan and those who reject this sacrifice, my coming will involve judgement.

Now I show them how I will make that sacrifice, and the kind of death I am to go through. "When I am lifted up, I will draw all people to myself."[6]

---

[3] John 12:23 (NIV)
[4] John 12:28 (NIV)
[5] John 12:30-31 (NIV)
[6] John 12:32 (NIV)

Of course, this crowd has just honoured me as their king, their Messiah. Talk of being 'lifted up' doesn't harmonise with their worldview. Someone is speaking up now, mentioning the law, saying that the Christ will remain forever. "Who is this 'Son of Man'[7] that he should be lifted up?"

Some of them still don't seem to understand the nature of my identity. I use an analogy I have used before[8] to explain that they will only have me a little longer. "Put your faith in the light while you have it, so that you may become children of light[9] and know where you are going."

I end the meeting at this point, gathering my disciples and heading for the temple. The bridge across Tyropoeon Street, which runs below in a shallow valley, takes us into the temple courtyard. It is already late now,[10] and things are quiet, so we decide to leave again and return to Bethany. After a leisurely hour's walk, we are back at Martha and Mary's, where we stayed last night.

A new morning dawns bright and early, and we head back towards the city. I'm hungry; we left Bethany not wanting to wake our hosts and therefore without breakfast. Ahead I can see a fig tree in leaf. I wonder whether there is any fruit on it, but as I reach the tree, I find nothing but leaves. It isn't really the season for figs after all.[11]

My disciples look bewildered as I rebuke the tree. "May no-one ever find fruit on you again!" The tree illustrates well the religiosity of the Pharisees, particularly: all leaves but no fruit. My Father and I desire so much more from your religion than the practice of mere traditions – it should lead you to a living relationship with us!

We're reaching the temple now. It is no longer graced by the quiet of last night, and I am appalled anew by the irreverent scene before me.

---

7   John 12:34 (NIV)
8   John 8:12; cf. John 1:4
9   John 12:36 (NIV)
10   Mark 11:11
11   Mark 11:13

If anything, it has become even worse than I found at the start of my public ministry.

It was almost time for the annual Passover festival, the first since starting my public life, when I reached Jerusalem from Capernaum,[12] and so the city was filling up with pilgrims fulfilling their obligation to celebrate the feast at the temple[13]. Back in its imposing courts, I remembered the time almost twenty years previously when, as an excited twelve year-old, I had sat and eagerly discussed prophecies with the temple priests and respected teachers of the law.

Now I was faced with a cacophony of noise: lowing cattle, bleating sheep and cooing doves, mixed in with the hoarse shouts of traders doing their best to attract the attention of both weary travellers and bemused locals. The latter were themselves weary, though more of the presence of so many visitors to their city, while at the same time appreciating the extra income gained by their appearance.

Jerusalem's temple authorities always profit greatly from the presence of all the extra visitors, though they would never admit it. Money traders do a roaring trade and make large profits for the temple. The unfortunate animals may be purchased with whatever currency people are carrying on them, the traders are not fussy. However, the temple tax of half a shekel[14] per person has to be paid with coins acceptable to the temple authorities, which means the silver shekels minted in Tyre or Syria[15]. Most foreign coins, including shekels minted further afield, sport images of foreign Greek or Roman gods, or of the Roman Emperor, who is revered as one, and are therefore not acceptable.[16]

All families, visitors and locals alike, are required by the law, and according to their means, to sacrifice an animal at the temple for the Passover festival each year, remembering the sacrifice made for the first Passover meal by our forebears on the desperate night before they

---

[12] John 2:12-13
[13] Exodus 12:14; Deuteronomy 16:16; cf. Matthew 26:17
[14] Exodus 30:15; Matthew 17:27
[15] Holroyd (www.ccu.edu/biblicalcoins)
[16] Unger (p.883)

commenced their exodus from Egypt. The sheer numbers of lambs slain each year are beyond imagination.[17] Travellers reaching the city do need to be able to buy their sacrificial animals when they arrive there. But not here in the hallowed temple courts! This place is supposed to be a place of sanctuary and prayer! Gentiles, who are not allowed in the main part of the temple, are supposed to be able to come to these outer courts to pray,[18] but the people here had turned the place into a den of thieves[19]!

My heart burned with righteous indignation and zeal for my Father's house.[20] I had to make a statement. Foreseeing my arrival, the prophet Zechariah stated that "on that day there will be no longer a trader in the house of the Lord Almighty"[21]. That day has come – I am now here! There is no room for sin in my Father's house; the corrupt practices of the old temple are to be replaced by the new temple: me!

I found some old hemp cords by one of the stands and plaited them into a makeshift whip. This I used to drive out the animal traders and moneychangers, turning over their tables. I told the dove sellers, who provided the poor with sacrifices they could afford, to get their things out of there.

"How dare you turn my Father's house into a market!"[22]

At this point, leading Jews stepped in and asked me to prove my authority with a miraculous sign.

"Destroy this temple," I said, speaking of myself in the future, "and I will raise it again in three days."[23]

Inevitably, they mistook what I said to refer to the temple building, and mocked me. "It has taken forty-six years to build this temple so far, and you reckon you can raise it in three days!"[24]

The excited crowd that had gathered round this spectacle soon dissipated after that, and the remainder of the Passover Feast passed

---

[17] See 'Sacrificial Lambs at Passover' note, page 309
[18] Isaiah 56:3-7; Mark 11:17
[19] Jeremiah 7:11; cf. Matthew 21:13; Mark 11:17; Luke 19:46
[20] Psalm 69:9; John 2:17
[21] Zechariah 14:21. NIV reads 'Canaanite'; footnote, and others, 'merchant'.
[22] John 2:16 (NIV)
[23] John 2:19 (NIV); see also NIV Study Bible footnote
[24] John 2:20 (NIV)

quietly, though I would minister to people's needs as our Spirit prompted me, in miraculous ways that were signs to the people, many of whom believed in who I was.[25]

One night while we were still in Jerusalem, a Pharisee and member of the Jewish ruling council, the Sanhedrin, came to see me. His name was Nicodemus. Now, the Pharisees are teachers of God's commandments as recorded by Moses. However, many generations of oral tradition have augmented them with numerous regulations, rigidly applied to all conceivable minutiae of everyday life. What we had intended as a supportive framework has been overburdened with detail.[26]

Nicodemus made one of those statements that showed he was searching for the truth. He addressed me respectfully as a fellow Rabbi: "You are obviously a teacher who has come from God, as no-one could perform such miraculous signs otherwise."[27]

He was soliciting a reply, so much was obvious; but what was his question? As our Spirit prompted me to see his spiritual need, I declared that to see the kingdom of God, one must be born again.

"How can a man be born again when he is old?" he retorted.

Poor Nicodemus! The Pharisees, you see, rejected the message of repentance and baptism offered by Cousin John,[28] but they are still caught up in centuries of Jewish cultural tradition. There are several defining moments in a Jewish man's life when he is considered to be 'born again'.[29] First, becoming a Jew under the Mosaic covenant;[30] in other words, converting to the Jewish faith. However, Nicodemus was born a Jew. Secondly, becoming a bar mitzvah, from which point you are obliged to observe the commandments. Then, getting married. My friends tell me that getting married certainly marks the birth of a new phase in your life, and to have become the member of the Sanhedrin he was, Nicodemus would have *had* to have been married[31]. Next:

---

[25] John 2:23

[26] cf. Matthew 15:1-9; Mark 7:1-13

[27] John 3:2

[28] Luke 7:30

[29] Wassell (Abound-in-Faith); Poyner-Levison (Beit Shalom Ministries)

[30] allowing for 'aliens' joining the community, e.g. Exodus 12:48; Numbers 15:15-16

[31] Wassell (Abound-in-Faith); Wilthew (2004)

becoming king, being ordained rabbi, or appointed rabban (the head of a rabbinical school). Well, Nicodemus still isn't a king, but he is both rabbi and rabban, which is why I addressed him as 'Israel's Teacher' a few moments later.

So, from his point-of-view, Nicodemus had already been 'born again' four times! He was, as a rabban, already 'old' and could imagine no further opportunities to be born again. He had done all the being born again he could possibly do! So I understood when he expressed surprise and asked, "How can this be?"

But in turn I was surprised that he didn't make the connection between the old covenant and the new one that I had already taught about and shown so many signs of.

"You are Israel's teacher, and don't understand these things?"[32]

I compared the sacrifice I was going to make with Moses lifting up the snake in the desert. Whoever was bitten by a real snake was saved by looking at the bronze snake he held up.[33] I too would be lifted up, for God my heavenly Father so loves the world that he gave me – his one and only son – so that whoever believes in me shall have eternal life.[34] He sent me here to save the world, and whoever looks to me will be saved and have life to the full, as we always planned for people to have.

Well, Nicodemus went away deep in thought, and I imagine will have taken on board what he had heard.[35] After this, my disciples and I left the bustle of the city and headed out into the rugged Judean countryside. We had some good quality time together, and baptised others who came and accepted our message.

Cousin John was also still baptising people, further north at Aenon, near Salim.[36] We heard that some of his followers got into a heated discussion with a certain Jew about ceremonial washing. They were also worried that I was now baptising more than he was. John graciously told them that his influence now had to decrease, while mine

[32] John 3:10 (NIV)
[33] Numbers 21:6-9
[34] John 3:16
[35] cf. John 7:50-52, 19:39-42
[36] John 3:22-23, 4:2

would increase. He had fulfilled his role, ordained before he was born, and was now deferring to the one whose presence he had come to announce and prepare the way for.

Word of all these events had got back to the Pharisees, who decided I was a threat to their authority and determined to kill me.[37] Why were these supposedly learned leaders of the people so blind to the salvation we had foretold through the prophets and longed to bring them? Their stubbornness continues to hold back our blessing from the people, for who else are they supposed to learn from?

For now, then, it was time to move on again, and so we headed back north towards Galilee, having to pass through Samaria on the way. When we had covered twenty miles or so and gone as far as Sychar, it had reached the sixth hour, the heat-laden middle of the day. I was tired from the exertion, so I sat down by Jacob's well, on the plot of land our forefather Jacob had given to his son Joseph. My disciples went off into town to find some food.[38]

The well still serves as the only water source for the whole village. It is hard work drawing up water from such deep wells – this one is over eighty cubits in depth[39] – and yet this is a task usually reserved for the women of each household. They typically come out in the early evening, after the overpowering heat of the day has subsided, and when doing the job is a little more comfortable.[40] So it was rather unusual when a Samaritan woman came to the well to draw water. The fact that she was a Samaritan was obviously not unusual; this was Samaria after all. No, it was the fact that she came out in the middle of the day, when the well would normally have been deserted. Her eyes shifted in a furtive glance towards me, risked but not intended to be noticed. At this point our Spirit gave me one of those insights.

"Could you draw me some water to drink?" I requested.

She was taken aback. My Jewish upbringing would have made me so too, except that I knew I was ultimately here for all people, not just

---

[37] John 4:1, 7:1
[38] John 4:4-6,8
[39] John 4:11. NIV footnote: depth of well found to be 138' (42m) in 1935.
[40] Genesis 24:11

the Jews. You see, Jews and Samaritans are like bugs and bleach – we don't get on. That has to do with some of our turbulent history.

After his invasion of Israel some seven hundred and fifty years ago, King Shalmaneser of Assyria deported most of the people to his country. He then brought foreigners in from Babylon and elsewhere, to resettle Samaria.[41] This ended up with mixed Jewish-Gentile marriages, which had been strictly forbidden under Moses,[42] and was one reason the remaining residents of Judah looked down on their compatriots. Some two hundred years later, the Jewish remnant of Judah was itself captured by the Babylonians, who destroyed the Jerusalem temple.[43] The people were again taken captive, but released by King Cyrus seventy years later (fulfilling Jeremiah's prophecy[44]), to go and rebuild the temple.[45] As Nehemiah recorded, the Samaritans gave them a hard time, opposing the rebuilding of the city walls and ridiculing them.[46]

So as you see, we Jews and Samaritans don't particularly get on. The returned Jewish exiles then, as the Jews to this day, regarded the Samaritans as second-class citizens. In fact – and on this point I'm almost ashamed to be Jewish – Jews regard Samaritans as unclean. If I were to use a drinking vessel of this woman, I would make myself ritually unclean. Hence her even greater astonishment at my asking for a drink.

Of course, I'm also a Jewish man and rabbi to boot. Jewish men hardly speak to their wives out on the street in public, much less an unknown woman, and for a rabbi to do so is even more unconventional.[47] But then, I never came to adhere to conventions, though I did come to fulfil the law.[48]

"How can a Jewish man like you ask a Samaritan woman like me for a drink?"[49]

---

[41] Kings 17. Deffinbaugh (2009); Historical Boys' Clothing (2009)
[42] e.g. Deuteronomy 7:1-4
[43] Kings 25
[44] Jeremiah 25:1-14; 2 Chronicles 36:21,22
[45] 2 Chronicles 36:22,23; Ezra 1:1-5
[46] Nehemiah 4
[47] Bohlin (2005)
[48] Matthew 5:17
[49] John 4:9 (GOD'S WORD)

After she had thus expressed her cultural surprise, I told her that if she knew the gift of God and who it was asking her for a drink, she would have asked for, and been given, living water. By this, I meant eternal life,[50] and I said that whoever drinks this living water would never thirst again.

"Sir, it's a deep well and you have nothing to draw water with. How are you going to get this 'living water'? Are you greater than our ancestor Jacob?"

Jacob had built the well for his family and livestock. When I said that whoever drinks the water that I give would never thirst again, she asked for some of this water, so that she wouldn't have to keep coming to the well.

At this point I brought into play what our Spirit had shown me. "Go and get your husband."

Her eyes narrowed slightly, and she denied having one.[51] I had hit a raw nerve. However, I affirmed her answer and proceeded to tell her she had had five husbands, and was currently living with a man to whom she was not married. The shame of all this was the reason she had come to the well at this time of day, knowing that she wouldn't have to face her townsfolk.

Shock flickered briefly across her face. Yet she quickly composed herself and deflected the conversation away from her own person to an old chestnut that the Jews and Samaritans had argued over for generations. To the Samaritans, Mount Gerizim is especially sacred.[52] The Jews hold that the temple in Jerusalem is the only place to worship God. How I long for these entrenched ideas to be superseded! They will be one day, and I told the woman that already people were worshipping God not with tradition but in spirit and truth. She countered with a Samaritan understanding that the Messiah (called the Christ) would come and explain everything to us.

---

[50] John 4:14
[51] John 4:17
[52] Deuteronomy 11:29, 27:12. Mount Gerizim is still where Samaritans re-enact the Passover. Wikipedia ("Mount Gerizim")

"I am he, speaking to you," I declared to her; the first time I had openly done so.

At that moment, our convoluted conversation was interrupted by the return of my disciples with some food. I could see that they were as surprised as the woman that I should be talking to her, though declined to say anything.[53] The woman disappeared without a word, leaving her jar behind, and my disciples tried to persuade me to eat something. I had still not even had a drink!

But I was on a roll, flushed from admitting to someone what I had long been reluctant to admit even to my human self, and from spreading the message of eternal life outside the four walls of the temple, outside Jerusalem even, to the people who needed to hear it. I told the disciples that my food was above their understanding, and indeed they misunderstood this, thinking someone else had been feeding me.

"My food is to do the will of him who sent me," I explained, "and to finish his work."[54]

I continued by saying that there were so many people that needed saving; the harvest was ripe. Wonderfully, some of them were already saved by the time the woman reappeared with half the town's population, who believed because of her testimony.[55] She had overcome her fear of judgement from people who knew her, to witness to what she had heard.

They asked me to stay in their town, which I did for two days, and many more again believed. This was the kingdom breaking out!

---

[53] John 4:27
[54] John 4:34 (NIV)
[55] John 4:39-41

12

Back in Galilee

From salvation-soaked Sychar we headed further north into Galilee and to my hometown Nazareth.[1] I felt buoyed up by the success of our mission and full of the Spirit. The Galilean people couldn't have been more welcoming.[2] Many had been in Jerusalem for the Passover, and had witnessed the scene in the temple and seen me in action elsewhere. However, I was also greeted with the news that Herod had imprisoned Cousin John because of his outspoken opposition to Herod's marriage to Herodias, his sister-in-law.[3]

On the Sabbath, I went into the local synagogue as normal. The elders had invited me to read from the Scriptures and comment on the passage. When it was time to read, I stood up, as was customary, and a bearded attendant handed me the well-used scroll containing the writings of the Prophet Isaiah.[4] I unrolled it towards the end, rolling the other end up as I did so, as far as the portion of text that talks about our Spirit resting upon me.

"The Spirit of the Lord has anointed me to preach good news to the poor,[5] bind up the broken-hearted, free the captives and

---

1 John 4:43; Luke 4:16
2 John 4:45; Luke 4:15
3 Matthew 4:12, 14:3-4
4 Luke 4:17; Isaiah 61:1,2
5 Isaiah 61:1; quoted in Luke 4:18 (NIV); cf. Isaiah 49:8 and Leviticus 25:10

downtrodden, give sight to the blind and announce the day of salvation."

Then I sat down to speak (as was also customary[6]), with everyone's eyes fastened on me intently. What did they expect me to say? People seemed to lap up my teaching in the synagogues,[7] but I knew their hearts were not really prepared to change.[8] I needed to challenge their preconceptions, particularly those about their supremacy in matters regarding God's salvation. They thought they were saved simply because they belonged to the Jewish people, made the right sacrifices, kept the right rules. It is hearts that we want,[9] an attitude of faith that relies on us and leads to justice being done, the poor being looked after, and all people being treated respectfully.

"Today, as you heard me read it, this passage has been fulfilled," I started, knowing that in their minds I was Joseph's son. While Isaiah was writing in the context of the Babylonian imprisonment, he was also hinting at the freedom from spiritual bondage and death that I was to bring. They had to understand that if they wouldn't listen, my mission would move to Gentiles who would. I said they would doubtless want me to do miracles in my hometown such as those they had seen me perform in Capernaum, and then continued by saying that a prophet is never accepted where he originates from. A little harsh, perhaps, given their initial welcome. But they had to see their own blindness!

I finished by citing instances in the Scriptures where not Jews but Gentiles had been helped by God's prophets.[10] After Elijah had pronounced judgement on King Ahab, who had turned away from us to worship Baal, he took refuge with, and assisted, a widow from Zarephath, a Gentile village near Sidon, even raising her son back to life through his desperate prayers. Naaman had been a commander of the army of the Gentile king of Aram, and was healed by Israel's leading prophet of the time, Elisha.

---

6   Matthew 5:1, 26:55; John 8:2; Acts 16:13
7   Luke 4:15,22
8   John 2:23-25
9   Hosea 6:6; Micah 6:6-8
10 Luke 4:25-26 ~ 1 Kings 17; Luke 4:27 ~ 2 Kings 5:1-14

At this, the synagogue erupted in an orgy of indignation. Clamouring voices competed from all sides; fists were raised to express resentment and anger. No rabbi should condemn Israel and pronounce God's favour on the Gentiles! Disorder was rapidly spreading, and it was aimed firmly in my direction. The incensed people rose up and drove me out of the synagogue all the way to the edge of town, which perches above a cliff-edge.[11] They were in a frenzy and intended to push me over the precipice. However, this was not in the plan, my time had not yet come, and in the confusion I managed to duck through the crowds and disappear. Time to leave.

I continued towards Capernaum, stopping for several days at Cana on the way, where I had given my first sign.[12] Another was about to follow, and salvation would accompany it. My desire always has been to show the love that my Father and I have for our people, and for them to respond in obedience and love of their own, prompted by our Spirit to serve us by serving others and addressing their needs.[13]

A certain royal official living in Capernaum, working in the service of King Herod, heard that I was in Cana, and must have travelled for five or six hours to come and see me. His son was lying sick at home, dying, and this man begged me to come and heal him.[14] I felt touched by his expectant faith, but expressed my concern that the people would only believe if they saw miraculous signs and wonders.

This did not deter the official, who urged me to accompany him before his ailing child died. I looked at him, saw the mixture of fear and faith in his eyes, felt my heart moved, and instructed him to go; his son would live. We later received reports that his servants met him the following day, while still on his way home, to say that his son was well again. They ascertained that he had recovered exactly when I had said that he would be okay. At that, the official and his whole household had believed – another family finding salvation and the friendship with

---

[11] Luke 4:29
[12] Luke 4:31; John 4:46; John 2:(1-)11
[13] Matthew 25:40
[14] John 4:46-47

us that we so long for! Moreover, a second sign had been performed to point the way there.

Finally, I too arrived at Capernaum, on the north shore of Lake Galilee, and determined to stay there for a while. This, incidentally, fulfilled another prophecy from Isaiah, which talked of a great light dawning over the land of Zebulun and Naphtali, two of the tribes of Israel dating from Jacob's time, who occupied the fertile land to the north and west of Lake Galilee.[15] I made my home right in the centre of what was their territory.

The kingdom of God was near, and I needed to go out and tell people about it. On the Sabbath, like the week before, I went to the synagogue and sat teaching the people.[16] I spoke from deep within me, from within my Father's heart and mine, and as the Spirit prompted, of the need for repentance and the nearness of God's kingdom.[17]

Suddenly, as I was speaking, a desperate-looking man some years older than me, who was possessed by a demon – an evil spirit – cried out at the top of his voice.[18] His stooping body convulsed as he did so, out of control, or rather, under the control of the evil force within.

"Ha! What do you want with us, Jesus of Nazareth? Have you come to destroy us? I know who you are – the Holy One of God!"[19]

Yes, even the evil spirits know who I am![20] But sometimes, Satan sends such demons as inhabited this shrieking man to corrupt what we created, causing mental disorders, violence, disease, rebellion against God.[21] The demon had no right to abuse the voice he was using, and he was distracting people's attention away from the teaching I was trying to give them and which they needed to hear.[22] Moreover, it was not good to gain public recognition, apparently from someone who was so obviously disturbed. I was not concerned for my reputation per se, but

---

[15] Matthew 4:13-16, NIV footnote

[16] Luke 4:31

[17] Matthew 4:17

[18] Using Luke 4:33 (before call of disciples); cf. Mark 1:23 (after call of disciples)

[19] Luke 4:34 (NIV)

[20] James 2:19

[21] John 10:20; Luke 8:26-29; Luke 13:11,16; Revelation 16:14 (NIV footnotes)

[22] Wilson ("Confronting Demons at Capernaum")

people needed to take seriously the message I had to bring, and anything that diminished that was undesirable.

Satan had no place here. "BE QUIET!" I thundered, indignation spilling over into a stern rebuke. You might not imagine me being angry, but when things exist so contrary to our intention of perfection, so harmful to one of our created children, or to the world we created for them, then our passion is aroused.

The demon threw the man to the ground one last time, without injuring him, and then departed from him for good. The man was free at last.

Of course, the news of this spread throughout the surrounding area like wildfire. The people were amazed and recognised that I taught with a higher authority, such that even evil spirits were bound to obey me. When my followers get hold of this, when they really understand what is possible in my name, why, they will find themselves doing even greater things![23]

The synagogue's congregation left in a buzz of excitement, and I walked over to Simon Peter's house. His mother-in-law was staying with them, but suffering from a high fever, and they asked me to help. Of course I would help! They had seen me deliver the man from the evil spirit, so they knew I could cope with a mere fever. But as eager as I was to help, it raised a nagging concern. Our mission could easily be undermined if healings were all I was allowed to do. If people came to me only expecting to be healed from physical ailments, but their hearts were not open to my teaching, then the saving work I had come to do would not be achieved.

However, for now I put such considerations aside, simply bent over Peter's mother-in-law and rebuked the fever. I felt healing power flow from me into her body, and the fever left her, banished. She was even able to get up and serve dinner for us. A refuge of relaxation and a chance to draw breath for a moment. Later that evening though, as the shimmering sun going down over Capernaum marked the end of the Sabbath, freeing its inhabitants from the restrictions on movement and

---

[23] John 14:12

carrying burdens, the people, who had noticed where I was staying, brought all their sick to be healed.

Their simple faith, though incomplete, touched me, and I had compassion for them. As earlier in the synagogue, demons that held some people as prisoners shouted out my name as I drove them from their victims. I rebuked them to be quiet. I needed to show by word and deed the sort of servant Messiah I was, rather than the Roman-conquering one hoped for by the people, before declaring myself openly. At this stage, if the people were to associate me with 'Messiah', with all that word's connotations, they would forcibly crown me king and my mission would be derailed.

By daybreak, I had already surfaced, and withdrew to a solitary place[24] to spend time with my Father. Attending to so many people's needs had been both exhilarating and exhausting. Life doesn't always go as you expect it: accidents happen and illnesses occur, which effects can drag you down with constant pain; you lose loved ones, especially distressing when it is sudden or, hardest to bear, when you lose a child; other people suddenly fall out with you or mistreat you, and feelings of worthlessness and depression can set in. Worst of all, evil spirits can sometimes take hold of a person and affect their entire being, just like the drugs you may be familiar with – or hopefully not – often affect people's once-normal behaviour and wreck their health, relationships and general well-being.

We hate all these things with a passion, my Father and I. So much unnecessary pain is caused by people following their own way instead of the good guidelines we gave them. That's why I was weary come the end of that evening, seeing so much pain and hurt. And also why I was exhilarated, having been able to help so many of the townspeople by delivering them of what was hurting them, and pronouncing forgiveness over them. At the same time, though, I had to consider the true nature of my mission, which was to preach a message of repentance and, at the end, to pay for the sins of the people and make them right with God again.

---

[24] Luke 4:42

Talking to my Dad would keep me on track with His purposes, just as it does for you when you pray to us for guidance and make time to listen to our Spirit prompting you. By the way, we don't mind how you address us in your prayers! As a human I have given you an example of addressing our Father in heaven. But he and I are one in our Spirit; I am in my Father and he is in me, and we even live in you through our Spirit![25] The thoughts of your heart are more important. No amount of fancy words will cover up wrong attitudes or motives, nor are they needed to solicit our attention. Just chat with us!

I wasn't alone for very long before the townsfolk came looking for me and, having found me, tried to persuade me to stay.[26] However, I had not come to work solely as a physician; I had the challenging message of repentance and the good news of the kingdom of God to preach, and stated plainly that I felt compelled to go to other towns with the same intent that had brought me to Capernaum, because that is why I was sent here.

And so I did just that, travelling around the area, visiting other towns, and teaching in their synagogues.[27] As before, sicknesses were healed, pain relieved, demons banished, epileptics freed from their seizures, the paralysed enabled to walk again.[28] All the imperfections, the deviations from what we had created as good, were treated and made good once more. The 'norm' was reinstated in people's lives. How often have you heard it said about some sad or bad state of affairs, "Oh, it's normal," or, "That's just how it is"? Nothing could be further from the truth; it's another of Satan's lies. It may be usual, sadly. But normal? Never!

As word of mouth carried these events to a wider audience, so many in that audience made their way to hear me speak and to ask for healing of their own. While a certain number made their way out of curiosity or even for entertainment, I found the faith of many of them humbling. People travelled miles – from all over the region of Syria, not

---

[25] John 14:9-21
[26] Luke 4:42
[27] Luke 4:44; Mark 1:39
[28] cf. Matthew 4:23-25

just Galilee – to come and experience me first-hand, following in my footsteps literally as these took me from town to town. People's dialects betrayed their origins as being from as far south as Jerusalem, some ninety miles away.[29]

Many saw everything that was happening and believed. For my part, I was delighted.

---

[29] Matthew 4:25; approx. 150km Jerusalem to Capernaum; 100km N to Sidon

13

Fishermen

Spring had given way to summer[1] when one clear, bright day I was walking along the shores of the Sea of Galilee. I had spent many weeks traversing the area around the north-western end of the lake, preaching and teaching, healing and driving out demons. Now it was time to gather around me a group of dedicated followers who would become my disciples – apprentices, learning from their master just as you would learn a trade, or like I had learned about carpentry and construction from my stepfather Joseph.

On a sandy beach bordered by palms, with walnut trees and olive groves in the background,[2] I came across my early followers, the brothers Andrew and Simon Peter. As you may recall, Andrew had been a follower of Cousin John, and had first started hanging out with me after my baptism, joined by his brother later that day. Now I wanted to ask them to join me full-time.

A multitude of people flocked round, listening to the word of God as I taught them from it.[3] It was difficult for many to see, and I imagined the surging crowd involuntarily forcing me into the water. Now, Andrew and Peter are fishermen by trade, and that morning they were sat in their boat at the water's edge, cleaning their nets after a fruitless

---

1   From the NIV Study Bible time-chart at Matthew 25
2   Josephus (War of the Jews III, 10, 8)
3   Luke 5:1

night's fishing. So I climbed into their sturdy, wooden boat, asking Simon Peter to put out a little from shore.[4] Andrew clambered aboard as well.[5] Once we had moved a few strokes from the shoreline, the expectant crowd had a much clearer view, and settled. I taught from the prophets, explored the system of sacrifices and what they were for, talked about a new covenant that would replace the old, and about their need for repentance.

When I was done, I decided to challenge Peter to trust me, and to recognise in me the fulfilment of the prophecies I had expounded upon. "Put out into deep water, and let down the nets for a catch."[6]

I knew it wouldn't make sense, and, sure enough, he started to complain. Doubtless, they were frustrated and had been grumbling that the fish stocks nowadays aren't what they were. Nevertheless, a little reluctantly – because it was me – he agreed. "Master, we've worked hard all night and haven't caught anything. But because you say so, I will let down the nets."

Sometimes we ask things of you that don't make sense, hoping that you will trust us anyway, and grow through the experience.

Simon and Andrew suddenly found the nets so full of fish that even with my help they couldn't drag them in. Their friends James and John, another pair of brothers who were also fishermen, were sitting on the edge of their boat nearby, also attending to their nets. All four would often ply the Sea of Galilee together. Working with a pair of boats could be useful for pulling in the nets when the catch was a heavy one, but also afforded the fishermen a sense of security when the winds that swept the sea whipped it up into a frenzy of frothy 'white horses' atop waves several feet high.

The lake is only thirteen miles long and eight wide, and not particularly deep, at most ninety cubits,[7] yet the storms that rage over it create a dangerously instable body of water. The fiercest storms occur when strong winds blow down from the southern end of the

---

4 Luke 5:3
5 Surmised from Matthew 4 and Mark 1
6 Luke 5:4b (NIV)
7 BibleWalks

mountainous area south of Mount Hermon, which we call Bashan and you know as the Golan Heights, to the East of the lake.[8] The men were used to such storms; they would have to learn to weather many others that would come our way. The worst for them – and me – still lies ahead.

But for now, it was a huge catch, and the nets were threatening to break. Simon and Andrew hailed the others over. We needed their help, and fast!

You know, when we ask you to do something difficult and the going gets tough, we always see to it that there are people around you to help. Have you never looked back and noticed that?

James and John arrived, and we filled both boats so full that they began to sink. The usually stoic men in the boats were visibly astonished at the catch of fish they had taken, and equally afraid of my presence because of it.

Peter vocalised the feelings of them all. "Get away from me, Lord; I am a sinful man!"[9]

I understood; when you realise that we are with you – that you are in the very presence of God – you become painfully aware of your every shortcoming. The prophet Isaiah described[10] the same emotion centuries ago; and long before him, Abraham had also felt it.[11]

Now I wanted them to work with me and, with a twinkle in my eye, gently told them not to be afraid; from now on I would make them 'fishers of men'.[12] Even they understood the pun! We strained at the oars and rowed the overloaded boats back to shore. The four men came with me, leaving everything in the capable hands of Zebedee, who was the father of James and John,[13] and who, with his hired helpers, wouldn't be worrying about needing to go fishing for a while!

---

8   In March 1992, damaging 3m waves crashed into downtown Tiberias (ibid.)
9   Luke 5:8 (NIV)
10   Isaiah 6:5
11   Genesis 18:27
12   Matthew 4:19; Mark 1:17; Luke 5:10
13   Matthew 4:21-22; Mark 1:19-20; Luke 5:10

14

Old to New Restored

Leprosy is a common disease in these parts and its consequences are far greater than the appearance of white, scaly skin that can proceed to disfigure faces or amputate digits from hands or feet. Leprosy means to people here what HIV-AIDS or Ebola will mean in your time. It is incurable and spells 'outcast'. In my culture, those unfortunate enough to contract leprosy are banished from settlements,[1] and must warn people that they are 'unclean'. You might be surprised to discover that in your modern world there continue to exist many leper colonies.[2]

Unclean: that is the greatest social stigma imaginable for any Jew. 'Unclean' means losing regular contact with one's family and friends; loss of one's home, income and dignity; and no longer being able to worship God with others. The Pharisees have embellished the commandments with many regulations dealing with ritual uncleanness, but in most cases simple washing restores the status quo. Skin diseases such as leprosy cannot be simply washed away, and are universally dreaded.

The physical numbing of nerve cells has the further consequence that any injuries frequently go unnoticed; pain no longer warns the

---

[1] cf. Leviticus 13:(1-)45,46
[2] Wikipedia ("Leprosy")

sufferer of present danger or that anything is wrong. Pain, while nobody desires it, is a natural mechanism we gave the human body to protect itself. It is actually a good thing. In a wider sense, it is the pain in your life – not seldom self-inflicted – that alerts you to the fact that something is amiss, brings realisation of wrong choices made. Why do you not come to me with your pain? For I am always right there in the thick of it, with you.

So it was with compassion that I faced a man who approached me in one of the towns around Galilee,[3] fell to his knees before me, and begged to be healed.

"Lord, if you are willing, you can make me clean."[4]

Not just 'healed', but 'clean', signifying all that would be returned to him as a result. I reached out and touched him – a simple, everyday gesture, yet one he would not have felt for a long time; a sign of acceptance rather than shunning; a sign that I cared.

Yes, I was willing, and informed him with words to underline the unspoken message already conveyed. "Be clean!" I pronounced, and instantly the man's skin was transformed, his features made whole, and decorated with the joy that was rapidly returning to his face. He was restored.

Once again, I was concerned that this would not be widely publicised, reluctant to openly declare my identity before I had had the chance to teach the people about the kingdom, and particularly instruct my disciples, who would continue the work. However, the man's restoration was not yet complete. Moses gave the ancient Israelites detailed instructions about skin diseases in his book about the Levites, 'And He Called'[5] (that you know as Leviticus), and I wanted to adhere to these. To be pronounced clean and restored to the community, the man would need to see the local priest for confirmation that his condition had been healed, and for a sacrifice of thanks to be given. Only then would he be able to return to normal life.

---

[3] Luke 5:12
[4] Matthew 8:2b (NIV); Mark 1:40 (NIV); Luke 5:12b (NIV)
[5] Leviticus 13, 14; Wikipedia ("Book of Leviticus", quoting Wenham, 1995)

That he did, but he also told everyone how he had arrived back there. As a result, it became difficult to enter any town without being swamped by excited crowds gathering around me.[6]

Not long after this, having returned to Capernaum,[7] I had entered a large house and was teaching the people present, which included many Pharisees and teachers of the law from across a wide area.[8] As I was doing so, to my amusement and the consternation of the building's owner, dusty flakes of plaster, then small chunks of the ceiling above me, started to descend around us, accompanied by a symphony of scraping noises.

Through the open door, I had spotted a group of men carrying someone on a bed-mat. They had paused, looking at the crowd spilling out of the door onto the street, and then disappeared out of view. I now guessed it was them on the flat roof. Their audacity provoked a chuckle within me, but their sheer faith bowled me over. These guys were here for a healing, whatever obstacles they had to overcome to achieve it! That isn't quite how it works, really, but having such faith is a good place to start and from which I can work. As our children come to us in trust, so my Father and I are prompted to respond, and our Spirit can move.

I guess you're questioning now why there are occasions we don't seem to respond. Why did a loved one have to die, even when you've come to me and asked for healing? Why did we allow another tragedy to occur? My friend, there is so much that you are spared because we don't let it happen in the first place. That sometimes includes illness or tragedy that would have happened had those loved ones lived longer. Losing a job that was stressing you towards a heart attack was our way of blessing and preserving you. I don't expect you to understand all that, and it doesn't explain everything; but be assured, we are in the thick of it with you, carrying you, weeping with you.

There is much else that we do allow to happen, it is true. Such things are often the consequences of the free choice we gave to

---

6 Mark 1:45; Luke 5:15
7 Mark 2:1
8 Luke 5:17

humankind from the start. Tragedy is never our plan, nor our aim; yet the usual earthly existence will contain it. That is the price we too have to pay for giving you the choice – and for Adam and Eve making the wrong one.

Hands reached through the growing hole, pulling the loosened lumps of clay and supporting sticks from around its edge. Finally, one last determined piece of ceiling lifted away to momentarily let a ray of sunshine flood through the roof. The new, unexpected opening soon darkened, filling with the silhouette of a bed-mat being lowered as gently as possible between two of the wooden beams supporting the roof. The young man lying on it, while visibly apprehensive, looked expectant, and didn't seem to mind the ungainly nature of his arrival in the hurriedly cleared space on the floor before me.

"Take heart, friend, your sins are forgiven,"[9] I said.

The man returned my gaze, unsure what to think and what I might say next. This was not the greeting he had expected. But I could see he was processing my assurance. Many people hold that when tragedy or hard times strike, or infirmity burdens life, these must signify divine judgement.[10] Yes, the consequences of the sin of an evil person who hates God can reach down to the third and fourth generation that comes after them[11] – and who knows what happened three or four generations ago! – but sin alone doesn't cause sickness unless the illness is a consequence of that sin.

Guilt had been a lodger in this man's mind for too long; his need for the pronouncement of forgiveness was greater even than his desire to walk again. And just maybe the forgiven would then learn to become the forgiver. That is the mysterious healing power of forgiveness. It is the greatest restorer of brokenness.

Forgiveness in the Pharisees' eyes, however, was definitely something only God could dispense, so their instant and inevitable reaction was that I was blasphemous. By proclaiming forgiveness, I was

---

[9] Matthew 9:2c (NIV); Mark 2:5 (NIV); Luke 5:20 (NIV)
[10] cf. John 9:2
[11] Exodus 20:5

claiming divinity. I knew through our Spirit what they were thinking to themselves.

"Why do you have such thoughts?" I followed this rhetorical question with another. "What's easier: to say his sins are forgiven, or to tell the man – a paralytic! – to get up, take his mat and walk?"

Silence.

So I continued, stating that I would prove my authority, and using the messianic title the prophet Daniel had been inspired to use about me centuries earlier: Son of Man.[12]

This further incensed the already apoplectic Pharisees. Why could they of all people, with their knowledge of the Scriptures, not see the signs?

"I tell you," I directed the patient, "get up, take your mat and go home!"[13]

And that's exactly what he did. I was as exhilarated as the crowd was amazed. Another life had been restored, and it would be a sign for many of God's love and power. The throng of people parted in wonder as he made his way out, and they praised my Father in heaven for something so remarkable, never seen before. For me, the greater reason for celebration lay not in his newfound mobility, but in the fact that he had accepted forgiveness. Yes, another life restored.

Down the road towards the lake was another whose life was far from perfect, and he knew it. Levi, who was the son of Alphaeus, was one of the local tax collectors. A despised breed, this motley assortment of characters is hired by the Roman authorities and collects taxes for the occupiers. As such, many of their compatriots regard them as traitors.[14] Under the thumb of the area 'publican', they seek to help themselves by overcharging whatever they can get away with, and tend to be actually quite well-off as a result.

Capernaum lies roughly mid-way along the East-West section of the 'Way of the Sea' trade route from Damascus in Syria to the seaport

---

12 Daniel 7:13-14. Only Jesus uses this title for himself in the Gospels.
13 Luke 5:24b (NIV)
14 Thompson (p. 2092)

of Caesarea.[15] The route continues from there south to Egypt. Isaiah mentioned this highway when he foretold[16] my coming. Regular caravans keep the tax collectors busy, and in profit. The latter may be regularly observed sitting in booths alongside the road.

It was in one of these that we came across Levi. I would soon christen him Matthew, which means 'Gift of the Lord'[17], as he was indeed that. Choosing him was a sign that my invitation to follow included those whom the rest of society shunned. If you are already my follower, will you in your day extend the invitation likewise? And if the margins are your territory, will you join me?

"Follow me," I said to Matthew, as I shall refer to him now.

He stepped out of his booth, leaving everything behind, and led me to his house, where he laid on a veritable feast.[18] He had quickly sent word to a large crowd of friends, many of whom were fellow tax collectors. I could learn something about recruitment from this guy! The comfortable house and its shaded courtyard soon filled up with the contented sounds of people enthusiastically enjoying food, punctuated with lively conversation and laughter.

A group of Pharisees passing the overflowing house noticed me in the merry crowd. Calling a few of my disciples over, they wanted to know why I chose to eat with such 'sinners'. Sharing such a meal is a universal sign of friendship; tax collectors were the last sort of people the Pharisees would consider having anything to do with.

I swallowed the tasty mouthful of food I was in the middle of savouring, and called over to them. "Surely, sick people, not healthy ones, are those that need a doctor. I haven't come to call the righteous," I explained, "but sinners."[19]

Now the Pharisees, as well as Cousin John's disciples, were fasting. Many Pharisees fast twice a week,[20] although the Levitical law only requires it on the Day of Atonement,[21] when the people are supposed to

---

[15] NIV map 6 "Palestine in New Testament Times"; Hein (*Via Maris*)
[16] Isaiah 9:1; Matthew 4:15
[17] Matthew 9:9 and NIV footnote for Mark 2:14
[18] Luke 5:29
[19] Mark 2:17 (NIV)
[20] Luke 18:12
[21] Leviticus 16:29,31, 23:29,32; cf. Psalm 35:13

deny or humble themselves by fasting. Sabbath rest is supposed to replace work. Trouble is, as the prophet Isaiah made clear, many of them have reduced fasting to mere habit, forgetting that humble self-denial is intended to bring them – individually and in community – back into close communion with God. Instead, they do as they please, exploiting each other and quarrelling. What we intended included justice, freedom, sharing and healing.[22]

Other bystanders obviously felt troubled by the fact that, while the Pharisees and John's disciples were fasting, my disciples and I were busy eating. What did they expect? Long-lost hope had been restored in the lives of both the leper and the paralysed man, and now Matthew was finding acceptance and a new hope of his own. Of course we were celebrating!

"You don't expect the bridegroom's guests to fast when he's still with them, do you?" I asked them, speaking figuratively of myself. "The bridegroom will be taken soon enough; then they will fast."[23]

Equally, I needed to make clear that I wasn't here to dispense with the old law, but to strip away the accumulated layers of regulations and tradition placed upon it, so that people could see afresh the true spirit of the rules we gave their ancestors so long before. In that sense I had come to do away with the old style of living, bringing a new way. Using illustrations of patching an old garment with a new, yet-unshrunken piece of cloth, and of putting new, still-fermenting wine into old, no longer flexible wineskins, both of which would spell the destruction of what was being repaired or stored, I tried to make clear that life needs to be guided not by laws but by our voice, our Spirit.

Good examples of this occurred over the next couple of Sabbaths. My disciples were wandering with me through the cornfields and plucking a few ears of corn to eat on the way through. The all-seeing Pharisees happened to be on hand to observe this blatant breach of their regulations, and complained to me that what my disciples were doing was breaking the law.

---

[22] Isaiah 58
[23] Mark 2:20 (NIV)

My Spirit brought to mind the passage[24] in the book named after Samuel, where the future King David needed food for his men and obtained some consecrated bread from the priest Ahimelech. While such was permitted to be consumed solely by the priests, having established that the men were ritually clean, the priest allowed them to partake of it, following the spirit of the law that had been given. My disciples were only doing likewise.

"The Sabbath was made for man,[25] not vice-versa," I stated, "so it's the Son of Man who determines what happens on the Sabbath."

That set their blasphemy antennae quivering anew, and so the following time we met in the synagogue, they were looking for any reason to accuse me. I was equally determined to give them one, though it saddened me deeply that they would perceive a need to convict me for what I was about to do.

A man with a shrivelled right hand had come,[26] and the Pharisees were watching closely, almost willing me, to see whether I would heal him. That much they apparently did believe: that I could do so. Why had they allowed their regulations to condemn bringing wholeness, even – particularly – on the Sabbath, when we gather to worship God together?

The man with the shrivelled hand could feel everyone's attention turning towards him as I asked him to stand up and move to the middle of the assembly.

"Which is the right thing to do on a Sabbath," I demanded, "good or evil; restore a person's life or ruin it?"

No reply. Their hardheartedness was merciless! I looked around them, bristling with anger, then commanded the man to stretch out his hand. In front of us all, he stretched it out and was able to move it freely. Restored!

The Pharisees turned heel and, as was later reported, started plotting with the Herodians – influential Jews who support the

---

[24] Originally one book (NIV intro.); 1 Samuel 21:6
[25] Mark 2:27a (NIV)
[26] Luke 6:6

Herodian dynasty authorised by Rome – how they might kill me. Their own hearts were already dead.

I withdrew from there to the lake,[27] accompanied by my disciples and a large crowd. Having learned from previous experience, I had the guys hold a boat ready for me, to prevent being crowded and going for an unplanned swim. Knowing or having seen what I had already achieved, illness-stricken people were pushing forward to be healed. As before, demons recognised me and I had to rebuke them.

These things, as Matthew will later record, actually fulfilled another prophecy of Isaiah, who had written about me as my heavenly Father's chosen servant, whom he loved and upon whom he would place His Spirit. I would proclaim justice and victory, and nations would put their hope in my name.[28] Written seven hundred years ago, that was a pretty accurate mission statement. It's still true for you today.

27 Matthew 12:15; Mark 3:7
28 Isaiah 42:1-4; Matthew 12:17-21

15

Teaching and Learning

In addition to the signs they had already seen me perform, I needed to start giving my followers some serious teaching about the kingdom that my heavenly Father has always planned for our world. There will be a new heaven and a new earth one day, when we will renew everything and render it perfect again.[1]

However, our kingdom is for living *now*, not merely sometime in the future. We long for all people to live in harmony with us, and with each other. When people get the first relationship right, they will find the second is a lot less of a struggle. The commandments we gave through Moses put a healthy framework in place for these relationships, but layers of man-made rules have masked the original spirit of our law.

In my desire to reach everyone, I was experiencing a problem. Though I knew I was one with my heavenly Father, I had limited myself to the finite presence of a human frame. There were physical and spiritual needs everywhere I went, but I could only be in one place at a time!

I decided to select and empower a core group of my disciples to go out and spread the message. I had reached the point where I needed representatives to help me. They would have my authority, even to drive

---

[1] cf. Revelation 21:1-5

out evil spirits.[2] In order to make the right choices, I spent some time up the mountain above Capernaum, drawing power from my Dad through the Spirit, seeking guidance, wanting to get it right.

Uniquely as a human, I do have the power to decide everything myself, but nonetheless I have limited myself to seeking and submitting to my Father's will. How often do you launch into a project or a decision in your own power, without chatting it over with us first? How much heartache might you have saved by listening to our gentle, guiding voice before we had to blow the circumstantial trumpet of a broken friendship, lost job or failed plans in order for you to hear our will for you?

Having heard my Father's will, I headed back down the mountain. The excited chatter of another expectant crowd rose to greet me. For weeks, people had been coming, seeking healing of a plethora of illnesses. Making my way through to my disciples, I heard dialects from across the whole region, all the way up to the Phoenician cities of Tyre and Sidon on the coast,[3] the latter perhaps sixty miles distant, a couple of days' walk. People pressed on me from all sides and I ministered to as many as I could while forging a path forward. A touch here, a word or a simple smile there, my Father's power working as the Spirit moved.

Reaching the front of the crowd, I selected and took to one side twelve special representatives from the wider group. Simon Peter and his brother Andrew had joined me soon after my baptism. Then there were my 'Sons of Thunder', James and John, the sons of Zebedee. I chose Philip and his friend Nathaniel Bartholomew, who had needed convincing about people from Nazareth. Next came Matthew the tax collector, whom we had recently acquired. Thomas, another character who sometimes needed convincing, joined the group, along with James, the son of Alphaeus; Thaddaeus, also known as Judas son of James;[4] and Simon the Zealot, a revolutionary. Finally, I selected Judas Iscariot. He didn't know it yet, but he would have particular role to play later on.

---

2   Mark 3:13-15
3   Luke 6:17
4   Luke 6:16 and NIV footnote

These twelve represented a wide cross-section of society. In a wider sense, they would represent the twelve tribes of Israel.[5] Only the tribes of Judah and Benjamin remained intact after the other ten tribes had formed the Kingdom of Israel and were later scattered in exile by the Assyrians, as I have already described. It has long been a hope of the Jewish people that one day all Israel will be reunited. In me, one day, that will happen.[6]

"I want you guys to work with me closely," I told them. "All these people, indeed the whole nation needs to know about my Father's kingdom and His love for His people. You're going to help me do that. Now listen and learn."

It was time to start teaching. I sat down on a gentle slope near the base of the mountain, in view of the expectant crowd of people spread out over the flat area below, and with the twelve close by.

How to tell them about inner healing and life for those in God's kingdom? This was my manifesto, my raison d'être. They needed to know how to live differently from their culture, with our heartbeat, in union with us. Living counter-culture involves turning commonly held preconceptions on their head. So I launched my teaching by talking about what sort of people are not just happy, which is a changeable emotion, but *blessed*. Not necessarily those who are successful, well-heeled, respected; but those who possess a contented joy that is neither dependent on material blessings nor quenched by external circumstances beyond their control. The first Psalm embodies this concept quite well.

"In God's kingdom," I started, "it's those who are poor in spirit that are blessed, and those who mourn, for as Isaiah wrote[7], they will be comforted. It's the meek who will inherit the land."

"Meekness is weakness," somebody called out. "Inherit the land? Meekness isn't going to rid us of the Romans!"

---

[5] Matthew 19:28; cf. Luke 22:29
[6] Jeremiah 23:1-9; cf. John 10:11-18, 11:49-52
[7] Isaiah 61:1

"What did King David write?" I asked. "Didn't he recognise that it is the humble before God who will inherit the land?[8] In their gentleness,[9] they are considerate towards others. When ordinary people submit to God, he can use them in mighty ways, championing the needs of those without a voice and bringing justice. They inherit the land by positively shaping the cultural landscape!"

No-one chose to argue with that. Murmurs of agreement faded in expectation of what I might say next.

"The righteous long for their community to live by God's commandments, and even if they are persecuted because of their righteousness, theirs is the kingdom of heaven!"

As I was finding, living counter-culture tends to engender some counter-culture of its own. My Father's children often experience persecution when challenging preconceptions, power-bases, or wrongdoing. Cousin John was in prison for doing so, and I myself had already escaped the clutches of people wanting to kill me. Such living means countering the deceitful lies of the devil, resisting his temptation to take the easy path, holding strong against opposition and threats. That is the path to our kingdom, and those who stay on it shall inherit that kingdom. Indeed, they are already living in it.

"Those who are merciful to others will be treated mercifully."

Do you remember me telling you about the forgiven being released to become the forgiver?[10] When you recognise your own need for mercy and forgiveness, and extend them to others, you will receive them yourself, both divinely and from the neighbour you have wronged. Mercy is also active compassion, taking pity, addressing the needs of others.[11]

Older people nodded in agreement, the lesson long since learned; others showed contrition. I was getting through!

"The pure in heart learn to see God in the everyday things of life; peacemakers are close to God's heart and will be called His sons!"

---

8 Psalm 37:11
9 πραεῖς (πραεις) = meek, gentle; including considerate, courteous (Barnes on Matthew 5:5)
10 See page 88
11 ἐλεήμονες (nom. m. plu. of ἐλεήμων) = merciful, compassionate (actively)

As Isaiah described,[12] bringing peace is central to my coming here: peace with our created friends, peace within families and communities, even between enemies. Peace spells wholeness in individual and community lives; its restoration reintroduces justice, well-being and contentment. 'Shalom', in a word. Those who strive to bring peace capture our heart's desire and become our children, co-heirs with me of my Father's kingdom.[13]

My audience were spellbound. This sort of teaching was new to them, and most seemed to appreciate my words. I imagined that many of them were indeed meek, did strive for peace, did live righteously – and did suffer for it, not least under the Roman occupiers for whom Caesar and no other is God. For my disciples' benefit particularly,[14] I underlined this last point.

"God goes out of his way to bless you whenever people insult and oppress you on my account."

I know that they, like many prophets before them, and indeed me, will personally experience persecution and lies, and worse. I wanted to reassure them that we would greatly reward them in heaven for the counter-culture life they strived to live. I likened such lives to salt[15] that both preserves foodstuffs such as meat, and draws the flavour out of them during cooking. Your life, lived in union with us, will display our unconditional love to those around you and so enrich them.

The Pharisees had already decided I cared nothing for God's laws given through Moses. However, nothing could be further from the truth, and I emphasised that until the end of time, the law retained full legitimacy. Not the least stroke of a pen would be invalidated.[16] I had a little dig at the Pharisees and teachers of the law present by warning my listeners that they wouldn't enter our kingdom unless they behaved more righteously than those they were supposed to be able to look up

---

[12] Isaiah 2:4; 9:6-7
[13] Matthew 5:9; cf. John 1:12-13
[14] Luke 6:20
[15] Matthew 5:13
[16] Matthew 5:18; Luke 16:17

to,[17] who applied a heartless rigidity to laws that we designed to uphold justice and freedom.

Now I turned my attention to the spirit of the law. Most commandments in the Scriptures are straightforward enough to understand and, with sufficient will, adhere to. But pride at keeping to the letter of the law masks a failure to listen to the Lawgiver's heartbeat, just as the original intention of the system of sacrifices has gradually been eroded to the point where making them has become meaningless. I started with murder.

"You know that the law prohibits murder,[18] and anyone who commits murder will have to answer for it. But I tell you that anyone who is angry with his brother will be subject to the same judgement."[19]

I tried to show that while not many people murder others, anyone angry with a brother is heading down the same path, the more so by calling him empty-headed.[20] Dubbing him a fool, however, is a dangerous step down Anger Avenue, which highway passes through shades of hate and leads ultimately to Dead End.[21] I used the Valley of the Sons of Ginnom, which we call Gehenna, south of Jerusalem, to evoke a picture of the judgement that Anger Avenue leads to. This was the place desecrated by King Josiah after pagan worshippers had sacrificed their own children to the false god Moloch.[22]

"So if you come to worship," I went on, "and remember someone you have wronged, who is angry against you, first go and sort it out!" Doing this is important; anger will consume people you have wronged, driving a wedge between them and you, and potentially affecting their own relationship with us. Similarly, if a person is taking you to court, attempt to settle the matter before it gets that far, for your own good!

I then turned to male-female relationships, potentially fraught with difficulty from earliest times, when Eve listened to the Deceiver and persuaded Adam to go against the house rules. In fact, there was only

---

[17] Matthew 5:20
[18] Exodus 20:13; 21:12; Deuteronomy 5:17; cf. Matthew 5:21(-26)
[19] Matthew 5:22 (NIV)
[20] ῥακά (Strong's 4469; Greek: empty; worthless) from רֵק (Chaldee origin)
[21] Matthew 5:22; cf. 1 John 3:15
[22] 2 Kings 23:10. Greek γέεννα, derived from the Hebrew

one house rule at the time! *One!* So I addressed particularly, though not exclusively, the men in my audience about adultery and lustfully wandering eyes.

"You know that the law prohibits adultery.[23] But I tell you that anyone who looks at a woman lustfully[24] has done so."

Faces dropped; some managed to assume their previous expression again before wives' eyes registered any change. Committing physical adultery was plainly against our laws, but heads rotating at walking speed soon manufacture illicit images that are no different. We created sexual desire in our human friends and provided the perfect framework of marriage for it.[25] A beautiful woman walking by may arouse a man's desire. Entertaining that desire soon results in an invasion of adulterous thoughts.

"Better to gouge your eye out than let it cause you to sin!" If I didn't already have their attention, I certainly had it now. "That's how drastically you need to cut sin out of your life," I explained.

Furthermore, divorcing one's wife (unless she has been unfaithful), while reluctantly permitted under the law,[26] causes her to commit adultery should she remarry; likewise, her new partner. It grieves us that people treat so lightly what we gave them for good.

"Again, you know that the law tells us to keep our oaths to the Lord and not break them.[27] But I tell you: Do not swear at all.[28]"

Lying also grieves us. People make oaths in our name[29] to emphasise honesty. What is promised will be done, as Moses described[30] in his writings about Israel's wandering from Sinai to the border of Canaan. The regulations for worship and holiness prohibit swearing falsely by our name. Sadly, unscrupulous use of oaths nowadays means that they no longer ensure truth; the spirit of the law is again being

---

[23] Exodus 20:14; Deuteronomy 5:18; cf. Matthew 5:27(-32)
[24] Matthew 5:28 (NIV)
[25] e.g. Genesis 2:18-24; Deuteronomy 24:5; cf. Matthew 19:4-6
[26] Deuteronomy 24:1-4; Matthew 19:7-9
[27] Leviticus 19:12; Deuteronomy 23:21; cf. Matthew 5:33(-37)
[28] Matthew 5:34 (NIV)
[29] Exodus 22:10-11
[30] Numbers 30:2

broken.[31] One should not lie in the first place, so one's honesty should not need emphasising with an oath.

"Let your 'Yes' be 'Yes',[32] and your 'No' be 'No'," I advocated. The crowd murmured approval, and I tackled another problem area.

"You know that our ancestors always maintained, 'Eye for an eye, and tooth for a tooth.'[33] But I tell you, if anyone strikes you on one cheek, turn the other cheek to them as well."

I knew that many of my listeners tended towards seeking revenge, rather than treading the path of the peacemaker. We intended our laws concerning revenge to limit retribution to the loss inflicted, but people now often use them to sanction punishment going way beyond the wrong perpetrated. Justice is required, yes, but commensurate with the crime committed.

Revenge, even restrained, precipitates a tit-for-tat downward spiral where eventually no-one remembers cause or effect. By contrast, I told my listeners to avoid being hostile towards an evil or needy person, and rather to react non-aggressively in a way that would shame the transgressor.

"You know that the law talks about loving your neighbour and hating your enemy.[34] But I tell you, love your enemies and pray for those who persecute you.[35]"

My Father above will ensure that justice is done.[36] Anyone can love those who love them, but the peacemaker loves his enemies and prays for them, and as such is a child of God.

The gathered crowd was listening intently, and I felt encouraged to press on. This discourse was already becoming lengthier than a typical Sabbath-day sermon, yet they were not displaying any of the usual shuffling signs of the onset of boredom. They were anxious to hear my words.[37] So next, I taught them a straightforward prayer,

---

[31] cf. Matthew 23:16-22
[32] Matthew 5:37 (NIV)
[33] Exodus 21:24; Leviticus 24:20; Deuteronomy 19:21; cf. Matthew 5:38(-42)
[34] Leviticus 19:18; Deuteronomy 23:6; Psalm 139:21-22; cf. Matthew 5:43(-48)
[35] Matthew 5:39 (NIV)
[36] cf. Romans 12:19-21
[37] cf. Matthew 7:28-29

honouring my heavenly Father and asking him to supply their daily needs:[38]

> "Our Father in heaven,
> hallowed be your name,
> your kingdom come,
> your will be done
> on earth as it is in heaven.[39]
> Give us everything we need for today.
> Forgive us our sins,
> as we forgive those who sin against us.
> Lead us away from temptation,
> and deliver us from evil."

I examined one of my pet hates, that of 'doing' for the sake of appearances.[40] Worship of any kind should be something between you and God, but the Pharisees in particular love to make a show of it. They openly parade their charitable giving, pray highfalutin prayers that even we don't understand, and quit customary and desirable hygiene so that all around them know they are fasting. They will get their just reward: their observers will think what wonderful people they are! However, the affirmation of my heavenly Father is a much greater treasure worth pursuing.

"Do not accumulate earthly treasures," I instructed. "They can be destroyed by moth and rust, or stolen by thieves."

'Things' divert your allegiance away from God. So I directed the people's thoughts towards treasure in heaven. If your spiritual eyes are open, you will see where heavenly treasures may be found; you will notice the downtrodden and encourage them, perceive a need and meet it, empathise with the mourning and comfort them. Your life will be alight with the love that flows from our heart. How dark it will be by comparison if your eyes and heart are closed to the world around you!

---

[38] Matthew 6:9-13; Luke 11:2-4
[39] Matthew 6:9-10 (NIV)
[40] Matthew 6:1-18

The extent to which your life shines brightly indicates the love in your heart for us. That will dictate, conversely, how tight your grip on your earthly treasures remains.

"You cannot serve both God and money!"[41] I concluded.

Someone in the crowd saw himself vindicated, and shouted out, "Teacher, tell my brother to share our father's estate with me."[42]

Settling such disputes is not what I'm here for. Leaving aside the usual rules[43] on dividing up an inheritance, I replied firmly, "Since when am I supposed to do the work of an arbiter for you?" Then, addressing the crowd once more, I warned them again against greed, saying that there's more to life than possessions. I told them a further parable to illustrate the point.

"A rich man had so many crops one year that he had nowhere to store his harvest. So he thought to himself that he'd tear down his barns and build bigger ones to store everything in. He'd say to himself, 'I'm sorted, take life easy; eat, drink and be merry!'[44] But God said to him, 'You fool! You will die this very night. Then who will get everything you have worked for?'[45] That's how it is with everyone that accumulates riches for themselves rather than with God."

Remember, when we put Adam in the garden, we gave him every seed-bearing plant and fruit as an inexhaustible supply of food. Despite their early protestations to the contrary,[46] we provided the Israelites with sustenance throughout their forty years wandering in the barren desert. So it always amazes me when people worry about what they're going to eat or drink, or especially what they're going to wear. I told my audience that life is too important to be constantly worrying about such everyday things, drawing a comparison with the third of Israel's kings, renowned for his unparalleled wisdom and unimaginable riches.

"Do the birds sow or reap or store up food for themselves? Of course not! Yet your heavenly Father keeps them fed. And see how he

---

41 Matthew 6:24c (NIV)
42 Luke 12:13b (NIV); see also verses 14-21
43 Deuteronomy 21:17
44 Luke 12:19 (NIV)
45 Luke 12:20 (NLT)
46 Exodus 16:3,35

clothes ordinary flowers with a glory that not even Solomon in all his splendour could have matched. Your heavenly Father knows all your needs and will supply them as you make it your priority to seek his will. So don't fret about tomorrow, for tomorrow will take care of itself. Today already has enough to worry about."

People nodded sagely. "Amen to that!"

Those who knew my background grinned when I talked about judging others and removing the wooden plank from one's own eye before attempting to remove a speck of dust from someone else's. I had soon learned in the workshop to close my eyes when stooping to blow shavings and sawdust from a workpiece, and liked the analogy myself!

While speaking out against such judgemental hypocrisy, it was important to recognise that some people remain unclean, like the undomesticated dogs and pigs that roam the streets or fields. Just as pigs would see no value in pearls and trample them into the ground, so there are opponents who refuse to accept the challenges of the valuable good news I am here to share with them, and who will turn against me, and you, in response.

Next, I elaborated on the prayer that I had just taught them. "Ask and it will be given to you; seek and you will find; knock and the door will be opened to you."[47]

While wanting our children to trust us for their needs rather than worrying about them, I made clear to my audience that we desire them to ask for their 'daily bread', and for guidance in their everyday lives. I modelled this when I sought my Father's will before selecting some of my disciples to be 'Apostles'.

"You know what is right for your children;" I declared, "how much more our heavenly Father knows what is good for you!"

I often muse over the abundance of blessing you unwittingly forgo because you forget to ask. We have so much we want to give you!

Following on from that, I wanted to turn around current, negatively biased Jewish thinking, propagated by such respected rabbis as Hillel the Elder, who died roughly twenty years ago[48]. He had been

---

[47] Matthew 7:7 (NIV); Luke 11:9 (NIV)
[48] "Hillel". Hillel the Elder †~10AD.

asked by a heathen to teach the entire Torah in the time he could stand on one foot. To this challenge Hillel replied, "What is hateful to you, do not do unto your neighbour." All very well, but this negative aspect permeated the mindset of many people. So I reversed it.

"Do to others what you would wish them to do to you."

That reinstated our positively expressed law given to Moses that you should "love you neighbour as yourself"[49]. If my listeners were to remember only one sentence, then this should be the one. For, as Hillel's reply to his antagonist had continued, it sums up all the law and the prophets.

I ended my monologue with a selection of word pictures, using familiar images to help people to recognise right teaching and right living. The devil, like when he tempted me in the desert, tries to make the wrong way seem easier than the right way.

"Choose the narrow path, for only that leads into God's kingdom. The highway to hell and the gate at the end of it are wide, and many err down that way; but few reach the narrow gateway to life."

So many miss the narrow gate, yet the directions are in our Word for all to see! I pleaded with my Father, even as I spoke, to help the people recognise and follow the way into our kingdom. The devil commissions many false prophets to lead people astray. Just as you can recognise good trees by their fruit, so you can detect such inwardly ferocious wolves from the bad fruit in their lives. Such people will not be recognised at the gates to heaven, but turned away, just as trees bearing bad fruit are cut down and cast onto the fire.

Wrapping up, I challenged my listeners to put my words into practice, likening doing so to building a house with its foundation firmly placed on rock. No storm can shake it loose. Conversely, those who ignore my words are building their lives on sand, which will be swept away when the next of life's storms hits.

Where are your foundations?

49 Leviticus 19:18

16

Healing Confirmation

Back in Capernaum, having concluded my talk on the south-facing slopes above the town with an illustration of obeying my words, a Roman centurion stationed in the town approached me.[1] His rank was such that his words demanded unquestioning obedience from the hundred soldiers under his command. Amongst the local Jewish population, however, this man – even though he was a Gentile – had gained much respect due to his love for our nation and for organising the building of the local synagogue.

Now, though, a look of concern cast a long shadow over his tanned features. He explained that a valued servant was lying at home paralysed and in terrible suffering. I started to move, ushering him in the direction from which he had come, ready to go with him, but he stopped me, and addressed me with a deference I would not have expected from a Roman soldier.

"Lord, I am not worthy to have you come under my roof."

Who knows what terrible deeds and experiences his job as a soldier had etched on his psyche. I was touched that he acknowledged both his own unworthiness and my cultural needs as a Jew, for by entering his Gentile house I would make myself ceremonially unclean[2].

---

[1]   Matthew 8:5-13; Luke 7:1-10
[2]   Mishnah Oholot 18:7, quoted by Smith, Lee; cf. John 18:28

The centurion then uttered some startling words: "But just say the word, and my servant will be healed."[3]

He went on to proclaim that he had soldiers under him, who obeyed his commands, and that he too was under authority. Here was a Roman soldier, a Gentile, who recognised my authority and expected me, at a word, to be able to heal his servant!

I was astonished and exclaimed to those around us that I had never come across anyone with such great faith, even in Israel. I gave them a warning: "Many from outside the kingdom will sit down at the banquet alongside Abraham, Isaac and Jacob; but many inside, who think they are invited, will be thrown out into the darkness."[4]

I ardently hoped that those listening would understand and take my words to heart. To the centurion I simply said, "Go! It will be done just as you believed it would."

He dropped to his knees to thank me, and returned with his group to base. They were able to confirm that the stricken servant had indeed been healed, at the precise moment I spoke.

Not long after this event, my disciples and I, accompanied by a large crowd, made our way to Nain,[5] which nestles in the fertile Jezreel Valley some nine miles south-east of my hometown, Nazareth, and a strenuous twenty-five from Capernaum. It stands between the towering citadels of Mount Tabor and Mount Gilboa. These local landmarks, which rise steeply either side of the valley floor, witnessed Deborah and Balak's erstwhile defeat of the Canaanite Sisera and his troops from Hazor,[6] after twenty years of cruel oppression.

Children were running ahead, chattering excitedly as they climbed trees, turned over rocks, explored crevasses either side of the road, their boundless energy defying the overpowering heat of the day. They were enjoying their unexpected excursion. Now and again, a parental admonition sailed over our heads, followed by frantic footsteps racing in the opposite direction, faces frowning with contrition over some or

---

[3] Matthew 8:8b (NIV)
[4] Matthew 8:11-12
[5] Luke 7:11(-17)
[6] Judges 4:1-24

other line overstepped. Laughter emanated from the crowd, whose expectant voices wondered aloud what I would do at today's destination.

Dusk was beginning to assert itself as we were entering Nain, where we were met by a dead man being carried out, lying wrapped in a burial shroud in an open coffin, and the only son of his weeping, previously widowed mother. My heart went out to the woman, who now had no means of looking after herself. Our early laws had sought to ensure that the community would provide for widows, as well as orphans and foreigners living in the land,[7] but there remained the emptiness of loss, the reproach that accompanied widowhood,[8] the suffocating feelings of failure and rejection.

"Don't cry," I said to her, my Spirit welling up within me. I stretched out my arm to touch the coffin, and those bearing it stood still. "Young man," I addressed her lifeless son, "time to get up!"

A hush descended over the funeral party and soon rippled back along the crowd behind me. The dead man sat up and began to talk,[9] a little uncertain of the purpose of his attire and his whereabouts on the shoulders of the men of his village. They awkwardly lowered his bier to the ground, in an ungainly fashion that reflected their shock. In the circumstances, I would not have been too surprised had they dropped it!

The man stood up, and I gave him back to his mother, from whose already tear-stained face flowed further tears of shock and joy. The onlookers were all filled with awe. Nobody spoke life into a corpse as they had just witnessed; that was the domain of Scripture's great prophets, of Elijah and Elisha[10]. So it was natural that they thought I was a great prophet who had appeared amongst them, and as such, they praised God for coming to help his people.

This was the first time I had raised someone from the dead physically. Driving out the demon from the deranged man in

---

7   Deuteronomy 14:29, 16:11, 24:19-21, 26:12
8   Ruth 1:20-21; Isaiah 54:4
9   Luke 7:15a (NIV)
10   1 Kings 17:17-24; 2 Kings 4:17-37

Capernaum had brought him new life, certainly, but not bodily, though his appearance had improved dramatically. In a sense, bringing somebody back to life is no different than healing an ailment, albeit involving hauling that person back to health from further down the line. Nevertheless, it was an exhilarating landmark. Isaiah's ancient prophecy[11] was coming to pass. The grave had been robbed of its occupant!

News of this event spread all over Judea and, via his disciples, as far as Cousin John, who was still being held in Herod's fortified hilltop palace at Macherus,[12] the other side of the River Jordan, overlooking the Salt Sea[13]. John, given his precarious predicament, had become understandably unsure about the prophecies regarding his own person and, consequently, those about me. The excitement we used to share surely shouldn't have ended like this. Had we got it wrong? So he sent word, asking whether I was the "one to come", the promised Messiah, or whether someone else was expected.[14]

How I longed at that moment for those occasions when we would eagerly explore the Scriptures together. Here I was in Galilee, doing all the things Isaiah had foretold: sight was being restored to the blind, the lame could walk again, those with leprosy were cured, the deaf could hear, even the dead were raised; and the good news was being preached to the poor.[15] This was exactly what we used to study, and what I had read from the scroll in the synagogue at Nazareth.

I did not want John to be brought down by the discouragement of his situation, so I instructed his messengers to return and report to him about all the miracles they had seen me perform. Hearing those words would immediately remind him of the Scriptures and assure him that he was right, and to keep on trusting. I added that whoever is not caused to stumble because of me[16] is blessed. You too may be caused to doubt

---

[11] Isaiah 26:19
[12] Josephus (Antiquities of the Jews XVIII.5.2)
[13] 30km S.E. of the mouth of the Jordan River.
[14] Matthew 11:3(-19); Luke 7:19(-35)
[15] Isaiah 35:5-6, 61:1
[16] (σκανδαλισθῇ) σκανδαλίζω: cause to stumble, offend (⇒Engl. scandal)

by times of difficulty; hold tight to what you know, to what you have seen and heard.

When his envoys had departed, I spoke to the still-present multitude of people about John's character and ministry, posing a series of rhetorical questions about what they had expected to see in him. What had attracted them enough to head out into the desert to see him, and had they accepted the challenge he had given?

Had they expected a reed, swayed by the wind? Reeds are common along the banks of the Jordan, particularly where spring rains regularly swell the river beyond its usual bounds. Their swaying one way and the other in a breeze symbolises a weak character in a man, a metaphor probably not intentioned by Herod Antipas when he designed the obverse of his coins! These portrayed a reed where his head would normally have been, thus assuaging Jewish sensitivities regarding banned images yet still using a symbol of fertility.[17] No, John was no swaying reed. He remained firm in his calling and message, calling people to repentance.

If not that, had they expected a man dressed in fine clothes? They will have been disappointed! No, such luxury-accustomed people may be found in palaces. John didn't model luxurious, soft-to-the-touch garments.[18] His rough camelhair clothes were as uncompromising as his message.

So what did they go out to see? A prophet? Yes, he was indeed a prophet, and the first that Israel had seen since Malachi over four hundred years ago, a contemporary of Ezra and Nehemiah. No wonder people were interested to experience for themselves what he had to say!

I confirmed John's role, and indirectly indicated my own identity. "John is the one about whom it is written: 'I will send my messenger ahead of you, who will prepare your way before you.'[19]" Furthermore, the prophecy that God would send Elijah had found its fulfilment in John. There had never been any man greater than John, and yet the least in the kingdom of heaven was greater than he. For John preached about

---

[17] Jensen (p. 235)
[18] μαλακοῖς ἱματίοις = soft raiment (Luke 7:25)
[19] Malachi 3:1, 4:5 (NIV); Matthew 11:10 (NIV); Luke 7:27 (NIV)

my coming; those in the kingdom would preach about my sacrifice and glory to come.

Turning my attention to the reactions I had observed in many of my listeners to both John's ministry and my own, I compared them with children at play, emulating their elders as they do the world over. We often see children giving a gentle flick of the whip to an imaginary donkey or camel, or to a pretend horse pulling a racing Roman chariot, like the ones that sweep along the Way of the Sea between Damascus and the coast. How often have you watched a child gleefully sitting behind, and clinging to, the steering wheel of your modern-day transport – wondering why the doors were unlocked, whilst hoping that it wasn't because the children had got hold of the keys to open them! Children here are just the same, often mimicking the shepherd-boy flutes that are played at weddings, or the persistent wailing of the women in any town who accompany a funeral.[20] Adults walking by would usually pay little attention to such amusement, either feeling above it or being too preoccupied to notice.

"People are like children playing at a market," I imagined aloud. "They call out to the passers-by, 'We played the flute for you, and you didn't dance; we sang a dirge for you, and you didn't mourn.'"

People had reacted to us in a similar fashion, particularly the Pharisees. John had worn clothes of mourning, and preached a message of repentance that they and many others had ignored, labelling him as demonic. I, the Son of Man, could often be found at the 'wrong' people's houses, enjoying a good meal with some wine, and they branded me a glutton and a friend of sinners. We couldn't get it right whatever we did! However, God's wisdom would be seen in the end.[21]

Soon after this, one of those 'wrong' kinds of people brought very similar reactions at the house of a Pharisee called Simon.[22] He had invited me to lunch, and I was happy to accept; maybe I could open a stubborn heart to accepting the kingdom of grace rather than an eternal life 'earned' (so people thought) by religious observance. However,

---

[20] Matthew 11:16-19; Luke 7:31-35
[21] Matthew 11:19; Luke 7:35
[22] Luke 7:36-50

despite the seemingly warm sincerity of his invitation, I perceived a distant reserve, with neither the customary kiss of welcome, nor the usual bowl of water for alleviating my feet of the all-pervasive road dust.

After we had reclined a while, propped up on one elbow at a low table, with feet trailing out behind, a head appeared in the doorway, eyes nervously surveying the scene. The woman to whom they belonged picked me out, sitting in the circle, and entered the room, clutching an expensive alabaster jar of perfume. She also brought with her a questionable reputation, and a tangible hostility towards her pervaded the atmosphere.

The despised woman made her way through the bristling room, impervious to its occupants' affront, intent on her mission. Tears had been forming in the corners of her glassy eyes before she entered the room. Now they flowed freely over my dusty feet as she knelt down, enough to wash the dirt from them, before she wiped them dry with her long, black, silky hair. She tenderly kissed my refreshed feet and then poured sweet-smelling perfume on them. Its fragrant scent permeated the whole house.

I looked across the table and met Simon's gaze. Had his eyes been able to talk, their lips would have been forming the condescending remark that, were I a prophet, I would know what sort of sinful woman was touching me. Hearing this unspoken slight through our Spirit, I wondered how to make him understand my obvious acceptance of this woman, and to realise how unforgiving his own position was. Prompted again by our Spirit, an illustration formed in my mind.

"Simon, I have something to tell you."[23]

He looked at me without expression. "Tell me, teacher," he said[24] noncommittally.

"Two men were in debt to a moneylender, one to the tune of five hundred denarii,[25] while the other owed fifty. Neither of them could repay him, so he cancelled the debts of both. Now, which of them would love him more?"

[23] Luke 7:40a (NIV)
[24] Luke 7:40b (NIV)
[25] NIV text note at Luke 7:41: a denarius was a coin worth about a day's wages

"The one who was forgiven more, I guess," Simon replied, with barely disguised reluctance. His nervous fidgeting indicated a growing awareness of where this was leading.

"That's right," I responded. Then, turning to the woman, I pointed out to Simon the shortcomings I had noticed on entering his house, contrasting his lack of courtesy with the love she was still lavishing on me. To that home truth I added further insult, to his mind, by pronouncing that her many sins had been forgiven, because she loved much, while he who had been forgiven little would love little.

Some of the assembled guests echoed his startled thoughts as they muttered to each other. "Who does he think he is,[26] that he presumes to forgive sins?"

I winked good-naturedly at the woman, who had recognised her own part in this story, and reassured her. "Your faith has saved you; go in peace."[27]

The nervousness in her eyes was gone, and they oozed serenity as she left, happy.

As summer once more wrestled power from spring,[28] and brightly coloured tree blossom gave way to a thousand shades of green, I travelled about with the Twelve from one town and village to another, proclaiming the good news of God's kingdom.[29] Several women accompanied us now, which fact was unusual in itself, as I mentioned when I told you about the woman at the well in Sychar.[30] I had cured them of diseases and evil spirits – seven in the case of Mary of Magdala – and they now followed us, helping to support us from their own personal means. Susanna and Joanna, who was the wife of Herod's household manager, Chuza, were two more of the many that helped and for whom we were grateful; their widespread contacts gave us a temporary base in many places.

---

26 cf. Gill (on Luke 7:49)
27 Luke 7:50 (NIV)
28 From the NIV Study Bible time-chart at Matthew 25
29 Luke 8:1
30 See page 70

In one of these,[31] a demon-possessed man was brought to me. The wretched figure could neither see nor speak, and so was only aware of people around him through sound and touch; aware, but unable to communicate except by squeezing the hand belonging to a familiar voice. Once again, my urge to reclaim wholeness for this child of God drove me to act. The demon had no place here, no right to squat! Healing authority flowed through me as I drove the evil spirit out of the man, so that he could both talk and see. Another one restored.

"Could this be the Son of David?"[32] the people exclaimed in their astonishment, using a popular Jewish title for the expected Messiah, based on the promise[33] of an eternal dynasty made to King David.

When the Pharisees heard this, they made the ridiculous statement that I could only drive out demons in the power of Beelzebub, the prince of demons. Indignation grew within me; didn't they understand anything? How can a kingdom survive if it fights against itself? The Pharisees should have known that from our history: when Gideon's whittled-down army of just three hundred men blew their trumpets, we caused the joint Midianite and Amalekite army to panic and turn on itself.[34]

I stated the obvious and further explained what had happened by likening it to burgling a strong man's house. This can only happen if you first manage to tie up the strong man! I could only dispossess Satan because I was able to bind him up. The deceased man's grave remained unexpectedly empty because I had authority over death.

Did the people understand now?

I needed to issue a warning to the Pharisees especially, but also to the crowd, who, though burdened by their many rules, generally upheld the Pharisees' teaching as reliable[35]. People like to assume that those in charge know what they are doing. They must not be led astray on this one! You are either with me or against me, gathering in the harvest of souls, or scattering them. Anything spoken about the Son of Man is

---

[31] Mark 3:20
[32] Matthew 12:23 (NIV)
[33] 2 Samuel 7:11b,16
[34] Judges 6:33, 7:22
[35] Josephus (Antiquities of the Jews XIII.10.5,6; XVIII.1.4)

forgivable: "Isn't he Joseph's son?" or the commonly held view of a Nazarene as echoed by Nathaniel. But to attribute works of the Holy Spirit to Satan is a blasphemy that cannot be forgiven.[36]

"You brood of vipers," I exclaimed, borrowing a phrase from Cousin John, "how can you who are evil say anything good?"[37]

Good fruit indicates a healthy tree, bad fruit a diseased one. In the same way, a man's words display his heart, and on the day of judgement will serve to acquit or condemn him. What do *your* words show of your heart?

Harboured hopes that the Pharisees would heed the warning faded abruptly with their next request. They wanted to see a miraculous sign from me![38] Hello? I had not long breathed life back into a dead man, and barely finished opening the eyes and mouth of one demon-possessed. What sort of miracle did they want! If they attributed the one they had just witnessed to the devil, nothing would convince them of my divine identity.

So I put it bluntly: "It is a wicked and adulterous generation that asks for a miraculous sign!"[39] God's people, who are supposed to be his bride, have turned their back on him[40] and refuse to accept the evidence before their very eyes. "No, the only sign that will be given is the one of the prophet Jonah."

Now, getting on for eight hundred years ago, my Dad and I sent Jonah on a pretty straightforward, if lengthy, errand to Nineveh, some six hundred miles north-east of Jerusalem, on the banks of the River Tigris. We told him through our Spirit to warn the Ninevites of imminent judgement that would befall them if they did not repent.[41] This didn't suit Jonah, so he paid for a boat fare from Joppa and sailed in the opposite direction. The boat was aiming westwards to the farthest limits of his known world, towards the Phoenician settlement of Tarshish, in what you know as southern Spain. In the end we had to

---

[36] Matthew 12:10
[37] Matthew 12:34 (NIV)
[38] Matthew 12:38; Luke 11:16
[39] Matthew 12:39; Luke 11:29
[40] cf. Ezekiel 16
[41] Jonah 1:1,2ff

resort to sending a violent storm; only then did the crew throw Jonah overboard (reluctantly, it has to be said in their favour). Finally, we provided free return transport by getting a large fish to swallow him whole. Jonah took three days to recognise his folly and apologise to us, by which time the fish had swum back to Joppa and, at our command, spewed him up on the beach. Needless to say, when we asked him a second time, he went without questioning his assignment!

"Just as Jonah spent three days and three nights in the belly of the great fish,[42] so the Son of Man will be entombed in the heart of the earth for three days and three nights."

I reminded them that the Ninevites had repented after hearing Jonah's message and so were spared judgement; this generation had rejected one who is greater than Jonah was, and would be condemned by those same Ninevites at the time of judgement.

Continuing in a similar vein, I called to mind the visit of the Queen of the South – the area known as Sheba[43] – saying that even she would condemn this generation. She had heard of King Solomon's fame and how his wisdom was linked to his relationship with the Lord, and had travelled with a large caravan bearing expensive gifts, to see him for herself. Overwhelmed by Solomon's wisdom and riches, she had praised God for his love of Israel. She had recognised all that in Solomon, yet here stood one greater than he was, and this generation was stubbornly rejecting him. Did they not have the faintest idea that I was talking about myself?

Giving a final illustration, I warned my listeners about the judgement that would befall those of this generation who would refuse to believe. When an evil spirit comes out of a man, it goes wandering in desolate places, vainly seeking rest. Finding none, it returns, but with the man restored to his right mind like the one in Capernaum had been, finds its house vacant, clean and tidy. So the evil spirit goes and finds a further seven, more evil than itself, and they go in and live there. This generation, having rejected me, will be like that man – who ends up far

---

[42] Jonah 1:17; Matthew 12:40; see 'Three Days and Three Nights' note, page 303
[43] 1 Kings 10:1; noted at Genesis 10:28 (NIV) as approximating to Yemen

worse-off than he was to start with. If my Spirit is not living in you, then there is an empty house in your heart waiting to be occupied.

The throng sat back, taking in what I had said. Someone leant over as murmured comments started filling the lull, and told me that my mother and brothers were outside, waiting to speak to me. I sensed that they had come to take charge of me – aware of the dangers such as those I faced in Nazareth, and considering me out of my mind that I should go around putting the Pharisees' collective nose out of joint as I did.[44]

So I posed a rhetorical question. "Who are my mother and my brothers?"[45] I answered it by indicating the disciples sat in a circle around me. "It is those who do God's will who are my mother and my brothers."

I was not, of course, neglecting either my family or the commandment to respect one's parents;[46] rather, I stated my love for my disciples and those doing God's will by depicting them as my family. We got to speak with each other just as soon as I could forge a way through the crowd.

---

[44] Mark 3:21
[45] Matthew 12:48 (NIV); Mark 3:33 (NIV)
[46] Exodus 20:12; Deuteronomy 5:16

17

Kingdom Crops

Later that day,[1] I made my way down to the lakeside with my disciples, and sat down to teach. Once again, the crowd that followed was so large that I got into one of the boats and started teaching the people from out on the water.

You could say that I had not enjoyed a universally positive reception. While many came to hear my teaching, there were those amongst them, certainly the religious leaders, who perceived a threat to their privileged positions. Others, even my own family, remained sceptical and didn't understand the significance of my ministry. However, many were responding to what they had heard, believing in me when they witnessed the healing power unleashed before them.

So as I spoke to the crowd, I started to prepare my disciples for their own role in this ministry by giving them an illustration of how it would work. I soon discovered, when we were alone later on, that teaching them was going to be an uphill struggle. They hadn't understood the analogy, and requested an explanation.[2] So I went through it again.

"You will be going out to spread the word about God's kingdom, like a farmer going out to scatter seed by hand. Some people will hear

---

[1] Matthew 13:1
[2] Matthew 13:10; Mark 4:10

the word, but Satan will pluck it away from them, just as birds would eat up any seed that fell on a path."

So far so good. My fishermen could picture themselves as farmers.

"Others receive the word with joy but don't proceed to root themselves in the faith, thus falling away when troubles come. They are like seed that falls on rocky ground with little soil; it sprouts forth quickly but is soon scorched by the hot sun and withers. Those who hear the word but get choked by everyday worries, so that the word cannot impact their life, reflect the seed that is choked by thorny weeds growing up around it and rendering it unfruitful."

I glanced round at my attentive disciples; they were still with me.

"Thankfully, there are those with a noble and good heart, who are open to the word they hear, persevere, and produce fruit in their lives many times what was sown, just like the seed that fell in good soil and produced strong plants swollen with grain."

I hoped they would be pondering over what sort of soil they represented. Where did they stand regarding my teaching? For that matter, where do *you?*

"Why do you speak in parables?" my disciples wanted to know.

Fair enough question; even they didn't always understand the deeper meaning, evidently, but some people neither understood nor were willing to consider and apply my teaching to themselves. I likened such people to the Israelites Moses had spoken to when leading them in renewing their covenant with us;[3] he had reproached them for not understanding, despite having seen all that we had done for them. They simply refused to see or hear. These people actually fulfilled Isaiah's similar description of them.[4]

My disciples understood – if at a second attempt – because they were willing to accept what they saw, and listened to my words with an open heart that believed. The significance of a heart that believes is borne out in a life lived according to our laws.

"Living for God's glory is like this," I told them. "When you light a lamp, you put it on a stand where it is visible; you don't place it under

---

3   Deuteronomy 29:2-4; Matthew 13:13; Luke 8:10
4   Isaiah 6:9-10; Matthew 13:14-15; Mark 4:12-13

a bowl or under your bed, where no-one can see it! Your life should shine out brightly, to cast light onto others around you. They should see me in you! That's what my parables are designed to do: not to obscure the truth, but to throw light on it."

Speaking to the crowd from the boat, I had remained with the agricultural theme and explained the kingdom of heaven some more with a couple of additional seed-sowing illustrations.

"It's like a farmer sowing seed and then waiting for it to grow. How it does so remains a mystery to him, yet somehow the soil produces corn. Bit by bit the corn grows until it is ripe, and the farmer brings his sickle along to harvest it. Another farmer might sow good seed on his field,[5] only to have an enemy come stealthily by night and sow weeds among the wheat. When they all appear together, he instructs his servants to leave the weeds in for the time being, since pulling them out will uproot the wheat too. At harvest, the weeds can be gathered up in bundles and burned, and the wheat will be harvested and brought into the farmer's storage barns."

Now I found myself having to explain the second farmer's crop to my disciples as well. While it was frustrating when those close to me understood little better than the crowds that came out of curiosity, I valued these more intimate times where we could talk alone, knowing that they were willing to attune their hearts to mine. I explained the wheat and the weeds to them.

"The farmer that spreads good seed on his land represents the Son of Man. He spreads the good news in the world, and his children who accept it grow. In contrast, the weeds are the children of the devil. At the end of time, our angels will weed out and cast into hell's fiery furnace anything that causes sin and all who do evil. The righteous will be gathered into God's kingdom and shine brightly like the sun."

I looked round at each of my disciples. "Do you understand now?"

Gentle nodding.

"So live your lives as expressed[6] by the prophet Daniel and shine brightly!"

---

[5] Matthew 13:24-29,36-43
[6] Daniel 12:3

Back in the boat, facing the crowd, I had given a final seed analogy that described me.

"The kingdom of heaven is like the miniscule mustard seed which grows over time into a large tree that birds nest in."

Daniel interpreted the meaning of such a tree in King Nebuchadnezzar's dream;[7] the tree, representing the king, was to be felled because of the king's pride, but would grow back when he had recognised the Lord, and become a refuge for the people. I had been thinking more, however, of the similarly described tree prophesied by Ezekiel that represented the coming Messiah.[8] Now that tree was here! From my humble earthly beginnings, the tender shoot planted by my Father was beginning to flourish into a splendid tree in which people of all nationalities could come and take refuge.

Scanning the crowd to check they were still with me – wanting to give the people as much as they could take in[9] – I had pressed on with another image depicting life in the kingdom. Did you know that the tiniest amount of yeast will work its way through a whole batch of dough and cause it to rise?[10] That's what I likened God's kingdom to.

I mentioned my humble human origins. You might consider yourself too insignificant to do any good in my kingdom. You never know, though, what effect a small word of encouragement sown in someone's life will have; it may take time, like the dough has to be left to rise, but it will surely grow and infuse their whole being, ripening all by itself[11] into the fruit of hope, renewed confidence, self-worth or inner peace. Where do you need to go sowing today?

After that, the afternoon had drawn on to the point where I decided it was time to leave and return to the house we were staying in, where the disciples joined me. Now, having explained the parable of the weeds to them over some food, I showed them what it is like when people discover the kingdom of heaven for themselves.

---

7 Daniel 4:11-12,20-21
8 Ezekiel 17:22-23
9 Mark 4:33
10 Matthew 13:31-33; Mark 4:30-32; Luke 13:18-21
11 cf. Mark 4:26-29

"It is like this: a man finds some treasure in a field, hides it again and in his joyful excitement sells all he owns in order to buy the field and secure the treasure. Likewise, a pearl merchant who discovers his dream pearl at a dealer's sells all he has to obtain it. Do you get it?"

They understood. After all, they had already left their livelihoods to follow me. Do *you* get it? Are *you* prepared to give up everything in order to obtain the greatest treasure?

Building on the allegory of the weeds, I warned the disciples again that the end of time would bring separation of the wicked from the righteous.

"The kingdom of heaven is also like this: a fishing-net catches all kinds of fish; the good ones are collected in baskets, but any bad ones are discarded. Those who have rejected the challenge to repent and the good news I bring will be thrown into the fiery furnace like those bad fish or the bundle of weeds. Those who accept my words, on the other hand, will be gathered up into the basket of the kingdom."

The challenge to my disciples remains the same. Are you going to be in the bundle or the basket? Where do you want to be?

18

Weather Madness and Madness Drowned

"Have you understood all these things?"[1] I asked my disciples.

"Yes," they assured me.

Sufficient parables for one day, but I shared one final comment, comparing faithful teachers of the law who were knowledgeable about the heavenly kingdom with a householder who can draw on the rich bounty of previous years as well as that newly harvested.[2] The law of Moses – the old covenant – is a treasure that shows our children what sin is, convicts them of it, and provides redemptive measures to remove that sin from our holy presence. In the new covenant, we – my Father and I in the power of our Spirit – are providing those measures, the necessary sacrifice, ourselves; not dismissing the old but raising it to renewed prominence, while providing a brand-new way of fulfilling it.

Evening was already approaching when I suggested to my disciples that we cross over to the other side of the lake.[3] They were itching for

---

1   Matthew 13:51 (NIV)
2   Matthew 13:51-52
3   Mark 4:35(-41); Matthew 8:23-27; Luke 8:22-25

some movement to loosen up their stiffened muscles; I was tired from a good lunch and an afternoon's teaching, and was hoping that the gentle lapping of water against the side of our fishing boat would ease me into some restful sleep. My disciples got their exercise all right, but my nap was rudely interrupted.

An urgent tugging on my arm replaced the gentle rocking motion that had soon induced my slumber. "Teacher, don't you care if we drown?"[4] several of my disciples chorused.

Well of course I cared, but why would they think they were going to drown? They had so little faith. Night had fallen, and indeed a howling gale was coming down from Bashan, churning the sea; yes, the bottom of the boat looked like they were intending to keep the few fish they'd caught on the way alive for a bit longer. But weren't the fishermen among them used to such storms? Even the landlubbers in the group knew to trust their friends, so why would they think I wouldn't care? Didn't they realise that we were on a mission together, and that the middle of the lake was not where it was destined to end? Did they still not know me well enough to know I would have it in hand?

"Be still," I rebuked the storm, having stood up to face the wind.

An instant hush descended around us, and the white-crested waves crashed for a final time and rippled into non-existence. The terror on my disciples' faces, however, showed no signs of subsiding, and their wide eyes burned with the question of who exactly was stood before them, whom even the wind and waves obeyed! I guessed it would still be a while before they realised it was the guy who created them in the first place.

My disciples nervously settled back into a steady rowing rhythm, and we reached the far side without further incident, landing at the lakeside village of Gergesa, in the predominantly Gentile Gadarene region,[5] halfway down the eastern shore of the lake. Steep cliffs rose close by, dotted with caves hollowed out by man and wind, and used as burial chambers[6].

---

4   Mark 4:38b (NIV)
5   Matthew 8:28ff; Mark 5:1ff; Luke 8:26ff. (Gentile: Jews do not keep pigs.)
6   Barnes (on Matthew 8:28)

The naked inhabitant of one of these – a live specimen! – came out to meet us. He was from Gergesa, but had not worn clothes or lived in a house there for a long time, driven to the solitude of the tombs by the evil spirits that had seized him, as can sometimes happen. The townsfolk had tried on numerous occasions to bind the man up with chains, adding to his suffering and degradation, but he broke free each time. It was a broken man, covered in physical scars from years of self-harm,[7] who greeted me at the top of his voice, pronouncing my divinity and demanding what I wanted of him.

"What is your name?" I asked.

"Legion," he informed me.

Now, a Roman legion comprises six thousand men; many demons had inhabited this desperate fellow. Demons are the evil spirits of deceased nephilim, the giant offspring of a number of fallen angels. Once servants of heaven, who were supposed to watch over the people, these particular angels had chosen their own direction, lusting after and marrying the daughters of men.[8] For their lustful disobedience, we cast them out of heaven and into the abyss – hell – to await judgement at the end of time.[9] The nephilim were big and strong, and these products of free choice inherited their parents' disobedience. They wrought violence amongst Israel's ancestors, and eventually we decided to eradicate them.[10] Only Noah and his family had remained faithful to us, and against all logic he obeyed us in building a wooden ark in which he saved his family and pairs of all the animals we had created.[11]

The flood destroyed the nephilim, but their spirits remained free to roam until the end of time as demons. Like their prince, the devil,[12] they are no respecters of truth, though they do recognise authorities and powers greater than themselves. That's why the demons occupying the man, thinking that perhaps the end of time accompanied my presence, begged repeatedly that I wouldn't order them into the Abyss, the eternal

---

7   Mark 5:5
8   Genesis 6:1-4; Numbers 13:33; Josephus (Antiquities of the Jews I.3.1)
9   2 Peter 2:4-5; Jude 6; Huie ("Fallen..."); Brown (Chs 3,4)
10   1 Enoch 8:1, apocryphal OT writing; Huie ("Sons-of-God")
11   Genesis 6-8
12   Matthew 12:24; Luke 11:15

place of confinement we have reserved for evil spirits and indeed Satan.[13] Instead, they appealed for permission to enter the herd of some two thousand[14] pigs grazing the grass nearby.

Demons can occupy animals as well as humans; only look at some fighting dogs, or a crazed horse. I briefly contemplated the pigs, regarded as unclean animals in our culture. That alone was no reason for them to deserve the demons, but they would serve as a stark warning to the people that demons and the consequences of sin are to be taken seriously. I granted them permission, and they relinquished the man. The hapless pigs' narrow eyes widened in terror as they sensed the demonic invasion, and within seconds they were frantically stampeding down the nearby steep bank into the lake, where they swiftly drowned.

Those who had been tending the pigs fled into the village with almost as much panic as the pigs had when headed to their demise. Meanwhile, my disciples found a few spare clothes in the back of the boat, still a little damp from the night's weather, though they would soon dry in the day's heat, and the man was able to dress himself. People trickled down in groups, until a sizeable crowd had amassed by the lake, eager to see for themselves what had happened. They found the previously uncontrollable man sitting there dressed and in his right mind. Those who had witnessed it told them how I had healed the man, and about the pigs, whose carcasses were floating in the water nearby. At least this side of the lake, some of them might make their way into a casserole.

The people to whom I had wanted to come, a Gentile community, reacted quite differently from those I remembered in Sychar, who had entreated me to remain with them,[15] and many of whom had come to believe in me. Those here were understandably afraid, but their reaction was to plead with me to leave their region. The loss of the pigs certainly represented a financial blow to their owners, as well as to the herdsmen, who had just lost any hopes of a bonus. Perhaps they wondered how much else they would lose! So many people worry about what they

---

[13] Revelation 9:1-2, 20:1-2
[14] Mark 5:13
[15] See page 73

might have to give up if they decide to believe in me. Yet it is always like obtaining the hidden treasure or that pearl of great price;[16] whatever you give up in order to follow me, my Father and I replace with so much more.

As I was getting into the boat,[17] the man who had been demon-possessed begged to go with me. However, I could better use him on this side of the lake, and told him instead to go home to his family and tell them how much God had done for him, and of His mercy. The man acquiesced, and held his hand high in a farewell greeting as we departed, a wide smile having replaced the wild desperation on his face. Another one restored.

Two more awaited on the far side of the lake. We had not long arrived back at Capernaum[18] when a crowd gathered. I started to teach them, talking about the signs they had already seen, and using illustrations they would understand to educate them about the nature of the kingdom of heaven. Before long, I could see a man picking his way among the people sat on the ground in front of me. His air and the quality of his flowing robes indicated a high-ranking member of the synagogue. It was somewhat surprising that a synagogue ruler would approach me in this manner, even more so that he proceeded to kneel down and plead earnestly with me.[19] There was a serious reason for casting off his usual reserve.

"My little girl's close to death," he faltered, lip quivering. "I beg you to come and lay hands on her, to heal her and save her life."

I reached out to Jairus, as he was called, and helped him back to his feet. Anxiety creased his features. The crowd parted like a pair of drapes as we walked forward, closing again behind us in what was already resembling a funeral procession. I could not let it come to that.

Suddenly I felt healing power flowing from me through my clothes. Now, people were pushing in on all sides, but this was no accidental contact. When I heal somebody, I always feel my Father's power flowing

---

16 Matthew 13:45-46
17 Mark 5:18
18 Matthew 9:1 (then vv18-26; Mark 5:21-43; Luke 8:40-56)
19 Matthew 9:18; Mark 5:22-23; Luke 8:41-42

out of me into the patient, carried there by our Spirit. That is true when I myself initiate the treatment, or when somebody comes to me in expectant faith,[20] as happened in this case.

I turned round, knowing that somebody behind me had more than just brushed against my garment.

"Who touched me?"

No-one dared to admit having touched me, and Peter eventually tried to diffuse the impasse by telling me the obvious. "Master, the crowd is pressing in on all sides."

"No, no," I retorted, "someone just touched me. I felt power flowing from me."

Whoever it was needed to know that they had rightly placed their faith in me, and I wanted the crowd to understand that too.

With no immediate escape route open to her, and seeing that she could not go unnoticed, a harried-looking woman came trembling and fell at my feet. In front of everybody, she told me everything that she had gone through. It was a bold thing to do, since the bleeding she had been suffering from for twelve years had made her unclean in the eyes of the Jewish law. The poor woman had used up all her money on treatments that were at best ineffective and at worst had made her condition more serious. She had dared to believe that I could turn her wretched situation around, and it was her great faith, as I informed her affectionately, that had healed her.

"Daughter, your faith has healed you. Go in peace."[21]

I had hardly finished speaking to the woman, when I could see a series of heads zigzagging towards me, or more accurately, towards Jairus, weaving their way past people on each side. The atmosphere became more subdued once again, as the sombre-faced men informed Jairus that his daughter had died, and told him not to bother me anymore. *But I am bothered!*

So many people cannot imagine me, Almighty God, wanting to be bothered with their little lives. How wrong they are! The prophet Isaiah vividly described us engraving you on our hands so we can never forget

---

[20] cf. Matthew 7:7, 21:22
[21] Mark 5:34 (NIV)

you,[22] just like you might write a name or number on your hand so you don't forget it. Engraving my hands is how I am ultimately going to show my love for you.

I ignored what the messengers had said. "Have no fear,"[23] I told Jairus. "Just have faith."

There are times when only faith can overcome fear and grief. I, the Word, through the power of my heavenly Father, spoke life into our created beings, as our Spirit breathed it into them. In the face of real, believing faith, I still love to speak life back into people or situations that have lost it. Reassuring Jairus, I could already sense my Spirit leading the girl's spirit back towards her prematurely deserted body.

As we approached the house, we were faced with a commotion. Wailing women, doleful flutes, noisy neighbours, all raised a mêlée of mournfulness that did little to comfort anyone. Taking only Jairus and his wife in with me, plus Peter, James and his brother John,[24] I threw everyone else out of the house, protesting that the girl was only asleep. They ridiculed me, knowing that the girl was dead.

In the dimly lit room at the back of the house, I approached the girl's motionless body. As I took her hand and spoke to her, my Spirit danced as he handed back her spirit.

"Talitha koum!"[25] *Little girl, arise!*

Her spirit returned,[26] life breathed back into her, and she stood up at once and started walking around. Her mother was beside herself with more emotions than she knew how to cope with, and I suggested she busy herself with finding some food for the girl to eat. Both parents were astonished and delighted in equal measure. I warned them in vain, as I had others before, not to tell anyone else about what they had seen. As it was, news of it spread through the whole region.

---

[22] Isaiah 49:16
[23] Mark 5:36 (NIV)
[24] Mark 5:37,40; Luke 8:51
[25] Mark 5:41
[26] Luke 8:55

19

Delegation

It wasn't long before I was crossing swords with the Pharisees again. One of them had invited me to his house to eat with him,[1] and as I sat down to recline at the table, he was surprised that I didn't have the usual ceremonial wash before the meal. This was not a requirement of the law, but of the Pharisees' added customs.[2]

The Pharisees are so concerned with outward appearances, and so unwilling to look at a person's inner values. I used the picture language of dirty crockery to address their hypocrisy. "You Pharisees pedantically wash the outside of a cup or dish, when it is not that which requires cleansing but the greed and wickedness you are full of on the inside."

Did they not think about the fact that we made the inside, as well as the outside which they took such pains over keeping clean?

"If you were to give your ill-gotten gains to the poor, then I might be convinced that you are attending to cleansing the inside as well."

These remarks did not appear to go down too well. The next certainly wouldn't.

"Woe to you Pharisees," I declared, "for you neglect the important values of justice and the love of God, while diligently tithing your garden herbs! You need to attend to the important issues in life, while

---

[1] Luke 11:37(-54)
[2] Mark 7:1-5

not leaving small matters undone. You love the best seats at the synagogue, and the greetings of others in the market place, instead of being humble before God. Your deceptive lifestyles and teaching are like unmarked graves, which people walk over unwittingly, becoming unclean in the process."[3]

An expert and teacher in the law interjected, "Teacher, what you're saying is insulting to us as well."

I could not resist aiming a few home truths in their direction as well. "You lawmakers burden people down with loads that are oppressive, while not lifting one finger to help them."

I reminded them of the ornate[4] tombs they build for the prophets whom their ancestors killed, thereby approving those ancestors' actions. We sent prophets to our people, but they were often ignored or even killed. Right through the Scriptures – from Abel (in the first book of Moses) to Zechariah (in the last book of our Hebrew Bible, 'The Events of the Days', which you know as Chronicles[5]) – prophets had been killed. Their blood will taint the hands of even this generation, who will be held responsible.

"Woe to you experts in the law,[6] because you have purloined the key to knowledge. You won't enter through its door yourselves, and you hinder anyone else who would do so."

The thought of the prophets' fate caused the purpose of my saving mission to sweep through my consciousness with intensity. *Father, help the Pharisees to get it*, I thought, *help me to persevere.*

It wasn't just the Pharisees who took offence at my words. I still wasn't faring too well in my hometown of Nazareth. It was a while since my townsfolk had tried to cast me down the cliff-face. Their antagonism had faded to the extent that I was able to preach in the synagogue again.[7] However, their reaction to my person had remained intact. I was still the local carpenter's son, and the brother of others they knew. They couldn't imagine me speaking with such authority, and took renewed

---

3 Numbers 19:16
4 cf. Matthew 23:29
5 NIV footnote at Matthew 23:35
6 Luke 11:52 (NIV)
7 Matthew 13:54; Mark 6:2

offence at me. I said to them quite plainly that only in his hometown and in his own house does a prophet count for nothing.

I was sad, because naturally I felt an affinity for Nazareth, having grown up there, and because the people there were just as in need of healing and hope as anywhere else. As I said about the through-the-roof healing, we love to respond to faith;[8] when faith is present we are bound to respond to it. Finding so little faith in my hometown, I was only able to lay hands on a few people to heal them. I was amazed at the lack of faith of most of the townsfolk.

We moved on again from there and went through all the towns and villages, teaching in their synagogues, preaching the good news of the kingdom and healing all sorts of disease and illness. The crowds were harassed and helpless, like sheep without a shepherd, and I had compassion on them.

"There is a plentiful harvest, but there are few workers," I remarked to my disciples on one occasion, referring to the people. "Ask the Lord of the harvest to send out workers into his field."

That thought ignited a spark within me. My disciples had been on the road with me for over a year now. I had taught them by word and example how to minister to people, how to speak healing, even to cast out demons. I do everything I see my Father doing, and in his power,[9] but that power was available to them as well, just as it is to you. I reckoned that their faith had increased to the point where I could send them out on their own.

I commissioned them with some excitement, directing them to the lost sheep of Israel and telling them to avoid Samaritan or Gentile territories for the time being. They were still apprentices after all! The time for them to spread further afield would come soon enough. I told them to preach the message that the kingdom of God is near; to heal the sick, raise the dead, and cleanse those who had leprosy; and to drive out demons.

I was empowering them for free, so they weren't to solicit or receive any payment for healing ministry. However, they should also

---

[8] See page 87
[9] cf. John 5:19-30

not take any supplies with them, but accept the hospitality shown to them at whichever town or village they entered. Should none be offered, I told them to shake the dust off their feet, just as you would stamp your feet after tramping across a muddy field. This was a symbolic use of the common custom among my people when they leave 'unclean' Gentile areas, to show the seriousness of anyone rejecting our message – Jew or Gentile. The custom dates back to Nehemiah, who shook the dust out of the folds of his robe to represent God rejecting anyone who broke their promise to help the poor among the returned exiles.[10]

As well as encouraging my disciples, I also had to warn them to be realistic about their undertaking. There would be those who would try them in local councils and even flog them in the synagogue of which they were part. On the positive side, because of me, they would be brought before governors and kings, having the chance to witness to them and to the Gentiles.

"Don't worry about what to say," I assured them. "The Holy Spirit will show you what to say and speak through you."

Our message would even end up splitting families, some believing, others not.[11] But your love for me should be stronger even than your love for your family.

"Students and slaves are not above their teachers or masters," I continued, "but may strive to be like them, taking the good with the bad. Some have already compared me with Beelzebub, so you can expect more of the same."

My disciples glanced at each other, uncertain despite my assurances. They had seen how my words could reap adverse reactions.

"Don't worry about proclaiming the truth to such people; they can maybe kill your body, but not your soul. You should be more afraid of God, for he can condemn both to hell and destruction.[12]"

They needed convincing of how much my Father and I valued them. "Sparrows are sold for two a penny," I stated, "yet none falls out of the sky without the Father's say-so. How much more will he look

---

10 Nehemiah 5:13; Matthew 10:14; Mark 6:11; Luke 9:5; cf. Acts 13:51, 18:6
11 Matthew 10:21-22,34-37
12 Matthew 10:28; Luke 12:4-5

after you! At the same time," I told them, giving another hint of what my mission would entail for me, "trouble may come your way, and if you're not prepared to come after me carrying your own cross, you're unworthy of me. But if you give up your own hopes and dreams for my sake, you will rediscover your life. Equally, if you extend hospitality to any such person – be they prophet, righteous man, or lowly disciple – or even just give them a cup of water in my name, you will receive your just reward in heaven.[13]"

Having sent my disciples off on their own, I travelled down to Jerusalem for a feast of the Jews.[14] I wondered how the disciples were getting on, trusting my Father in heaven that he was looking after my 'sparrows'. Catching up with them was going to be fun!

On the Sabbath in Jerusalem, I made my way to the rain- and spring-fed twin Pool of Bethesda, near the city's Sheep Gate to the northern side of the temple. The gate had been rebuilt over four hundred years ago by the high priest Eliashib and his fellow priests, under Nehemiah.[15] The original pool dated back twice as far, when a dam built across the short Beth Zeta valley had provided a reservoir of rain water for the city.[16] People with various illnesses gathered there constantly, for they attributed healing properties to the water, the surface of which moved periodically.

Colonnades surround the two pools. I walked through the one that runs between them, surveying the needy people all around and waiting for my Spirit to prompt me. My eyes met the empty gaze of an invalided man lying near the pool. He expected nothing; I was just another person passing by. His unwashed clothes spoke of a lengthy period of inactivity; but it was the resignation in his eyes that drew me to his plight. I squatted down beside him and learned that he had been in this condition for thirty-eight years.

"Would you like to get well?"

---

[13] Matthew 10:41-42
[14] John 5:1(-15)
[15] Nehemiah 3:1
[16] Wikipedia ("Pool of Bethesda")

You might consider that a strange thing to ask, but after such a long time, the man would struggle to live a normal existence again. No-one would bring food or give him any money to pay for some. He would have to support himself. His indirect reply revealed the real answer.

"Sir, there's nobody to help me. Whenever the waters are disturbed, while I'm struggling to drag myself into the pool, somebody else beats me to it."

Unable to move quickly to the waters when they moved and to receive healing as the first to enter them, he had given up on ever being healed, at least without help. But did he really *want* to be? Had he grown acclimatised to life as it was, having stopped believing for something that he no longer expected anyone, including me, to give him? Have *you?*

"Get up," I said to the man, "pick up your mat and walk!"

The man had to make a decision: either to remain dependent upon others or to choose to re-enter the forgotten territory of self-reliance. I could see him wrestle with this for a moment before resolution formed across his features, and he made the decision to obey. At once, his weakened muscles became strong, and joints stiff from immobility loosened as if oiled. I smiled broadly at him as he stood up and took some faltering steps.

As he did so, I spotted a huddle of Pharisees heading towards the man, who was carrying his mat as I had commanded him. Not normally a problem, only today was the Sabbath, and mats were not to be carried. I shunned the discussion that would inevitably follow, and slipped out through the crowd in the opposite direction.

Later, I found the man in the temple, and exhorted him to stop sinning, lest anything worse should befall him. Having chosen healthy independence, I wanted the man to recognise his need for dependence on my heavenly Father. Physical ailments are bad enough, but the consequence of unconfessed sin is eternal separation from us.

The Pharisees must have observed me talking to the man, because they soon started persecuting me for having done 'work' on the Sabbath[17] and inciting the man to do so too.

"My Father is continually working," I told them, "so I'm not going to stop doing his redemptive work just because it's a Sabbath."

To working on a Sabbath, they now added the charge of blasphemy, because my statement had made myself equal with God my Father.

I tried explaining it further by telling them how I work. You see, I choose to only ever do what I see my Father doing, working to fulfil His purposes. He has even entrusted me with judgement, though I judge only as I hear from him, in a just way that is pleasing to him. Because my Father has given me his authority, all will honour me as they honour him. Likewise, by honouring me with your life you honour him who sent me.

"My Father has granted me to have life just as he does," I proclaimed to them. "He embodies life and he gives it.[18] Whoever listens to what I say and believes in the Father who sent me, no longer lives under condemnation but has eternal life. Even those who are dead will soon hear my voice and rise, the righteous to live, evildoers to be condemned."

Proclaiming and restoring life – that's what I'm here for! *Father, help my people to believe!*

I could see that the Pharisees still refused to believe; they had already demanded proof despite the evidence of the healing I had just brought. So I told them that my Father himself testifies in my favour,[19] as some had witnessed at my baptism.

"You entertained John's message for a while, but didn't accept his testimony. Nor do you believe the far greater evidence my Father is displaying through the work he has given me to do. You believe in the law of Moses, but not in the messianic prophecies he wrote[20] about me.

---

[17] John 5:16(-30)

[18] John 5:26; cf. Deuteronomy 30:20; Job 10:12, 33:4; Psalm 36:9

[19] John 5:32(-47)

[20] e.g. Genesis 3:15, 49:10; Exodus 12:21 (1 Corinthians 5:7); Numbers 24:17; Deuteronomy 18:15; Luke 24:27

Moses himself will condemn you through the law you claim to believe in."

Back in Capernaum a few days later, my disciples rejoined me from their expeditions. Like little children interrupting each other to tell all the details of a story, they reported everything they had taught and done while I had been down in Jerusalem.[21] They had been worthy representatives; I had known they would be! *Thank you, Father, for being true to your word.* We swapped stories until late into the night.

But my joy was short-lived. The following morning some of John's disciples came with the devastating news that Herod had had him beheaded.[22]

---

[21] Mark 6:30; Luke 9:10
[22] Matthew 14:12

20

Breadcrumbs

For a moment in time, my humanity took precedence, and I mourned over Cousin John just as you would over a lost, close relative. Memories flooded back: our times of studying the Scriptures together, of growing up to realise our respective destinies, our intertwined roles in my Father God's purposes. He had fulfilled his calling, to prepare the way – for me. *Father, keep me strong in my own calling!* Many had repented at John's words and he had baptised them, just as he had baptised me, albeit reluctantly. And now he was gone; now it was only me.

Except it wasn't solely me; I had my faithful band of disciples, and they had just returned from their first solo missions full of uplifting stories. I had to remain strong for their sake. Any doubts on my human part would knock their confidence. We needed to get away on our own, gather ourselves and continue in our mission.

To that end, we collected what we needed and took one of the boats to a solitary place towards Bethsaida,[1] which lies further along the top of the lake from Capernaum, the other side of where the Jordan enters it. Unfortunately, people on Capernaum's shoreline recognised us as we left.[2] Here and there, we could see glimpses of figures running

---

[1] Matthew 14:13; Mark 6:32; Luke 9:10
[2] Mark 6:33

along the lakeside, and by the time we landed, the remote spot was anything but solitary. Many of John's followers formed part of the crowd. They were like sheep without a shepherd, and I felt compassion for them.[3] They needed me, so after a quick prayer to my Father for strength and insight, I started teaching the people that had gathered.

At some point, as the sun started its downward journey to the horizon, I could see my disciples starting to fidget and whisper among themselves. They waited for a suitable pause and came over to state the cause of their discomfort. It was as I had suspected: it was getting late, we were in a remote place, and I should think about sending the people away to buy food for themselves. However, I had already been considering what I was going to do.

"You feed them!" I told them, knowing that the five thousand or so men and their families would present rather a challenge.

"It would take two hundred denarii to buy enough bread to feed this lot!" Philip protested[4] with an expression that suggested I had seriously lost it. The others murmured their agreement. He said it as if they actually had the equivalent of about eight months' wages on them, which would have greatly surprised me, as would anywhere being able to supply that amount of bread in the first place!

"Go and look how many loaves we've got," I told them instead.

Andrew, Simon Peter's brother, returned shortly with a tousle-haired boy. "This young lad here has got five little barley loaves plus a couple of fish," he stated sceptically, "but I can't see them being enough to feed that many!"

Barley grows widely in this area,[5] but the bread made from it is quite coarse.[6] It was a poor man's meal at best, and ordinarily completely inadequate for the task at hand. However, as well as being a reminder of the way Elisha satisfied a hundred hungry men,[7] its inadequacy was ideal to show that my Father can and will more than provide through me.

---

3 Mark 6:34 (cf. Matthew 9:36)
4 John 6:7; Mark 6:37. 5000 men: Matthew 14:21; Mark 6:44; Luke 9:14; John 6:10.
5 Deuteronomy 8:8; Ruth 1:22
6 Gill (on John 6:9)
7 2 Kings 4:42-44

I directed them to cause the people to sit down on the lush grass in groups of about fifty. Taking the loaves and fishes, I looked up to heaven and gave thanks to my Father, breaking the loaves as I did so. This was also a picture of my body being broken in the sacrifice to come, but I didn't expand on that symbolism for now. Instead, I simply divided everything up between my disciples and instructed them to do the same among the people. It was a good meal, so good that all were able to eat as much as they could or wanted. So that nothing went to waste, I encouraged my disciples to collect all the leftovers, which filled twelve baskets full. That was richly symbolic; I am here to provide a perfect and complete sacrifice for all the tribes of Israel.

Dismissing the crowd after that was no easy matter. I started by sending the disciples ahead of me to set off in the boat to Bethsaida.[8] Up above the shore, everyone wanted to crowd around me. Many had made the connection with Moses' foretelling of a saviour prophet whom God would raise up and were asking whether I was that prophet.[9] It was clear that the people wanted to come and make me king by force, but they had the wrong expectation of such a king. I used the first opportunity to escape the crowd and headed up the nearest mountain to spend some time alone and pray to my Father.

Meanwhile, and now in the darkness of the fallen evening, the disciples were not making any headway towards Bethsaida. In fact, they were being blown in the opposite direction.[10] I came down from the mountainside and spotted my disciples a considerable distance out on the lake, silhouetted in the reflected moonlight. For several hours, I paced along the lake shore, continuing in communion with my Father. Then sometime during the fourth and last of the Roman night watches,[11] as the first hint of the rising sun appeared over the Bashan, from which direction the strong winds were blowing, I made my way out to them.

The white-crested waves lapped against my ankles and soaked the hem of my garment. But the water presented no obstacle to me. While I

---

[8] Mark 6:45 (Matthew 14:22)
[9] John 6:14-15; Deuteronomy 18:15,18
[10] Given their later landing position in Gennesaret (Matthew 14:34; Mark 6:53)
[11] 03:00-06:00 (NIV footnotes at Matthew 14:25)

had limited myself to a human frame, I could still draw on all the powers of my Father. We had created the water, after all, and, as Job had recognised, it is within our character to tread on its waves to subdue it.[12] If the surface needed tensioning that bit more to carry me rather than the pond skaters and other insects it normally supported, well, that was just a word spoken in command.

However, the disciples, despite everything they knew about me, were still freaked out by what they thought was an apparition walking towards them. Doom and terror filled their faces, and I called out to reassure them. Their memories are so short-lived! I'd only just provided for the crowd, and had they already forgotten the storm a few months ago? They were exhausted, it has to be said, and in no mood to do the mental gymnastics required to connect together all the pieces of the complex jigsaw I presented to them.

"Don't be afraid! It's me: Jesus!"

Peter shouted back, saying that if it was me I should tell him to come to me on the water. I love Peter's impetuous faith! I could see that the rest of the Twelve looked as aghast at Peter's recklessness as they had at my unexpected appearance.

"Come," I shouted back, laughing, and indeed, he climbed out of the boat and headed out on the water towards me. After a few brief moments of excited delight spreading over his face at this new party trick, Peter looked up, registered the howling wind, and realised with horror what he was actually doing. Suddenly terrified, he began to sink.

"Lord, save me!"[13] he cried.

He was already close enough that I could just reach out my hand and grab him. We walked back to the boat together and climbed in. In my spirit I commanded the wind to calm down; my disciples were completely amazed by its obedience and my method of travel. They still didn't really understand, yet realised enough to worship me as the Son of God.[14]

---

[12] Job 9:8
[13] Matthew 14:30 (NIV)
[14] Mark 6:52; Matthew 14:33

They calmed down, mirroring the weather, and we plied the oars together. We soon landed at Gennesaret, as the wind had driven the boat in that direction. As had become usual, no sooner had we arrived than people recognised me, and word of our whereabouts soon spread. I was able to heal many; some, like the woman with bleeding, just touched my garments in faith. So my teaching had convinced some after all! Thus we made our way the three miles back to Capernaum.

There, some came and asked when I had arrived that side of the lake, saying that they had only seen the one boat leave the other side and that I hadn't been part of the crew.[15] Knowing that they would have been party to my catering, I used the theme of bread to illustrate what I wanted to speak to them about now.

I first provoked them by saying they had only come looking for me because they had eaten the loaves and gone away full. "Better to work for food that does not go off and believe in the One God sent."

"What miracle are you going to perform that will make us believe in you?" they challenged me, just as the Pharisees had done. "Moses gave our ancestors manna to eat in the desert."

Had I not just performed a sign?! Their wilful lack of understanding was disheartening in the extreme.

"That 'bread from heaven' didn't come from Moses," I explained patiently, "but from my Father. He is now offering you the real bread from heaven, which is the one who has come here from heaven to give life."

"Sir," they said, "from now on give us this bread."

This was as muddled as the woman at the well in Sychar demanding the living water I offered.

"*I am* the bread of life,"[16] I told them, using both the metaphor and the title my Father had used of himself during a mammoth session convincing Moses to challenge the Pharaoh.[17] "All that come to me shall never hunger, and all that believe in me shall never thirst. For by my Father's will they shall have eternal life."

---

[15] John 6:25(-59)
[16] John 6:35 (NIV)
[17] Exodus 3:14

At this the Jews in my audience began to grumble about my claims to have come from heaven, in the light of my local background, as they knew it. I hinted strongly that only I have seen the Father, who directs anyone who listens towards me. Our ancestors ate manna yet died; I am the living bread from heaven that brings eternal life. This bread is my body, which I will give for the life of the world. This caused more disquiet among the Jews, which I rebutted by saying even more clearly that they had to partake of my body and blood in order to gain eternal life. Of course I was speaking figuratively, yet my life will indeed be given and my blood will be shed, that others may live.

That was a sermon such as the Capernaum synagogue had never heard before. In fact, it proved too much for many, who found my teaching too hard. I asked my disciples whether they too wished to leave.

Peter, typically, spoke for all when he asked to whom else they should go. "Your words give eternal life," he said. "We believe and know that you are the Holy One of God."

Peter, when he gets it right, sure gets it right! I was proud of him, yet replied with the somewhat shocking statement that even though I had chosen the Twelve, one of them was a devil. For I knew that one of them had to betray me. The disciples looked uncertainly at each other, saying nothing further. Nor did I; it would become clear to them soon enough, but that was something to be faced later.

Of the crowds of people that came from all over the region, there was one time a group of Pharisees and teachers of the law who had come up from Jerusalem to see what to make of me.[18] They didn't take long to find something to complain about.

My disciples had started eating without making the ceremonial cleaning demanded by the traditions of the elders. They have all sorts of rules governing the washing of oneself and of any cooking utensils.[19] (And that's just washing.) So the Pharisees and teachers of the law asked me why they were eating with 'unclean' hands. I retorted by asking them why they put their tradition before God's laws.

---

[18] Matthew 15:1(-20); Mark 7:1(-23)
[19] Mark 7:3-4

143

For example, they get round our laws about honouring one's parents by saying that whatever they fail to do to help them is a 'gift to the Lord'. Not much logic in that, particularly since the attitude we have is that anything you do for someone else, you do for us.[20] No, Isaiah was right when he wrote that, "Such people pay me lip-service, but their hearts remain a long way from mine. They think they're worshipping me, but are simply reciting useless human rules."[21]

"It's not what enters someone's mouth that makes them 'unclean'," I said to the crowd at large, "but what leaves it."

Later, once we had gone into the house we were staying in, my disciples expressed concern that I had offended the Pharisees with what I had said about them.

Reminding them about the weeds, I said that anything my Father has not planted will be uprooted. "Don't bother with the Pharisees; they are blind guides. One blind man leading another will end up with both of them falling down a hole."

A puzzled expression still adorned most of their faces. Peter asked me to explain the parable.[22] Doh! They're still not getting it! I tried again.

"Anything entering your mouth passes through your stomach and out the other end. But words coming from your mouth originate from your heart; it's all the unclean thoughts, expressed in words and actions, which show a person to be unclean."

The Pharisees were utterly failing to grasp my message, and even the Twelve were struggling to understand all of it, despite their growing faith and all they had achieved when I sent them out. The people, on the other hand, saw my miracles and wanted to force the timetable of my mission and make me their Messiah immediately! So I decided to spend a little while in the region of Phoenicia, along the coast north of Mount Carmel. After a couple of days' trek from Capernaum, we stopped at a house near Tyre, hoping for a time of rest and prayer. However, even

---

[20] Matthew 25:40
[21] Isaiah 29:13
[22] Matthew 15:15(-20); Mark 7:17(-23)

there some people recognised me, and word soon spread of my whereabouts.

One sunny morning, accompanying a refreshing breeze blowing from the Mediterranean Sea, a woman arrived at the house.[23] Her features were Greek, and it turned out that she had been born locally of Greek immigrants. Phoenicia, as part of the former Greek empire, had been swallowed up by the Romans, but their language was still used widely here.[24] Now she was outside the house, shouting my name and imploring me to drive out the demon from her possessed daughter. Why did she recognise me as 'Son of David' when even most of my own people refused to?

The woman wouldn't let up, and when they encouraged me to do something about the disturbance, I reminded my disciples of what I had told them before sending them out on their own, that we were primarily to reach the Jewish nation. I am, after all, a prophet to my own people, in the line of David and as Jewish as can be. However, I was on Gentile territory right now and faced with the persistent faith of the woman now kneeling before me, begging me to heal her daughter.

Such faith always moves me, though on this occasion I wished to test it a little more. "It is not right to take the children's bread and toss it to their dogs,"[25] I said, by which I meant that my main responsibility was to reach the Jews.

The woman was unperturbed by what she understandably took to be a very Jewish attitude. "That's right, Lord," she countered, "but even they get to eat whatever scraps end up on the floor."

So much faith! She, a Gentile, acknowledged me as Lord and fully expected me to be able and willing to free her daughter from her oppression. I could but respond by fulfilling her last-hope appeal.

"Woman, you have great faith! Your request is granted."[26]

---

[23] Matthew 15:22(-28); Mark 7:25(-30)
[24] MacCulloch (p.43)
[25] Matthew 15:26 (NIV)
[26] Matthew 15:28

I could tell that my disciples were storing this one away; despite telling them to avoid Gentile areas, I had healed this Gentile woman's daughter.

This area, Phoenicia, was where the great prophet Elijah had stayed with the poor widow while on the run.[27] While not on the run myself, I wanted to avoid returning to Galilee until things had settled down. From Tyre, therefore, we took a northerly detour towards Sidon and turned eastwards along the Litani River valley, skirting round the southern flanks of Mount Lebanon. From here, we spent another day travelling southwards along the upper reaches of the River Jordan, as far as Capernaum. After spending the night there, we picked up one of our boats[28] and had a pleasant day's rowing down the eastern side of a calm Sea of Galilee to another mainly Gentile region, the Decapolis.[29] Here, though I had gone up on a mountainside, great crowds came to me once again, and I ministered to the sick they brought to me.

One in particular was a deaf man who could barely talk. His friends begged me to lay hands on him, in order that he might be healed. The man looked at me, incomprehension clouding his face. Having lost his hearing, and increasingly his speech, he was largely cut off from much of what was going on around him. He likely didn't know who I was or really understand why his friends had presented him to me.

I motioned to the man and led him to one side, away from the piercing gaze of the crowd. Facing him, first holding up my fingers for him to see, I placed them in his ears. Then, again so he knew what was going on, I dabbed a finger in the spittle on my tongue. He understood, obediently opening his mouth and sticking his tongue out towards me. I touched it with my moistened finger, and then, so the man knew where I was drawing my power from, looked towards heaven, before sighing deeply and commanding, "Ephphatha!" Be opened! At this, the man's ears were opened[30] and his tongue loosened so he could speak clearly again.

---

27 1 Kings 17:9
28 cf. Matthew 15:39 and Mark 8:10
29 Mark 7:31
30 Mark 7:35a (NIV)

Knowing that there would probably be some in the crowd who had seen me previously, and still cautious of them casting me in their role of Messiah, I told the man and his friends not to tell anyone. However, this fell on what should have been no longer deaf ears, and they talked about it widely. Nonetheless, people were finally beginning to make the connection, saying in their amazement that I had done everything well, even making the deaf hear and mute speak, just as Isaiah had prophesied[31]. Again, I had to wonder that people here seemed to understand this and accept me more than my own people did.

Many of the crowds had accompanied us for the three days we had been there, and I began to feel sorry for them having nothing to eat.[32] I didn't want to send them away on an empty stomach, given the remote terrain and the considerable distance some would have to travel in the debilitating heat. I put this to the disciples, who already seemed to have forgotten how I had catered for the crowds a few weeks previously. Hadn't they liked my bread; were they hoping against a repeat menu? This time they did realise the hopelessness of trying to buy enough bread for so many, some four thousand men this time, and their families, in such a remote place. So I asked them how many loaves they did have.

"Seven, and a few small fish,"[33] came the reply.

At least they didn't ask again how so little was supposed to help so many people. Perhaps they had learnt something after all. You know, many people consider themselves to have nothing they could serve me with, and so never do. I don't need what you haven't got; all I ever require from you is the little you have and the belief that I will do something with it.

As before, I directed the crowd to sit down, thanked my Father in heaven for his gifts, and broke them into the disciples' hands for them to distribute to the crowd. All ate and had plenty; even my disciples seemed satisfied. This time, they filled seven baskets with the leftovers, more than replacing their outlay. Remember the wine? Not just enough but the best in abundance!

---

31 Isaiah 35:5; 43:8
32 Matthew 15:32ff; Mark 8:2ff
33 Matthew 15:34b (NIV)

Having sent the crowds away strengthened for their journeys, I got into the boat with my disciples and traversed the lake to its westernmost tip, near the village of Magdala[34]. Here we spent a quiet few days, resting, talking together, and eating up the spare bread.[35] The rest and relaxation soon ended with the arrival one day of a group of Pharisees and Sadducees,[36] who had come to question me. They tested me – they certainly tested my patience! – by asking once again for a sign from heaven.

I sighed deeply with frustration, wondering why these learned men couldn't see what many ordinary, uneducated people had understood and accepted from the many signs I had already performed before them. I gently mocked their lack of comprehension, and replied as before.

"You know how to forecast the weather from the colour of the sky, yet you can't interpret the signs of the times! It's a wicked and adulterous generation that looks for a miraculous sign, but I'm not going to give it one beyond that of Jonah."

This time I didn't elaborate but left them to figure it out.

The Twelve and I got back in the boat once more[37] and set out for Bethsaida on the other side of the lake.[38] At some point I could see them muttering to each other, and I realised through my Spirit that they had forgotten to bring bread with them, except for one loaf they had in the boat. I had asked a few of them to find some bread to take with us, and now they were likely blaming each other for failing to bring any. Or maybe they thought they could save some money by bringing only one loaf. I mean, if seven loaves would feed four thousand, surely one would do us!

Be that as it may, I alluded to the theme of their grumbling by warning them to be careful of the yeast of the Pharisees and that of Herod. Since the time of the first Passover, yeast has represented sin,[39] so it's a well-worn analogy. But my disciples? – they thought I was

---

[34] Matthew 15:39: ὄρια Μαγαδάν = region of Magdala; Mark 8:10: Dalmanutha
[35] cf. Matthew 16:5 and Mark 8:14
[36] Matthew 16:1(-4); Mark 8:11(-12)
[37] Matthew 16:5(-12); Mark 8:13(-21)
[38] Mark 8:22
[39] Exodus 12:15-20; cf. 1 Corinthians 5:7-8

referring to their lack of bread! Frustrated, I asked them whether they had forgotten how many baskets of bread they had collected after feeding both large crowds.

"How could you fail to grasp that I wasn't on about bread?"

They had not forgotten, and it finally dawned on them that I was exhorting them to avoid taking on board any of the Pharisees' unbelieving legalism and the more obviously sinful nature of Herod.

Just as yeast is a symbol of sin, physical blindness is a picture of being lost spiritually, which is what I was talking about when I told my disciples that the Pharisees are like the blind leading the blind. At Bethsaida, a group of people came to me with a physically blind man in tow, and implored me to touch him in order that he might be healed.[40] It was not evident that the man himself had any faith, but I would respond to his friends' faith, and could heal him in such a way as to show the Twelve how spiritual healing works.

Motioning to my disciples to accompany us, I guided the man out of the village, explaining as we went along. I wet my fingers and placed them over his eyes, praying to my Father for our healing Spirit to flow through me in healing power.

"Can you see anything?" I wanted to know.

"Men moving around," he confirmed, looking up, "but they're unclear – shapes like trees."

When spiritual enlightenment comes upon a person, they understand some things, but by no means is everything clear to them. That only comes with ongoing spiritual nourishment and further work of the Spirit.

Again, I placed my hands over the man's eyes, and told him to have another look. This time his sight had returned fully, and all had become clear. Another one restored, thanks to the faith of his friends! I prayed that his own faith would have grown as a result, and told him to return home rather than go back into the village.

Bethsaida, you see, was one of those places in which I had worked miracles, but which had not accepted my message. As such, I wanted

---

[40] Mark 8:22(-26)

the healing to be performed outside it. Indeed, because of its unbelief the city would be worse off come the day of judgement than Tyre or Sidon.[41] How does *your* community measure up?

---

[41] Matthew 11:20-24 and Luke 10:13-16; cf. Isaiah 23:1; Zechariah 9:2-4

21

Who I Am

My disciples and I are making our way back into Jerusalem from our Bethany base at Martha and Mary's. Yesterday I cleared out the traders from the temple courtyards for a second time. I spent the rest of the afternoon at the temple, healing the blind and the lame who came to me there. This was the sort of thing the temple was for – healing and restoration. The very people who were King David's enemies after he had conquered Jerusalem, whom he would not allow into the palace,[1] now came to me for healing in the temple, my Father's house.

As Pharisees are wont to be, they were resentful of the marvellous things I was doing, but particularly of several children running around the courtyard and playfully crying out, "Hosanna to the Son of David," mimicking the cheers the adults had been making. (They had learnt well!)

"Can't you hear what those kids are shouting?" the Pharisees finally erupted.

"Can't miss it!" I responded approvingly. "Haven't you ever sung the song that says, 'You put praise on children's lips'?"[2]

And with that I left them and returned to Bethany.

---

[1] 2 Samuel 5:8(6-10)
[2] Matthew 21:14-16; Psalm 8:2

Now, just ahead, is the fig tree on which I looked for fruit yesterday in vain.[3] Peter has just run forward to have a look at the tree, which has withered from the roots up.

"Rabbi!" he's saying, having turned round, and waiting for us to catch up. "Look! The fig tree you cursed has withered!"[4]

"Trust God!" I tell him. "Honestly, whatever you pray for in faith, you will receive. And whenever you pray, forgive any person you bear a grudge against, then my heavenly Father will forgive your wrongdoing."

We're nearly at the city wall now, climbing up out of the Kidron valley. This last section was easier sitting on the donkey! The city is crowded for the Passover, taking place in a couple of days. My disciples following, I head once again to the temple.

We haven't been here long, and now a group of senior clerics is heading in my direction. They look as if they've got a bone to pick with me. Well, I did chuck their profitable traders out last night, I suppose.

"Who gave you the right to do all this?" they demand.[5] "Who gave you authority to do this?"

Since they probably know that the answer to that is going to indict me in their eyes, it is a trick question. Well, two can play at that game! I'll ask them a question, and see how they answer; if they get it right, they might be willing to accept the answer to their own question.

"Where did John's baptism come from – heaven or men?"

That's foxed them. They're huddling together, discussing each option. I know what they're thinking: if they say heaven, I'll ask them why they didn't believe in him; if they say men, they'll court disfavour from the people, who believe John was a prophet.

"We don't know." What a surprise!

"Then nor will I say who gave me the right to do such things."

That hasn't pleased them any more than the answer would have done.

---

[3] See page 65
[4] Mark 11:21 (NIV); see also verses 22-26
[5] Matthew 21:23(-27); Mark 11:28(-33); Luke 20:2(-8)

After I had healed the blind man at Bethsaida, we moved on again and headed north towards Caesarea Philippi. On the way, I asked my disciples what people were saying as to my identity.[6]

"Some say John the Baptist;" they replied, "others say Elijah; and still others, one of the prophets."[7]

"But what about you?" I persisted. "Who do you say I am?"[8]

Peter, spot-on once again, answered immediately. "You are the Messiah."[9]

My Father had blessed Peter by revealing that to his heart. His name means 'rock', and I told him that on this 'rock' I would build my church. He would unlock the gospel to all people, rather than it being kept under the lock and key of the Pharisees who didn't accept its truths. Peter, with the guidance of our Spirit, would announce God's judgement on what should be permitted and what forbidden. By that I included which parts of the law to insist upon and what to declare was not necessary.[10]

"Don't tell anyone that I am the Christ; it is not yet time."

But it was time that I started to explain to them what was going to happen to their Messiah, and what the cost of following me entailed.

"The Son of Man must suffer many things[11] and be rejected by the religious leaders, and he must be killed and after three days rise to life again."[12]

I looked around at my disciples to see whether this was sinking in, and wasn't convinced. So I talked about it quite openly with them.

Peter was getting more and more agitated, and finally took me to one side and rebuked me. "No way, Master! That must never happen to you!"

Peter, Peter. Like I said, he can get it so right. But when he gets it wrong... I had to quash this train of thought. It was enough that the

---

6   Matthew 16:13; Mark 8:27; Luke 9:18
7   Mark 8:28 (NIV)
8   Matthew 16:15 (NIV)
9   Messiah (Hebrew) = Christ (Greek) = "the Anointed One"
10 cf. Acts 15:1-31
11 Mark 8:31 (NIV); Luke 9:22 (NIV)
12 Matthew 16:21(-28); Mark 8:31(-9:1); Luke 9:22(-27)

general crowds wanted to make me king, but Peter was my leading disciple and was a strong influence on the others. His statement was not just of his own thinking, however; it was a thought planted by the devil to tempt me away from the atoning sacrifice that I'm here to make.

"Get behind me, Satan! Stop tempting me to sin; you are not thinking God's thoughts, but thinking like men."

The startled disciples remained silent; I suppose they thought they couldn't say anything right, and yet hadn't Peter just been praised for recognising who I am?

I called the wider crowd closer and spoke again. "If you want to follow me, you must stop putting yourself first and be prepared to take up your cross – yes, even to die for me. Try holding on to your life and you will find yourself losing it; give up your life for my sake and you will rediscover it. What do you benefit from gaining the entire world if you lose your own soul? Even the world is not enough to redeem your soul! When the Son of Man comes in his Father's glory with his angels, he will reward you according to what you have done." *Father, help them to understand my words!*

While they were pondering that, I made one final startling statement. "I assure you that some of you standing here will not die before seeing the Son of Man coming in his kingdom."

These words were fulfilled about a week later.[13] I took Peter, James and John up a high mountain where we were all alone, in order to pray. They told me later that, as I was doing so, my face brightened until it shone dazzlingly like the sun, and my clothes became whiter than anyone in the world could possibly bleach them. For my part, I was feeling that infusion of warmth you soak up when sitting in the sun on a particularly warm day. It seems to travel down your spine and produce a warm tingle the opposite of a cold shiver.

From out of this explosion of light stepped Moses and Elijah, two great prophets and past saviours of the people. Moses, leader of the great exodus, had later descended Mount Sinai with the stone tablets of the law, after meeting with us, his face radiant. But his disobedience

---

[13] Matthew 17:1(-13); Mark 9:2(-13); Luke 9:28(-36)

over how to bring forth water from a rock meant that he never entered the Promised Land. He was limited to viewing it from Mount Nebo, a few miles east of the northern end of the Salt Sea, before dying there in Moab, where we buried him.[14]

Elijah was famous for calling down fire on a water-soaked altar, before we sent rain upon the land after a three-year drought. But even more amazing was that he did not experience death; we sent angels on chariots of fire to whisk him off to Paradise.[15] I'll tell you about that place later.

So there we were, Moses representing the law, Elijah the prophets, and me, talking together about the 'exodus' of my impending death in Jerusalem, which will happen soon in fulfilment of all the law and the prophets. With it will happen another exodus: my Father's glory will leave the temple.[16]

Peter's incredulous voice rang through the cool air of the mountaintop, interrupting the moment. "Lord, it's good that we're here. If you like, we can put up three shelters for you to stay in – you, Moses and Elijah."

He, like the others, was frightened and didn't really know what he was saying. Perhaps he was hoping to reinstate the place where my Father God would meet with His people.[17] Or maybe he was thinking the Feast of Tabernacles had come a couple of months early. That notwithstanding, our Spirit had opened his eyes to recognise who was talking with me. Now though, my Father himself came in a cloud that enveloped the three of us, and spoke both to reassure me and for the benefit of my three closest followers. He echoed his words at my baptism.

"This is my Son, whom I love; with him I am well pleased. Listen to him!"[18]

The sound of my Father's voice to my human ears filled me once again with courage and conviction. He was walking this with me, just

---

14 Exodus 34:29; Numbers 20:12; Deuteronomy 34:1-6
15 1 Kings 18:16-46; 2 Kings 2:11
16 See 'The Temple' note, page 309
17 Exodus 29:42-43
18 Matthew 17:5 (NIV); Mark 9:7

as we walk through your lives with you, in good times and bad times. He was giving me the strength to continue. I would need every ounce of my strength and his to fulfil all that I had come to achieve.

The cloud that had enveloped us slowly lifted, and I found myself alone. The disciples, who on hearing my Father's voice had thrown themselves flat on the ground, looked up again as I walked towards them, and registered that I was on my own again.

"Get up," I told them. "Don't be afraid."

While it had terrified them, they had been party to this in order to build up their own faith, which in the months ahead would be tested to the limit. Events to come would bring them to the brink of desperation, and I needed them to have this experience to cling on to. Later, they would recount what had happened.

"Don't tell anyone what you have seen, until the Son of Man has been raised from the dead."[19] This reminded them of what I had told them the week before.

On the way down the mountain, my disciples appeared puzzled. Eventually their question formed enough to find a voice. "You've got to die and then... come back, right? So why do teachers of the law maintain that Elijah has to come first?[20]"

"Elijah will appear in advance to prepare people for the restoration of the kingdom, yes. So why does Scripture talk about the Son of Man having to suffer pain and rejection? Well, Elijah has actually already come, but people didn't realise who it was, and chose to maltreat him, just as the Scriptures say."

My disciples would have remembered from Scripture how Elijah suffered because of Ahab's wife Jezebel, just as John had now been beheaded because of Herod's wife Herodias. Elijah had come before Elisha, whose ministry was one of judgement and redemption. John had come as Elijah did, in preparation for the judgement and redemption I was now here to bring.

"Similarly," I continued, "they will abuse the Son of Man too."

---

[19] Matthew 17:9 (NIV)
[20] Malachi 4:5-6

156

Finally, they understood that I had been talking about Cousin John, and also took on board the fact that I too was going to die.

We reached the bottom of the mountain and found the other disciples at the centre of a commotion,[21] arguing with some teachers of the law. As soon as the people noticed me approaching, they ran to greet me in wonder.

"What are you bickering about with them now?" I asked the scribes, half in jest, half in apprehension. I noticed the disciples looking somewhat sheepish, subdued.

Before they could answer, a desperate-looking man, who had been waiting on the fringes, approached me anxiously and knelt down before me.

"Lord, have mercy on my son,"[22] he started. "He is possessed by a spirit that has robbed him of speech.[23] It throws him to the ground, and he is suffering greatly." The man was close to tears as he catalogued his son's woes. Then he continued with a statement that explained the demeanour of my followers and made my heart sink. "I asked your disciples, but none of them was able to cast out the spirit."

"What an unbelieving and corrupted generation!" I lamented. "How long am I supposed to put up with you all?"

They were taken aback by my venting such feelings. I was frustrated with the lack of faith of them all. My disciples knew better than any what I had done in my Father's power, and had also done it themselves when I sent them out with my authority. The teachers of the law, who belonged to the Pharisees, were forever wanting a sign despite all the signs I had performed, and were now arguing with my disciples over their failure. Even this father was starting to doubt whether I could do anything, given that my disciples couldn't.

"Bring the boy to me,"[24] I commanded.

As soon as he came, the evil spirit within him recognised me and threw the boy to the ground.

---

[21] Mark 9:14(-29); Matthew 17:14(-21); Luke 9:37-43
[22] Matthew 17:15 (NIV)
[23] Mark 9:17b (NIV)
[24] Matthew 17:17; Mark 9:19c (NIV)

"Has this been going on long?" I enquired of his father.

"Since he was a child," the man said wearily. "The spirit often tries to destroy him by throwing him into fire or water. Please have mercy on us and help us, if you can."

"'If you can'?" I retorted. "Everything is possible for one who believes."[25]

Therein lay his doubts. Maybe they are yours too. Maybe you wonder whether I can really help you or not.

"I do believe," the boy's father exclaimed. "Help me overcome my unbelief!"[26]

That was an honest faith I could respond to. Seeing a crowd running to the scene, and desiring to avoid even more publicity for publicity's sake, I rebuked the evil spirit and ordered it to come out of the boy, never to return. The spirit uttered a final shriek and convulsed the boy violently before departing from him.

Lying motionless on the ground, the boy resembled a corpse so much that many of the shocked onlookers now doubted. "So much for that – he's dead!" one of them exclaimed.

As I took him by the hand, however, he came to; I helped him to his feet, and he stood up. Doubt was transformed into amazement at the greatness of God, brokenness into wholeness. Another one restored.

A little later, once we had entered a nearby house and could enjoy the privacy inside, the defeated disciples asked why they hadn't been able to drive out this particular demon.

"This kind can come out only by prayer."[27] It was a gentle rebuke. The empowering I had given them previously wasn't to be taken for granted. Just as my power comes from my Father in heaven, so their power – and yours – comes from seeking me in prayerful faith. If you have enough faith, even as small as a mustard seed, you can do anything. Even if you were to tell the mountain that we had just been up to move, it would.

---

[25] Mark 9:23 (NIV)
[26] Mark 9:24 (NIV)
[27] Mark 9:29 (NIV)

We left that place and moved on through Galilee.[28] I didn't want anyone to know where we were, because I needed space to teach the Twelve. And that needed to start with another reminder that I must die.

"The Son of Man is going to be delivered into the hands of men. They will kill him, and on the third day he will be raised to life."[29]

My disciples were appalled, both that I should be betrayed and that I would be killed. Their clouded minds could not comprehend a Messiah who would die, and they seemed to take no comfort in my statement that I would rise again. Their sense of foreboding prevented them from asking me any more about it.

As we approached Capernaum, their minds had obviously turned to other things, and they were having a heated debate about something.[30] Before I could ask them about it, the collectors of the two-drachma tax, which I have already told you about – the half shekel one – came to Peter and asked whether or not I pay the temple tax.[31] My Spirit gave me insight into these two matters, and I tackled the second one first when we arrived at the house, using the opportunity to help Peter grow in faith.

"What's your opinion, Simon?" I asked. Using his first name always gets his attention. "Do kings demand tariffs or raise taxes from their sons, or from other people?"

Simon Peter wasn't making the connection. "From others," he answered, unsure as to where I was going with this one.

"Then the sons are exempt," I continued.

"Ye-s."

"But we don't want to offend them, so go to the lake and throw out your line. Take the first fish you catch; open its mouth and you will find a shekel. Take it and give it to them for my tax and yours. "[32]

This time he understood, at least that I was talking about the temple tax, and headed off for the lake, albeit with a very definite 'If you say so...' look on his face that had replaced the puzzled expression

---

28 Matthew 17:22; Mark 9:30(-32); Luke 9:44-45
29 Matthew 17:22-23 (NIV)
30 Luke 9:46
31 Matthew 17:24(-27)
32 Based on Matthew 17:27 (NIV)

from wondering how I had known about the question of the tax. I would have loved to have seen his face when he opened the mouth of the lucky fish! Only later did he realise the deeper significance of my question. The temple is God's dwelling-place; I am the King's Son.

Having sorted out the temple tax with Peter, I tackled the other disciples.[33] "What were you arguing about back there?" I enquired.

Silence.

The sheepish look had returned to their faces, and I imagine they had thought I hadn't noticed or had forgotten about it.

"If anyone desires the place of honour," I started, sitting down, "he must occupy the lowliest position and serve everybody else."

Outside, there were some neighbourhood children playing. One of them, only six or seven years old, was taking a breather and was leaning against the doorpost, finding what we were discussing suddenly more interesting than running around. He reminded me of myself in the temple as a twelve-year-old, listening to the teachers of the law and their debates. I waved him into the middle of the room, and with an embarrassed 'What, moi?' expression, he tentatively shuffled forward.

Indicating the boy stood next to me, I said to my disciples, "Honestly, unless you learn to humble yourself like this little child, you will never enter the kingdom of heaven. Do so, and there you will be the greatest!" 'Oops' was emblazoned on each of their foreheads. "Whoever receives even a small child like this with the open arms of my love, receives me, and ultimately my Father who sent me. But woe betide anyone who causes one of these little ones that believe in me to sin. They'd be better off drowned in deep water with the sort of large millstone turned by a donkey[34] hung around their neck."

Sombre faces stared back at me as I underlined the last point by repeating what I had said on the mountainside about dealing with sin when talking about adultery. Sin needs to be dealt with radically, for it destroys lives and has residency in the fire of hell as its eternal consequence.

---

[33] Mark 9:33(-37); Matthew 18:1-9; Luke 9:46-48
[34] ὀνικός = "pertaining to an ass" (Strong's Concordance), usually translated "heavy"

Indicating the child again, I told my disciples not to belittle anyone with a childlike, expectant faith, for they too are ministered to by angels[35] who see the face of my Father in heaven. My disciples had been arguing about who might be the greatest, but in heaven all our children are equal.[36]

I noticed John's head nod suddenly, not so much in agreement to anything – or from weariness – but as a visible sign he had just remembered something.

"Teacher," he piped up,[37] "we noticed a man using your name to drive out demons, but he wasn't one of us, so we told him to stop."

A-ha! John was being defensive on my behalf, if a little bigoted, just as Joshua had complained to Moses when the elders Eldad and Medad had prophesied in the camp in our Spirit's power, without having been at the Holy Tent with the others[38]. Moses had expressed a desire that the Lord would make prophets of all His people!

"Don't stop him!" I replied. "No-one who performs a miracle in my name one minute is going to speak evil of me the next. Anyone who is not against us is for us.[39] Even someone who merely proffers you a cup of water in my name because you belong to the Messiah will gain the reward of God's approval."

I value all service done for others in my name, and therefore for me, from the greatest to the least. From preachers and teachers, to those who visit and provide for the needy, and others who welcome those gathering to worship and provide for their comfort in different ways: all follow our calling to serve, as they are able. As I said before,[40] you shouldn't think you have nothing to offer; just offer what you do have.

---

35 Matthew 18:10; cf. 1 Kings 19:6-7; Psalm 34:7; Acts 23:8; Hebrews 1:7,14
36 Matthew 10:40-42
37 Mark 9:38(-41); Luke 9:49(-50)
38 Numbers 11:25-29
39 Mark 9:40 (NLT)
40 See page 147

22

Water and Light

I had been going around Galilee, purposely staying away from Judea, because the Jews there were out to kill me.[1] But when the Feast of Tabernacles was near, my brothers urged me to go to Judea, so that my disciples there could see the miracles I did.

"No-one does anything secretly when he is seeking a public profile. You should get out amongst the people and show them what you can do."

There was a certain logic to that, but it wasn't the logic of the Suffering Servant[2], the One whose purpose lay in death. My brothers are products of their culture like everyone else, and await a Roman-conquering Messiah. I'm the awkward one of the family who refuses to toe the line of tradition and expectation. If only my people would realise that what they are waiting for is perfectly fulfilled in me.

"You can go there whenever you like; people don't hate you. I can't, because they hate me for showing up their evil deeds for what they are."

I told them to go to the Feast, and that I would follow when the time was right. Notwithstanding that, when they had left for the Feast, I gathered the Twelve, and we prepared to head for Jerusalem. I sent

---

[1] John 7:1(-10)
[2] Isaiah 53

messengers on ahead to prepare things for me in a Samarian village where we would stay en route.[3] However, when we arrived there, the people did not welcome us, because we were heading for Jerusalem. Remember, I told you that the Samaritans hold Mount Gerizim sacred and the true place of worship.

I could see James and John consulting with each other before coming to me and asking whether they should call fire down from heaven to destroy the people. They were doubtless thinking of Elijah calling down fire on King Ahaziah's troops[4]. It was nice that they wished to defend my honour, but – oh! – they still had so much to learn. Vengeance is my heavenly Father's and his alone. No, I came to save lives, not destroy them. Instead, we continued to another village to seek rest there.

The next day, as we set off down the road, a teacher of the law stopped me.[5] "I am prepared to follow you anywhere," he proclaimed.

"Foxes have their dens and birds their nests," I replied mysteriously, "but the Son of Man has no place of his own to rest." This man with his privileged position needed to know that wealth and power were not part of what it meant to follow me (though the influence they afford may be used to further my Father's kingdom as our Spirit directs).

The next man we saw needed to understand the urgency of following me, and this time *I* challenged *him* to do so.

But the man replied, "Lord, first let me go and bury my father."[6]

"Let the dead bury their own dead," I retorted, "but you go and proclaim the kingdom of God."[7]

The raised eyebrows of some of those listening reflected their interpretation of my exhortation as an assault on common decency. The man needed to attend to his father and his affairs, and was expected to do so. It would take time, was the right thing to do. Anyone could

---

[3] Luke 9:52(-56)
[4] 2 Kings 1:9-12
[5] Luke 9:57(-62)
[6] Matthew 8:21 (NIV); Luke 9:59 (NIV)
[7] Luke 9:60 (NIV); Matthew 8:19(-22)

understand that. But how often do you put off following me until circumstances might allow, or become easier?

Many, though, understood my intent. It is common for us to speak of someone who has no regard for the law as being 'dead'. We talk about them being 'dead to the world' or 'dead to the law' or, positively, 'dead to sin'[8]. I was showing them that following me and proclaiming the good news were more important than seeing to the affairs of 'the dead'. By putting me first you will actually be enabled to love your family more.

Yet another man approached me, saying that he too would follow me. "But first let me go back and say goodbye to my family."[9]

I replied, "No ploughman that keeps looking back is of any use in God's kingdom."

Those who had anything to do with farming understood what I meant. You cannot plough a straight furrow if you keep looking back; it just doesn't work. If you want to walk in a straight line, you have to keep your eyes not down on the ground but ahead on your goal. Following me with my kingdom as a goal is exactly the same. You cannot keep looking back at worldly distractions.

I myself was feeling distracted, but more because I knew that my time was now short and there was much to achieve. I had sent out the Twelve, and they had come back having done all that I had enabled them to do. Now it was time to expand the outreach team. I had recently been reminded of Moses' seventy elders, plus the two I told you about, Eldad and Medad,[10] on whom our Spirit had rested for them to prophesy[11]. Now I decided to send out that many myself.[12] Many of the wider group of disciples had been with me on and off for a long time now, and believed. Their faith had grown to a point where they too could go ahead of me and prepare the way in towns I was going to pass through.

---

[8] Gill (on Matthew 8:22); cf. Romans 6:11; 7:4
[9] Luke 9:61 (NIV)
[10] See page 161
[11] Numbers 11:16-26
[12] Luke 10:1(-22)

So I selected them and sent them out two by two, giving them much the same instructions as I had given the Twelve: travel lightly; accept any hospitality given, and move on where none is forthcoming.

"If people listen to you, they're listening to me; if they reject you, they're rejecting me; but woe betide any that reject me, for they're rejecting him who sent me. Woe to you, Korazin and Bethsaida! If Tyre and Sidon had seen the miracles that were performed in you, they would have repented long ago; but not you."

Over the coming days, as we gradually moved south towards Jerusalem, the disciples trickled back in pairs, full of joy and relating how even the demons had submitted to them in my name. This was it. Satan was suffering defeat! I had given my disciples power to overcome the enemy, and they were doing it!

"Rejoice, for your names are written in heaven!" I told them.

I was full of joy in my Spirit for all he was doing through us, and praised my Father in heaven for revealing the truth to those who were open to accept it. My disciples could count themselves blessed for experiencing everything they were seeing and hearing;[13] many prophets and kings had wanted to see the promised Messiah, but had not done so.

The disciples were exhilarated but tired from their work. I knew that others were feeling burdened by the circumstances of life or by the expectations of others, including those who represent the law.[14] I spoke comfort to them all. "Come to me, all who are weary and heavy-laden, and I will give you rest. Place my yoke over your shoulders and learn from me, for I am gentle and humble at heart, and your souls will find rest in me. For my yoke is made to sit well on you and my burden is easily managed."

These are my words to you, too, whenever you feel you can no longer go on.

We eventually arrived in Jerusalem, and every fibre of my being wanted to go to the temple, my Father's house. However, my disciples were wary of my going there, for we knew that the Jewish leaders

---

13 Matthew 13:16-17; Luke 10:23-24
14 Matthew 23:4; cf. Acts 15:10 and (yoke/burden) 1 John 5:3-5

wanted to take my life. Half-way through the Feast, I could stand it no longer and went up into the temple courts to teach.[15]

The Jews from Jerusalem reacted to my teaching with amazement, wondering how I could have amassed so much learning without having formally studied.

"What I teach doesn't come from me," I informed them, "but from the one who sent me. Anyone concerned with pursuing what God wants, will discern that my teaching is from him."

I went on to say that only a truthful man seeks to honour the one who sent him. Moses had given them the law; why were they trying to kill me? They circumcised boys on the Sabbath if that was the eighth day, as the law demands, so why were they angry with me for healing the whole man on the Sabbath?

"Quit judging by outward appearances; look beneath the surface to judge correctly," I challenged them.

At this point, I became aware of some of the crowd expressing surprise that I was speaking publicly, even though the temple hierarchy was trying to kill me.[16] They were wondering whether the authorities had actually concluded that I was the Christ, whose origin they believed would be unknown; by contrast, they thought they knew exactly where I came from.

"You might know me and where I grew up," I cried out to them, "but you don't know the one who sent me, who is true. I do, for I have come from his side; he sent me here."

This was too much for many blasphemy-sensitive ears, whose owners would have most liked to seize me. The chief priests must even have sent temple guards to arrest me, as several turned up but were disobedient to their orders in the face of the eager crowd.

Many of the crowd did choose to believe in me, reasoning that the Christ they were expecting could not do anything more miraculous than "this man" did. Well, "this man" is the Christ after all! I was heartened by their belief, but equally disheartened that those in authority still refused to believe. If they're going to get it, it needs to be soon!

---

[15] John 7:14(-24)
[16] John 7:25(-44)

"I will be with you just a little while longer," I said, casting an eye towards the Pharisees in particular, "and then return to the one who sent me, where you cannot follow to find me."

This caused confusion in them; surely I couldn't mean going to the Jews living scattered amongst the Greeks, and teaching the Gentiles there! Well, actually... They should have known from the prophet Isaiah that the good news was not just for the Jews.[17]

Now, in case you didn't know, part of the celebrations of the Feast of Tabernacles, Sukkot, involves a Levite priest carrying water from the Pool of Siloam to the temple altar.[18] It reminds us of God's provision of water during the exodus through the desert, and for our annual crops, the ingathering of which the feast celebrates. Tabernacles is a joyous feast for everyone, with songs sung, including Isaiah's song of praise that contains the line, "With joy you will draw water from the wells of salvation."[19]

The Pool of Siloam, by the way, is fed through a tunnel over a thousand cubits long, carved out in Isaiah's time by King Hezekiah's workforce to provide water from the Gihon spring that overlooks the Kidron Valley.[20] It was built to secure the city's water supply in case of invasion.

On the last and greatest day of the Feast, I had returned to the temple. At the point of the water being poured out, I staged an invasion of my own by standing up where everybody could see me and shouting out another verse from Isaiah: "If anyone is thirsty, let him come to me and drink." As I had tried to explain to the Samaritan woman at the well, and Isaiah had prophesied[21], I continued: "Streams of living water will flow from all that believe in me." I was talking of my Spirit, who dwells in all believers. He dwells in you and enables you to do all that I do.

People in the crowd were divided, some thinking I must be the Messiah, others contrasting where they thought the Messiah must come

---

[17] Isaiah 42:6, 49:6; Matthew 24:14; John 10:16; cf. Paul in Acts 13:46, 18:6
[18] Morris (p.420)
[19] Isaiah 12:3 (NIV)
[20] 2 Kings 20:20; 2 Chronicles 32:2-4,30; see 'Hezekiah's Tunnel' note, page 309
[21] Isaiah 55:1, 58:11

from (Bethlehem[22]) with where they knew I had grown up (Nazareth). The chief priests and Pharisees, whose temple guards had gone back empty-handed, had the same dilemma.[23]

That evening, tired from the day's confrontations, I withdrew from the city and walked up the nearby Mount of Olives to spend time talking to my Dad.[24] I passed Gethsemane, the garden I still come to with my disciples when here,[25] and climbed the Bethany road towards the Miphkad Altar by Bethphage, near the top, just outside the city limits.

At the crest of the hill, lining the other side of the road, several stipes stood like guards. The Romans had planted these wooden stakes in the ground; it was and still is one of their places of execution.

The altar, by contrast, is where the priests slaughter the red heifer of the purification sacrifice.[26] Its ashes are kept for use in the water of cleansing; it is for purification from sin but specifically to cleanse future contamination by, for example, touching a dead person or a grave. Just nine of these sacrifices have been made over many years; Moses and Ezra performed the first two.[27]

I spent a while sitting a little way from the altar, perusing the view across the olive-tree-strewn valley. The towers of Herod's palace, set against the far, western wall of the city, stood silhouetted against the sunset glow. Below me stretched the red heifer causeway, an arched bridge built between the Miphkad Gate in the temple's eastern wall[28] and the altar of the same name on the Mount of Olives. The high priests themselves financed its building.[29]

This causeway is about a thousand paces long, the distance the Israelites under Joshua were required to stay from the ark[30], and the distance outside the camp at which Moses made judgements[31] and

---

[22] Micah 5:2
[23] John 7:45-52
[24] John 8:1(-11). See 'Pericope Adulterae' note, page 301
[25] John 18:2
[26] Numbers 19:1-10; cf. Deuteronomy 21:1-9
[27] Numbers 19:1-10; Ezra 3:6; Mishnah Parah 3.5
[28] Mishnah Middot 1.3; Shekalim 4.2
[29] Mishnah Shekalim 4.2
[30] Joshua 3:4
[31] Exodus 33:7; Numbers 35:5

where sacrifices were burnt[32]. Its arches stand offset above each other, in a figurative attempt to avoid any possible contamination from any grave underneath while the priestly procession makes its way to the altar.

Above its far end rose the innermost temple building, the Holy of Holies – my Father's house – a hundred cubits tall[33]. The eastern wall of the temple is lower, so that the priest performing the sacrifice on the Miphkad Altar has line of sight to the priest at the temple entrance.[34] As I gazed across, I contemplated my own sacrifice. For I too must be led "outside the camp"[35] and will be the sacrifice that cleanses my people for all time. One day they might realise that the Messiah will make the tenth and final red heifer sacrifice,[36] but will they have accepted me as the Messiah?

The sun was barely up the following morning before I was back in the temple courts, where pious believers were already at prayer. It was much less crowded now, following the end of the Feast. Many of those there gathered around me, and I sat down to teach them as they and I had grown accustomed.

Shortly after I had begun, a kerfuffle of clerics made its way through the attentive listeners. Some teachers of the law and Pharisees were all but dragging a dishevelled woman towards me. They made her stand before everyone and brought their accusation.

"Teacher, this woman was caught in the act of adultery.[37] The law of Moses says we should stone her. What's your view?"

My Spirit prompted me to see this as a trap. The usual game. They wanted me to say something they could twist into an infringement of the law or a threat to the Roman governance. They were bringing only the woman involved, without the man, and so were infringing the law themselves.[38] I bent over silently and started writing in the sandy surface of the ground, to show that I had no intention of entertaining their

---

[32] Leviticus 4:12,21, 8:17, 16:27; Talmud – Yoma 68a; Zebahim 105b
[33] Mishnah Middot 4.6
[34] Mishnah Middot 2.4
[35] cf. Leviticus 16:27; Numbers 19:3; Hebrews 13:10-14
[36] cf. Maimonides (1135-1204), Hilchot Parah Adumah (Red Heifer Laws) 3:4
[37] John 8:4 (NIV)
[38] Deuteronomy 22:22-24

demand. Without looking up, I could tell they were trying to make out what I was writing.

כַּבֵּד אֶת־אָבִיךָ וְאֶת־אִמֶּךָ [39]

Honour your father and your mother.

לֹא תִּרְצָח ס

You shall not murder.

לֹא תִּנְאָף ס

You shall not commit adultery. [40]

"If any of you is without sin," I said, straightening up, "let him be the first to throw a stone at her." I stooped down again and continued scratching words in the dust.

לֹא תִּגְנֹב ס

You shall not steal.

לֹא־תַעֲנֶה עֵד שָׁקֶר ס

You shall not bear false witness.

לֹא תַחְמֹד פ

You shall not covet.

Footsteps moving away from me indicated the capitulation of the woman's accusers. Eventually none of them was asking further questions, and the remaining crowd fell silent.

"Woman," I said, straightening up again, "have your accusers all gone? Did no-one condemn you?"

"No-one, sir," she stammered.

[39] Exodus 20:12(-17). Hebrew from biblehub.com.
[40] Exodus 20:12a,13-14 (NIV)

"Neither do I," I declared gently, adding the redemptive instruction, "Go, but sin no more."

"Thank you, Father," I prayed silently, "for helping me to find a way of mercy while honouring the law!"

As I had reminded my disciples, I was here to bring life. There are always those who deserve death by the law – every person in fact – but my innermost desire is that all should have an opportunity to amend their ways and so bring glory to my heavenly Father.

I looked around at the people passing by the edges of the group of people listening to me. People going about their everyday business or, in this case, their habitual visit to the temple. Most of them paused briefly to place their oblation in one of the trumpet-shaped offering chests.[41] These are located in the Women's Court where I was sitting, as are the huge candelabras lit as part of the Feast of Tabernacles which went on day and night.[42] Now the feast was over, attendants were cleaning out the remains of the extinguished fires in each one.

"*I am* the light of the world," I proclaimed, waving a hand towards the candelabras and alluding to a well-known text from Isaiah.[43] "Whoever follows me will never walk in darkness, but will have the light of life."[44]

The Pharisees still present challenged me, saying that as my own witness, my testimony was invalid. I retorted that my Father was my witness.

"Where is this father of yours?" they wanted to know.

I told them straight: "You don't seem to have a clue who I am, so you're not going to know my Father either."

"Who are you?" they demanded.

"Exactly who I've always claimed to be," I said in response. "And after you have hoisted up the Son of Man, you will realise who I am, and that I act not by myself but speak only as instructed by the Father.

---

[41] John 8:20
[42] Morris (p.436-437)
[43] Isaiah 9:1-2
[44] John 8:12b (NIV)

Having sent me, he has not abandoned me, for I do everything to please him."

I could see that many were coming to faith in me while I was speaking.[45] Others had their doubts. The Pharisees had none; they simply refused to accept my testimony.

I challenged those who had started to believe in me to live by my words. "You will really be my disciples if you continue to live by what I've taught you. Then you will know the truth, and the truth will set you free."[46]

"We're descended from Abraham," they replied haughtily, then continued with a blatant disregard for history past and present. "Never been slaves to anyone. What do you mean by 'set you free'?"

"This is a fact," I said, "anyone who continues in sin is a slave to sin. Now, slaves may be sold or dismissed, but a son belongs to his family for ever. When the *Son* sets you free, you're not only free, you get to be part of the family!"[47]

I acknowledged their being descended from Abraham, but spelt out to them that the father they were emulating was in fact the devil. I did what I saw my Father doing, bringing them truth from God; they were trying to kill me, which Abraham would never have done. That was the work of the devil, in whom there is no truth whatsoever.

At this point someone shouted out that I was a demon-possessed Samaritan.[48] Murmurs of agreement echoed round the increasingly disgruntled onlookers.

"I am possessed only by the desire to honour my Father and seek his glory," I corrected them, "yet while he seeks my glory, you dishonour me. If only you would keep to my teaching, death couldn't touch you!"

Now the people thought their view of me justified. "Abraham and the prophets all died, yet you reckon keeping your words is supposed to give us eternal life?!"

---

[45] John 8:31(-47)
[46] John 8:32
[47] John 1:12; Romans 8:14-21; 1 John 3:1(-10)
[48] John 8:48(-59)

"My Father, whom you claim as your God, is the one who glorifies me,"[49] I stated. "Your father Abraham looked forward with joy to my time."[50] I was very close to proclaiming my true identity.

"You are not yet fifty years old," they mocked, "and you have seen Abraham?[51] Yeah, right!"

"I tell you the truth," I replied as calmly as I could, "before Abraham was born, *I am!*"[52]

There it was. I had said it outright. They could listen no more; for them it was blasphemy of the highest order, and they scavenged around for stones big enough to throw at me. I used the moment to slip away and was able to hide from them. My time had still not yet come.

My disciples and I were still in Jerusalem come the Sabbath, and were making our way to the temple when we happened across a blind man sitting at the side of the street, begging.[53] It was apparent that he had been blind from birth, and my disciples wanted to know who it was that had sinned, the man or his parents, that he had been born blind. They were alluding to the view held by some rabbis that, "There is no death without sin, and no suffering without iniquity," which others refute.[54]

There are typically no obvious reasons why such things happen. While it is true, as I have already described,[55] that the consequences of one's sin may reach down several generations, a newborn baby has done nothing wrong to deserve such a calamity. In this case, nor had his parents.

"It enabled God's power to work in the man prominently," I explained. Indicating the limited time of my ongoing human presence, I continued, "We have to carry out the work I was sent to do, while the sun's still up. Once it has set, no-one can work. As long as I am in the world, I am the light of the world."

---

[49] John 8:54 (NIV)
[50] cf. God's promises in Genesis 12:3; 18:17-19; 22:18
[51] John 8:57 (NIV)
[52] John 8:58 (NIV)
[53] John 9:1,8,14 (1-41)
[54] Talmud – Shabbath 55a,b
[55] See page 88; Exodus 20:5

My disciples appeared uneasy, rightly interpreting my hints that I shall not always be with them as at present.

"It is also true," I encouraged them, "that, just as we caused the moon to reflect the sun's light to lighten the darkness, so you are to reflect my light, as you follow my example and work in my power to bring light to your communities." Will *you* take this challenge too?

Approaching the blind man, I spat on the ground and made some mud with the saliva. "It's me: Jesus," I said to him gently, and told him what I was about to do. I put the mud on his eyes, then told him to go and wash in the Pool of Siloam. That is the pool I told you about before. Its name means, 'one who has been sent'.[56]

We carried on walking through the city, and had something to eat from one of the market stalls. One of my favourites was their selection of warm, flat loaves basted with butter and herbs. Couldn't beat it in the cool of an autumn evening.

A little later, we heard that the man and his parents had been in trouble with the authorities, who had thrown the man out of the temple.[57] We walked back in that direction, and eventually found the man near the Tyropoean Bridge, not far from the temple.

"Do you believe in the Son of Man?" I asked him.

Bearing in mind he had probably not heard of me nor indeed seen me up to now, his reply was unsurprising but encouraging. "Who is he, sir? I want to believe in him."

"You're looking at him," I told him, "the one speaking with you right now!"

Recognition flickered across the man's face as he remembered where he had heard my voice, and realised that it was I who had restored his sight.

"I believe, Lord," he said, falling down in worship before me.

Some Pharisees appeared from the direction of the temple. I guessed they had been involved in throwing the now sighted man out. So for their benefit I spoke up.

---

56 NIV footnote at John 9:7
57 John 9:35(-41)

"I have come into this world to judge it, to give sight to the blind, and to show those who think they can see that they are actually blind.[58]" I was speaking metaphorically, at least in the second case. I am here to enlighten people spiritually, so they can repent and be saved.

The Pharisees realised what I meant and that it didn't show them in a favourable light. "Are you saying we're blind, or what?"

"If you were blind," I replied, "you wouldn't be deemed guilty for missing the mark; but since you insist you're able to see, you remain guilty."

The Pharisees were responsible for teaching and upholding the law; instead, they burdened the people with impossible laws of their own. They should have recognised from Scripture that my Father had sent me, yet their hearts remained closed to the truth. In that sense, they were blind. Nevertheless, their guilt would fathom new depths with what they would do to me in a few months.

The Pharisees thought they were in God's favour and were his instrument for leading and teaching the people, just as a shepherd leads and cares for a flock of sheep. But they were blind impostors. Shepherds are often used in our culture as a symbol of a caretaker of God's people. King David enjoyed a meteoric rise from shepherd-boy to king (granted, with some fleeing from Saul in-between).[59] My Father himself was described by the prophets as the "Shepherd of Israel", Ezekiel particularly describing him as searching for and looking after his sheep.[60] So I tried showing the people and the Pharisees that I was that same true shepherd.

"I tell you the truth, only the man who enters the sheep pen by the gate is the true shepherd; anyone else is a robber.[61] The shepherd calls his sheep by name and they follow him because they know his voice. They run away from anyone whose voice they don't know."

I could tell I was already losing them, so I tried again.

---

58 Based on John 9:39 (NLT)
59 1 Samuel 16:11, 17:15,34, 21:19; 2 Samuel 2:4
60 Psalm 23:1, 80:1; Isaiah 40:10-11; Ezekiel 34:11-16
61 John 10:1(-21)

"I am the gate, and everyone who comes through me will be saved. The thief comes to steal, kill and destroy them; I come to give them life – life to the full. I am the good shepherd, prepared to lay my life on the line for my sheep. The hired hand doesn't care for what are not his sheep and flees as soon as he sees the approaching wolf, so it is able to attack and scatter the flock."

This time I was getting through to some of them. So I expanded the picture to show that not only Jews but also Gentiles would become part of the kingdom.

"I have other sheep from outside this sheepfold. I must call them in as well, and they will listen to my voice. Then there will be one flock with one shepherd."

I finished by saying that my life would not be taken but that I would lay it down willingly and take it up again, as my Father commanded. At these words the Jews were again divided. Many of them labelled me as demon-possessed and raving mad, and wondered why they were listening to me. Others were affected; how could a man possessed by a demon open the eyes of the blind?

One of those who had been listening intently, an expert in the law, stood up and posed a question. "Teacher, what must I do to inherit eternal life?"[62]

That was easy, in one sense. In fact, he ought to have known the answer. He was carrying the portion of Scripture known as the 'Shema' on his forehead as many men do, in a tiny, black, quadratic leather case. This contains four fragments of parchment, on which are written portions of the Torah, the books of the law that we gave to Moses.[63] Together, they make up the 'tefillin', or phylactery.[64] The thin leather strap coiled round the middle finger of his left hand showed that he also had one tied to his arm, close to the heart. If only the wearers would internalise the contents in their hearts as well as their minds.

---

62 Luke 10:25 (NIV)
63 Exodus 13:1-10, 13:11-16; Deuteronomy 6:4-9, 11:13-21
64 Greenstone et al ("Phylacteries"); Rich ("Tefillin")

"What is written in the law?" I asked him, indicating the tefillin on his forehead. "How do you read it?"[65]

"'Love the Lord your God with all your heart and with all your soul and with all your strength and with all your mind,'[66]" he replied, "and, 'Love your neighbour as yourself.'[67]"[68]

"That's right," I told him. "Do this and life will be yours."

Uncertainty still dominated the man's features; dissatisfied, he was forming another question.

"But who is my neighbour?" he finally asked.

Intending, as I was, to go as far as Bethany that evening, I told a story about a man travelling on the dangerous road from Jerusalem down to Jericho, who fell into the hands of robbers, was stripped of his clothes, beaten and left for dead.

"A priest happened to be travelling that way too, but on seeing the victim lying there, passed by on the other side. So too a Levite. But a Samaritan travelling that way found the man and showed compassion for him. He patched up the injured casualty, put him on his donkey and took him to an inn where he cared for him. The following day, he gave the innkeeper two silver coins to care for the man, and promised to reimburse him any extra outlay when he returned."

I certainly had the attention of the expert in the law, though he did not look too impressed with the outcome of the story. As I have said,[69] the Jews don't have a lot of time for the Samaritans. Now I pressed the point home. "Now, which of these three would you say was a neighbour to the man who was attacked by bandits?"[70]

"The one who showed mercy to him," replied my enquirer grudgingly, unwilling even to speak out the word 'Samaritan'.

"Go and do the same," I told him, looking him straight in the eye, willing him to open his heart to the laws he knew in his head.

---

[65] Luke 10:26 (NIV)
[66] Deuteronomy 6:4-5
[67] Leviticus 19:18
[68] Luke 10:27 (NIV)
[69] See page 71
[70] Luke 10:36 (NLT)

He hung his head slightly and departed, taking with him much to think about.

23

Finding What's Lost

Mary and Martha's house[1] always provides a refuge from the busyness and controversy I encounter at the temple. I often stay with them and their brother Lazarus when down in Jerusalem. The two sisters are very different in nature. Mary always enjoys sitting at my feet with the others, listening to whatever I'm saying. Martha, on the other hand, flits in and out, always checking on the state of something cooking over the fire, and generally running the household.

We went to Bethany now, the Feast of the Tabernacles over, and enjoyed their hospitality for a few days. Martha was her usual distracted self, and at some point came over to me, irritated, and spoke a little accusingly.

"Lord, don't you care that my sister has left me to do the work by myself? Tell her to help me!"[2]

"Martha, Martha," I answered gently, taking her hand, "you get worried and het up about many things, but only one thing is needed. Mary has chosen what is better, and you shouldn't want to take it away from her."

---

[1] Luke 10:38(-42)
[2] Luke 10:40 (NIV)

Are you sometimes so distracted by everything that needs doing that you forget to simply sit and listen out for my voice? Go look at the birds and the flowers in your garden or in a park. Remember?

One of those days, some people I was talking to mentioned the Galileans whose blood Pilate had mixed with their sacrifices.[3] Pilate is the Roman prefect of Judea, and well known for his brutality. A few years ago, he used sacred Corban[4] monies from the temple to build an aqueduct.[5] When, understandably, tens of thousands took to the streets to protest, Pilate had the disturbance quelled violently. His soldiers went into the crowd undercover and then, at a prearranged signal, used their daggers to slay the rioters.

Whatever these folk thought of Pilate, here was a teaching opportunity. I asked them whether they thought the murdered Galileans must be worse sinners than all the other Galileans because they had suffered that way.

There were blank stares and the vague hint of a shrug from the one who had made the gruesome statement.

"Of course they weren't!" I exclaimed, answering my own question for them. "But unless you repent, you too will all perish."[6]

Sceptical question marks replaced some of the blanks.

"What about the eighteen who died when the tower in Siloam collapsed on them[7] – were they more guilty than everyone else in Jerusalem?"

Back to blanks. Just as my disciples had wondered whether the blind man or his parents were to blame for his predicament, many people here assume that calamities such as these happen in judgement of some serious sin.[8] But we use such things, however and why ever they happen, as signs – prompts to make people ponder their lives, opportunities for learning righteousness,[9] for repentance and healing.

"Not all all! But if you don't repent, you're all going to perish."

---

[3] Luke 13:1(-9)
[4] Corban: a gift dedicated to God; cf. Mark 7:11
[5] Very possibly what Luke refers to; Josephus (Antiquities of the Jews XVIII.3.2; War II.9.4)
[6] Luke 13:3b (NIV)
[7] An unknown incident (NIV footnote at Luke 13:4)
[8] Proverbs 24:16; John 9:2
[9] Isaiah 26:9

Were some of them beginning to understand? I told them a parable about a fig tree to help them along. (The health of a fig tree is often used in Scripture to illustrate the spiritual health of an individual or of Israel as a whole.[10]) So, the vineyard owner with a fig-tree in one corner, that had not borne fruit for three years, told his gardener to cut it down. The gardener had him agree to a stay of execution for one more year, during which time he would tend the tree and fertilise it. If it didn't bear fruit the following year, then it could be cut down.

Did they understand that my heavenly Father would cut them down? Here I was, doing all I could to tend their hearts. Now was their year for repentance and bearing fruit!

On a Sabbath soon after this, I went to teach in the synagogue of one of the towns in the area.[11] Amongst the congregation, I spotted a woman who was doubled over and unable to stand up straight. Someone told me that an evil spirit had crippled her for the past eighteen years. I imagined how difficult her life must have been, and what pain she suffered trying to do everyday chores. Just getting to the synagogue for worship must have taken an immense effort. I love to see such faith; it is a faith you can learn from when you observe an elderly, infirm person using dogged determination to come and worship me with their church family.

When it was time for me to speak, I summoned the woman to the front. "Woman," I proclaimed, having quietly banished the spirit, "you have been released from your infirmity." When she had hobbled to the front, her gentle features barely visible, I laid my hands on her crooked back and, as so often before, rejoiced as I felt the healing power flow from me into her stiffened frame. Instantly the woman stood up straight, was able to look people in the face without cocking her head sideways, and started praising God.

Our rejoicing was cut short by the intervention of the ruler of the synagogue. Indignant that I had dared to heal the woman on the Sabbath, and therefore 'worked', he told the crowd bluntly that there

---

[10] e.g. Jeremiah 8:13, 24:2-8; Joel 1:7,12; Habakkuk 3:17
[11] Luke 13:10(-17)

were six days for work and they should come for healing then, not on the day of rest and worship.

"You hypocrites!" I exclaimed, bristling with anger. "Doesn't each of you on the Sabbath untie your ox or donkey from the stall and lead it out to give it water?[12] This woman is a daughter of Abraham! Satan has imprisoned her for eighteen years! Are you really saying it's wrong to release her on the Sabbath?"

Humiliated silence from my opponents contrasted with murmurs of approval from the rest of the delighted congregation. Father, please soften their hardened hearts!

My disciples and I made our way back towards Jerusalem, teaching in the towns and villages en route. In one of them, someone asked me whether only a few people were going to be saved. Wrong question; you need to make sure *you* are saved.

"Make every effort to enter through the narrow door,"[13] I replied. "For once the owner of the house has closed it, no more will be able to enter, however much they plead to be let in. There will be weeping and gnashing of teeth when people realise they are excluded from the banquet within, which is open to all peoples, if only they will enter."[14]

It was like with the conditionally reprieved fig tree: now was the time for people to make the decision and enter the kingdom.

In another town, some Pharisees approached me with the news that Herod wanted to kill me.[15] "Leave this place and go somewhere else," they advised.

The Pharisees shared my devotion to God but believed it could be lived out in daily life by adherence to the Torah and many other rules. We came to theological blows because I held to the spirit of the law, rather than the law itself. I also identified myself with the prophecies of the Scriptures.[16] Since some of the Pharisees wanted rid of me,[17] I

---

[12] Luke 13:15 (NIV)
[13] Luke 13:24 (NIV)
[14] Luke 13:28-29; cf. Isaiah 25:6-8
[15] Luke 13:31(-35)
[16] e.g. Luke 4:21
[17] e.g. Mark 3:6

accepted their warning now as genuine. However, I still had those prophecies to fulfil!

"Go tell that fox," I replied, "I will drive out demons and heal people today and tomorrow, and on the third day I will reach my goal. I must keep going yet, for surely no prophet will die outside Jerusalem!"[18]

I am going to die in Jerusalem, and soon now; it's why I came. So news that Herod wanted to kill me did not faze me. And on the third day, my goal to overcome death would be achieved. However, the reality of it hit home. Not just that, but it seemed that so few people were willing to enter through the narrow door I had just been talking about. There was so much opposition; not just a lack of understanding, but a refusal to understand. I was deeply saddened by the thought that I would die for many people who would not accept me and so perish anyway.

"O Jerusalem, Jerusalem," I lamented, and continued with a reminder of the warnings we gave to Solomon and Jeremiah.[19] "If only you knew what would bring you peace. But your house will be left to you desolate."

Six hundred years ago we abandoned Jerusalem to Babylonia for her disobedient devotion to false gods.[20] Now she is close to abandoning me, and she herself will last barely two generations more. *Father, may my sacrifice not be in vain!*

While nothing would interfere with the timescale my Father had set, I heeded the warnings of the Pharisees insofar as we headed north again towards Galilee, going village by village.

On another Sabbath, I was invited to eat in the house of a prominent local Pharisee.[21] He and others were carefully watching me; it was obvious that there was an ulterior motive to the invitation. It was a Sabbath and healing was 'work'. In front of me was a man suffering

---

[18] Based on Luke 13:32 (NIV)
[19] 1 Kings 9:7-8; Jeremiah 22:5
[20] Jeremiah 12:7; 44:1-6
[21] Luke 14:1(-14)

from dropsy. His fluid-swollen limbs caused his face to crease in pain every time he moved.

This time I posed the question up front, and directed it at the assortment of clerical experts. "Does the law permit healing on the Sabbath or not?" But they answered with silence.

I was feeling the same anger that had risen up in me just a few Sabbaths ago after healing the crippled woman. I reached out and touched the man, asking for my Spirit's enabling, and restored his health. Because he had only been invited to bait me with, and so to save him further embarrassment, I instructed the man to leave. Then I returned my attention to my host and his circle of friends.

"If one of you has a son or an ox that falls into a well on the Sabbath day, will you not immediately pull him out?"

Again, silence. They couldn't think of any response.

Those responsible for preparing it announced that the meal was ready. As they invited us to recline at the table, I noticed how some of the guests made a beeline for the places of honour. I told them a thinly veiled parable about humility, saying that if you're invited to a wedding reception and choose a seat by the head table, the host might well have to humiliate you by offering your seat to a more distinguished guest. If you take the lowest place, however, then it's more likely he will honour you by moving you to a better seat.

"For those who exalt themselves will be humbled, and those who humble themselves will be exalted."[22]

My host smiled politely, failing to disguise his growing doubts about whether inviting me to a meal with all his distinguished friends had been a good idea. I turned to him with an equally direct challenge.

"When you throw a banquet, don't invite those who you know can invite you back; but rather, invite the poor, crippled, lame and blind. They won't be able to return the favour, but your reward will come when the righteous are resurrected."

---

[22] Luke 14:11 (NLT)

As I said when I mentioned the Pharisees' failure to honour their parents, anything like this that you do for someone else, you do for my Father and me.[23]

When one of those at the table with me heard my suggestions on banquet invitations, he enthusiastically pronounced his own conclusion, like a schoolchild giving an answer in class. "Blessed is the man who will eat at the feast in the kingdom of God."[24]

He is indeed blessed, but unfortunately neither this man nor his friends are going to be there if they don't have a change of heart. Many of my people assume they will enter the kingdom of God because it is their birthright. But as I told Nicodemus, it requires a new birth.[25] They, like you, can only enter my Father's kingdom if they accept my words, admit their need of repentance and change, and receive me into their hearts.

To help them see this, I told them another parable about being invited to a feast. This time, the banquet was prepared, and the servant was sent out with invitations. One by one, the people made excuses for why they couldn't come: one had to go and see his new plot of land, another try out his new oxen, and yet another had just married. When the servant returned bereft of guests, the master was angry and sent him out into the alleyways and countryside to bring the poor, crippled and blind to the feast. "I tell you," said the master, "not one of the people I first invited will get a taste of my banquet."

As well as accepting the invitation to the banquet – accepting me into your heart – you have to be clear about the cost of following me. My disciples have been finding this out, and will do so yet. Many in the crowds that follow me believe in me, but fall away when the cost becomes too great, like the seed that fell on the rocky soil or among the weeds.

So it was with many in the crowd that followed as I moved on from the Pharisee's banquet with my disciples. I longed for them to believe, but wanted them to be prepared for what it would take to

---

23 Matthew 15:3-6; Mark 7:11-12; Matthew 25:40
24 Luke 14:15 (NIV); see also verses 16-24
25 John 3:3

follow me truly. They needed to wrestle with my words so that they understood them for themselves. I stopped and turned round, causing a pile-up further back in the procession of people along the road.

"If you come to me but by comparison do not hate your father and mother, wife and children, brothers and sisters – even your own life – you cannot be my disciple. Likewise if you're not prepared to follow me all the way to your own cross."[26]

There was consternation on the faces of the crowd. Surely I wasn't advocating breaking at least one of the commandments?[27] No, the commandments are to be upheld. But as I'd told previous enquirers,[28] to be able to follow me and carry your cross sometimes means having to put your calling ahead of family. That's why my coming here was always going to divide some families, as one follows the call that others won't accept.

Being aware of the potential costs involved in following me is like someone building a tower. If he starts and then runs out of money, everyone will ridicule him. Similarly, if a king decides to go to war and realises he has too few soldiers, he will send a delegation well ahead of him to arrange peace terms.

Having explained this, I repeated the challenge to those listening: "By the same token, if you won't relinquish all that you have, you won't be my disciple. You're here to make a difference. Salt is good, but if it loses its saltiness, it is good for nothing and is thrown out. Have salt in yourselves, and be at peace with each other."

We arrived at another northern Judean town and found somewhere to eat. It wasn't long before the town's tax collectors and other 'sinners' gathered around us to listen to what I was saying.[29] Local Pharisees and teachers of the law, on observing this, muttered between themselves (and for the 'benefit' of everyone else) that I not only welcomed sinners but even ate with them. *O Father, help me to enlighten them!* I tried to do so with another sheep parable.

---

[26] Matthew 10:37-39; Luke 14:26(-35)
[27] Exodus 20:12
[28] Luke 9:57-62
[29] Luke 15:1(-7); Matthew 18:12-14

"Now suppose one of you owns a hundred sheep and one of them wanders off. Will you not leave the ninety-nine in the open and go looking for the lost one? And when you find it, will you not lead it back joyfully to the others, then call friends and neighbours and celebrate its safe return? That's just how it's going to be in heaven, with greater jubilation over one sinner who repents than over ninety-nine righteous people who don't need to."

I wanted the story to illustrate my body, the body of believers that you call 'the church'. I had already talked of myself as the Good Shepherd, having a flock in one pen but also sheep from another pen who would become part of the flock. The flock represents my body. Sometimes one of the 'flock' wanders off, distracted by problems, disappointments or temptations that the devil puts in his way; the shepherd goes after that 'sheep' and rejoices when he finds it and it returns to the flock.

If someone wanders away from your 'flock', your church, do you go looking for that person? Have *you* wandered off? I want to come looking for you!

I told them a similar story about a woman having ten drachma coins and losing one.[30] Such a woman turns her whole house upside-down before finding it. When she does, she rejoices with her friends and neighbours, just as the angels in heaven rejoice over one sinner who repents. Do you do all you possibly can to find that lost person?

Seeing that the people were connecting with the idea, I told them a third allegory about the younger of two sons asking for his inheritance.[31] Now, the younger of two sons tends to receive half of what his brother would inherit,[32] but not before the due time. The younger son in my story wanted it *now;* he was all but wishing his father dead! However, the father acquiesced (not by dying, I hasten to add), and divided his property between them. The younger son went away with all his belongings, burning his bridges as he did so. Wild living in a far-away country, combined with the onset of a famine, soon left him

---

30 Luke 15:8-10
31 Luke 15:11-32
32 Deuteronomy 21:17

penniless and so desperate that he would have eaten the food of the pigs he was employed to feed. Eventually the young man came to his senses and thought to himself that even his father's servants had more than enough to eat. He came to a decision. "I will go to my father," he decided, "and say to him: 'Father, I have sinned against both heaven and against you, and I am no longer worthy to be called your son. Please take me on as a hired servant.'"[33] That he did. As always, his father was looking out for him and saw him while he was still a long way off. Filled with compassion, the father ran and embraced his son, who gave his rehearsed but sincere speech. The father would have none of it and instead had his servants kill the fatted calf, and organised a huge welcome-home party. For him, his son had been dead; now he was alive and found!

My point was the same as before, though this story portrayed the father – my Father – as giving his son free choice. The father was still there, and the son was still his son; he just had to repent and return for his relationship to be restored. Do you recognise yourself in the younger son, my friend? Is it time you came back? Outstretched arms await you.

There was a further idea I wanted to get over to those listening. The Jews here think that God is theirs. They tolerate Gentiles, as I've mentioned, though only because our law has made provision for them. My heart's desire is for my people to embrace all those who repent, regardless of their ethnicity.

So I added an older brother to my story, who came in from his field duties and was first curious then angry about the party his father was holding for the younger brother. After all, he had worked away for years with not even a goat to barbecue with his mates. The father went out and pleaded with him to join the celebrations. "My son," he declared, "you have consistently stood by me; everything I have will be yours. But we just had to celebrate together, because this lost brother of yours is suddenly alive and well again!"

I left the ending open, and left the Pharisees in particular to consider what response they would make towards the lost and 'other

---

[33] Luke 15:18-19 (NLT)

sheep' that I would yet call into my kingdom. What about you? Does your church family welcome back those who were lost, who may have caused much hurt through their wandering away? Do you?

24

Last Winter

Time was drawing on towards winter,[1] and the tops of the Judean and Samarian hills were sporting their first dusting of snow. It would soon be time for the Feast of Dedication at the temple. However, for now we were travelling northwards through Samaria and had arrived in another small town.

I still had so much to teach my disciples, but I also wanted to reach the Pharisees among my listeners. I longed for them to move beyond their dead traditions to a living faith. They might consider themselves to occupy privileged positions within the faith life of the nation, but they needed much more to court favour with me, the Son of God, in order to enter my kingdom. That was the point of the story I told them now involving a rich man whose estate manager had mishandled his wealth and so was about to lose his position.

"The manager said to himself, 'I can't dig and I won't beg, but I'm going to need a place to stay when I lose my job. And I know exactly what I can do to make people open to putting me up.' So he summoned all his master's debtors and reduced the amount they owed, so that each would look with favour on him when he was out of a job and needed help. Now, the master commended the dishonest manager for acting so shrewdly."

---

[1] John 10:22

My listeners were trying to figure out why I seemed to be condoning the dishonesty displayed by the manager and praised by the master. This of course was not what I was implying. Rather, the Pharisees needed to lose their love of money, and act wisely by acquiring and using their wealth in a way that would curry favour with my Father, by acting justly and looking after the poor. In fact, they would do good to follow the psalmist's advice to kings to be wise, submit to the Son, and take refuge in him.[2]

"Whoever can be trusted with very little," I continued, making the point, "can also be trusted with much.[3] So if you couldn't handle worldly wealth with integrity, who will entrust true riches to you? And if you can't be trusted to look after somebody else's property, why should anyone give you any of your own?" Repeating what I had told my listeners on the mountainside above Capernaum,[4] I finished by saying, "No-one can serve two masters. He will serve one with devotion and despise the other. You cannot serve both God and Money!"[5]

The Pharisees love money. I knew that those present had been listening, and they were sneering at my remarks. They didn't seem to understand that as spiritual leaders of the children of Israel – our children – they were not acting with trustworthiness. I didn't mince my words with my next remark: "You're happy to justify yourselves before people who value greed, but God detests greed – and he knows what's in your hearts."

Despite their continued disdain, I tried again with another story, willing them to accept my words and amend their ways. The Spirit had brought my friend Lazarus to mind (I would find out why soon enough) so, unusually[6], I gave one of the characters in my story a name – *his* name, not as a comparison or anything, just... well... because he was in my thoughts.

"There was an affluent man who wore fine garments and enjoyed daily luxury. Outside his gate lay a beggar named Lazarus, covered in

---

2   Psalm 2:10-12
3   Luke 16:10 (NIV)
4   See page 103
5   Matthew 6:24 (NIV); Luke 16:13 (NIV)
6   This once (NIV footnote at Luke 16:20). Narrative: Luke 16:19-31.

sores that dogs came and licked. He would have gladly eaten any of the scraps from the rich man's table. Lazarus died and was welcomed into paradise. Then the rich man died, but was cast into the torment of hell, from where he could see Abraham a long way off, with Lazarus beside him. He begged Abraham to send Lazarus with some refreshing water to ease his agony, but Abraham reminded him about all the good things he had received in his lifetime, while Lazarus had received only bad things. Besides, no-one could cross the great chasm between them."

Did they recognise themselves yet?

"The rich man accepted that, but requested that Lazarus be sent to warn his family. Abraham retorted that they had Moses and the prophets to warn them, but the rich man persisted, saying they would believe if someone from the dead were to go to them."

I thought about how the Pharisees had reacted when I had told them about rebuilding the temple in three days, and knew how they would react to what I had actually meant. I alluded to this as I concluded Abraham's words.

"If the rich man's family won't pay any attention to Moses and the prophets, not even someone rising from the dead is going to convince them."

That was certainly prophetic when later on it came to the Pharisees and my friend Lazarus. Would any of these listeners be convinced? Would they learn to share their wealth in this life, care for the poor now, make do with 'enough', use their wealth wisely? These are the things that my Father and I love to see our children doing, moved by our Holy Spirit, just as I do what I see my Father doing. When that happens, the meaning of Lazarus' name is fulfilled: 'God is my help.' Are you convinced enough to be my help to others?

I had taught much on repentance, commitment, and life in the kingdom. Now it seemed good to give my disciples some examples of handling everyday situations. Seeking out fellow-believers who have wandered away from their faith is one thing. Sometimes, however, some or other transgression requires extending forgiveness to them. Sin always needs dealing with, but initially in a fashion that encourages repentance and restoration. Measures that are more drastic may need to be taken later.

"If a fellow-believer wrongs you, mention it to them privately," I proposed.[7] "If they accept what you say, you've won them back. Should they refuse to listen, take one or two others with you, so that, 'Every matter may be established by the testimony of two or three witnesses,'"[8] I continued, quoting the familiar law[9].

A few of my disciples wore expressions that confirmed the need for this teaching. Nevertheless, I was nurturing them gently towards leadership of the wider group of believers. For their number will grow exponentially after I have left them.[10]

"If they won't listen to them either," I continued, "take the matter to the church; and if they won't listen even to the church, treat them as you would a pagan or a tax collector."[11] (Tax collectors who remained in sin, anyway. One of the Twelve was a reformed such character, after all.)

As I had recently told Peter, I now told all my disciples that, with the guidance of our Spirit, they would announce God's judgement on what to bind or what to loose. I added an assurance of my presence. "I also tell you this: If two of you agree here on earth concerning anything you ask, my Father in heaven will do it for you.[12] For wherever two or three meet together in my name, I am there among them."

The Twelve still looked as if they were wondering how to measure up to these standards. However, they knew enough to place their trust in the right place.

"Increase our faith!" they said to me, much as the father had done, whose demon-possessed boy my disciples couldn't heal.

"Even if your faith were no bigger than a mustard seed," I replied, looking around me for a suitable object, "you could order this mulberry tree to uproot and plant itself in the sea, and it would obey you."

---

7 Matthew 18:15(-20); Luke 17:3-5
8 Matthew 18:16 (NIV)
9 Deuteronomy 17:6, 19:15
10 cf. Acts 2:41
11 Based on Matthew 18:17 (NIV)
12 Matthew 18:19 (NLT)

On the other hand, there is no room for pride in getting it right, nor for thinking that what you do can earn your salvation. I gave my audience a final illustration.[13]

"When your slaves[14] come in from ploughing or tending your sheep, are you going to tell them to come and sit down for a meal with you?"

There have been slaves from earliest times, and early on we laid down laws for their protection through Moses[15]. Sometimes people willingly become slaves in order to escape abject poverty.[16] There are people in your world who, having been in prison before, re-offend for similar reasons: 'inside' they are ensured shelter, food and security.[17] Others, even more desperate, may find themselves caught up in, and enslaved by, prostitution. These things are why we put so much emphasis on helping the poor and needy.

People here, then, are used to the concept of slaves and their duties, much as well-off people in your world may have servants. A good master cares for his staff, servants or slaves, and may even rely on them. Nevertheless, they remain his servants, and no-one would expect them to eat with their master.

"Of course not!" I continued. "You'd tell him to get your meal ready; he can eat afterwards. Nor would you go out of your way to thank him; after all, he's just doing his duty. In the same way, having done all you were required to do, have the attitude of an unworthy servant who has simply done what he was supposed to."

Peter had been mulling this over. Had he not dealt with one of his fellow disciples very well, or was he pondering the responsibility I had given him and now the rest of the Twelve?

"Lord, how many times should I forgive a fellow-believer who wrongs me? As many as seven times?"[18]

---

13 Luke 17:7-10
14 δοῦλον (δοῦλος) = [bonded] servant, or slave
15 Exodus 21
16 Leviticus 25:39-41,47-48
17 Ministry of Justice (pp 130, 136, 137)
18 Matthew 18:21(-35)

Ah... Peter was trying to be generous! Our rabbis usually teach that you only have to forgive someone three times. This goes back to the words of judgement "for three transgressions, and for four" we pronounced[19] on pre-exile Israel and Judah through Amos. Both had become prosperous but taken on the pagan worship of their neighbours. However, adherence to these three times precluded any forgiveness when later repentance was evident.

"Seventy times seven!" I proclaimed to Peter, to his initial astonishment. But as he thought about it, I could see understanding dawning across his features as he connected the Scriptures my Spirit reminded him about.

Way back, through Moses, we had instructed the Israelites to let the land lie fallow every seventh, or Sabbath, year, and even spelled out the punishment for not doing so.[20] Your recent ancestors regularly practised a form of this called crop rotation, including a year lying fallow. Organic farmers and many gardeners still do, for it makes good agricultural sense, allowing the soil to replenish the nutrients required for different kinds of crops, and offering natural defence against pests and disease.

Well, the Israelites failed to do this for a period of four hundred and ninety years, starting from the Exodus. So, decades after Jeremiah had foretold[21] it, and a good century after Isaiah had prophesied[22] it, we allowed King Nebuchadnezzar of Babylon to take Israel captive[23] for a period of seventy years to give the land back the seventy Sabbath years it had lost. Even then, the people were to look after themselves and even seek the good of the place in which they found themselves – for their own good.

We told Jeremiah to write to them, encouraging them that we had plans to prosper and not to harm them, to give them hope and a future. They were still our people, and we were still their God![24] If you, my

---

[19] Amos 1:3,6,9,13, 2:1,4,6 (cf. Proverbs 30:15,18,21,29)
[20] Leviticus 25:1-5, 26:33-35,42-43
[21] Jeremiah 25:8-12
[22] 2 Kings 20:16-18; Isaiah 39:5-7
[23] 2 Chronicles 36:5-21; Ezra 5:12
[24] Jeremiah 29:4-24

friend, find yourself in a desert place of exile, remember that we still have plans for you; you are still our precious child.

The rebuilding of the temple was completed during this period, in the sixth year of King Darius. (At the end of this time, Nehemiah organised the rebuilding of Jerusalem's city walls, completed in the twentieth year of King Artaxerxes[25] following a royal dictate.) After completion of the temple, the nation celebrated its 'Hanukkah', or Dedication.[26] The Feast of Hanukkah we were now about to celebrate commemorated the wresting back of control of the temple from the Seleucid king Antiochus Epiphanes by the Jews under the leadership of Judas Maccabeus,[27] some two hundred years ago.

So the sin of the Israelites had been duly punished, they rededicated themselves to us and were thus restored. Sin always requires punishment, which is what I am here to take now, to bring about the restoration of Israel once and for all. And 'now' just happens to be approaching midway through the last of another set of 'seventy sevens'.

Some five hundred and fifty years ago, we sent our messenger Gabriel to explain our salvation plan to the prophet Daniel.[28] It started with that royal decree authorising the rebuilding of Jerusalem, and sixty-nine 'weeks' (representing four hundred and eighty-three years) would then pass before the Anointed One appeared. That happened when I was baptised by Cousin John and started my public ministry. Halfway through the final 'seven', the Anointed One will be 'cut off' from the land of the living.[29] Thus, I do not have long now.

So you see, when I told Peter 'seventy times seven', it had the weight of much prophecy behind it. How many times are you to forgive? As long as repentance is evident[30] and until restoration is achieved! To illustrate it, I told Peter and the rest of my disciples a story about a king who wanted to settle accounts with his servants.

---

25 Nehemiah 2:1, 6:15 (March/October 445 BC, NIV footnotes)
26 Ezra 6:15-16 (March 516 BC, NIV footnote)
27 MacCulloch (p.65); 1 Macc.4:36-59; 2 Macc.10:1-8; Josephus (Antiquities of the Jews XII.7.6-7)
28 Daniel 9:21(-27)
29 Daniel 9:26; Isaiah 53:8
30 cf. Luke 17:3-4

"The first owed the king a colossal ten thousand talents. The man couldn't pay, so the king ordered his family and possessions to be put on sale in order to recoup the debt. When the servant begged for mercy and patience, the king took pity on him, cancelled the debt and let him go. But when that servant went out, he found a fellow-servant who owed him a mere hundred denarii. Ignoring the man's similar pleas for mercy, he had him thrown in jail. This outraged the king's remaining servants, who reported to him all that had happened. He hauled the first servant back in and told him he should have shown the same mercy as he had been shown, then had him thrown in jail to be tortured until he had paid his entire debt. This is how my Father in heaven will deal with any of you that don't forgive other believers from the heart."

Contrition showed on their faces; my message had got through.

We were about to enter another village, nestled in rolling hills between Galilee and Samaria,[31] when ten lepers approached us, stopping at a distance and calling out in a loud voice, "Jesus, Master, have pity on us!"[32]

As I came closer to them and saw the condition of their faces and hands, I did indeed have pity on them, both for their physical condition and for their exclusion as lepers from any real contact with their community. Calling on our Spirit to bring healing to them, I sent them to the local priests for confirmation that they were healed. They could have pointed at their flaky skin and ridiculed me, but as they took the literal steps of faith towards the synagogue, so they were healed.

A little later, when my disciples had sorted out some modest accommodation where we could stay overnight, one of the healed men returned, singing away at the top of his voice – not with his habitual warning of "Unclean!"[33] but praising God. He threw himself at my feet and thanked me profusely. The fact that he was a Samaritan surprised me greatly.

"Didn't I heal all ten of you?" I enquired of the prostrate man. "What about your nine friends?" To my disciples I added, "Did only

---

[31] Luke 17:11(-19). See 'Gospel Harmony' note, page 301
[32] Luke 17:13 (NIV)
[33] Leviticus 13:45

this foreigner come back to thank God?" Looking down again, I told the man, "Stand up; your faith has healed you," and sent him on his way.

He stood, beamed at me, and gave me a sincere hug that said more than any words could have expressed. It was a heart-warming conclusion to the day, and I enjoyed a good night's sleep there.

We finally left Galilee the following morning, and spent several days making our way towards Jerusalem, since the time for the Feast of Dedication there would soon arrive. Where we paused to stop over, there was more opportunity for teaching. It was in my thoughts constantly that I did not have very long now.

My disciples would soon have to overcome major doubts, fear and loss, which would test their faith in me to breaking point. There are times in life when desperation would oust trust, and staying close to me as I stay close to my Father helps you through. I used a parable to show my disciples that they should always pray and not give up.[34]

"There was a town whose judge neither feared God nor respected people. A widow there kept coming to him with a plea for justice. After some time of refusing her request, the judge acquiesced, not because he cared about her plight but to get some peace from the woman. How much more will God see to it that his chosen ones get justice, and without delay?"

My heavenly Father and I are passionate about justice. Sometimes, though, our ideas of time and your ideas of time clash; what is 'without delay' to us can be an interminably long wait to you. When that is apparent, we love you to persist in your petitions and prayers, as much as we love it when you tell us what we know already, just as any parent would with their child. Don't lose heart; justice will prevail, your needs will be met, even when the opposite seems true.

When you pray, it is important not to fall into the trap of smug superiority. Some people are confident of their own righteousness, but fall into sin when they look down on everybody else. We are wholly opposed to such pride, but show grace to the humble at whom it is

---

[34] Based on Luke 18:1 (NIV); see also verses 2-8

aimed.[35] I illustrated this with a picture that would be familiar with plenty of my listeners.[36]

"A Pharisee and a tax collector were praying in the temple. The Pharisee stood there and prayed, 'God, thank you that I am not like other people – robbers, evildoers, adulterers – and especially that tax collector. I fast twice a week and give you a tenth of my income.'"[37]

My disciples were in danger of becoming smug themselves; the Pharisees are generally not the most helpful or popular people we encounter. Before they could start thinking themselves a cut above the Pharisees, I showed them what the right attitude was.

"But the tax collector stood at a distance. He would not even look up to heaven, but vocalised his posture of remorse: 'God, have mercy on me, a sinner.' It was this man, not the other, who went home righteous in God's sight. For all who sing their own praises will find themselves unexpectedly hoarse, while those who know they can't sing will get a whole choir singing for them."

Somebody stopped humming, and they all became a little more reflective.

We finally entered the city through the East Gate and from there continued towards the temple area via Solomon's Colonnade[38] – a cloisters-like covered promenade built along the eastern wall of the city. Here I often walked with my disciples; it was quieter than the main temple courtyards and sheltered from both the heat of summer and the cool winds of winter. However, it was not so quiet that I went unnoticed, and it was not long before a group of local Jewish leaders surrounded me.

They came straight to the point. "How long are you going to keep us in suspense? If you are the Christ, tell us plain and simple."

"I already told you," I responded, "but you don't believe me, despite the miracles I do on my Father's behalf. That's because you're not my sheep. My sheep listen to my voice; I know them, and they

---

[35] Proverbs 3:34; cf. Isaiah 57:15
[36] Luke 18:9-14
[37] Luke 18:12 (NLT)
[38] John 10:22,23(-39); Josephus (Antiquities of the Jews XV.11.3)

follow me. I give them eternal life and they will never perish. My sheep are my Father's; no-one can snatch them from our hands. I and the Father are one."

The expressions on the faces of my enquirers changed from mere challenge to downright outrage. They scrabbled about for stones to throw at me; the situation was becoming dicey. Before it could escalate any further, I challenged them: "Which of the many righteous acts I have shown you from my Father are you stoning me for?"

"We're not stoning you for any 'righteous acts'," they replied, "but for blasphemy because you, a mere man, claim to be God!"[39]

Well, at least they had understood what I had said. But acceptance of it was nigh on impossible for them, outside of their experience or expectation. Yet the Scriptures they claimed to value so highly were full of me; they just couldn't fathom it. I quoted to them at first a psalm of Asaph,[40] one of King David's Levitical worship leaders, then the prophet Jeremiah, underlining the authority of the Scripture they thought I disregarded.

"If Scripture says that the Father called human judges 'gods', and that he sent one into the world whom he had set apart as his own, why are you trying to pin blasphemy on me for saying that I'm God's Son? Do not believe me unless I do the righteous acts of my Father, in which case believe at least the miracles, that you may understand that the Father is in me, and I am in the Father.[41]"

That was too much for them; in their minds I had confirmed their blasphemy charge. I wondered whether any of them would ever be able to accept that I was their promised Messiah, and reminded myself that my sacrifice was for all, regardless. Once again, they tried to seize me, but I was able to escape their grasp and departed from the temple area and the city with my disciples.

We stayed over at Martha and Mary's, then continued east across the rugged Judean hills and along the Jericho road until we had crossed both that city and the River Jordan, reaching Bethabara, where Cousin

---

[39] Based on John 10:33 (NIV)
[40] Psalm 82:6; 1 Chronicles 15:17,19, 16:5,7,37, 25:2,6; Jeremiah 1:5
[41] Based on John 10:38 (NIV)

John used to preach and baptise[42]. Here, although John had never performed any miraculous signs, many had received his message and were baptised, and they believed in me now as I spent some time teaching and healing amongst them. It was a refreshing change from the unbelief I encountered in Jerusalem, but at the same time my joy was tinged with sadness that the leading Jews, who should have recognised me, were blind to me.

The local Pharisees soon came on the scene and it was plain to see that they had come to test me with another trick question.[43] If they could manoeuvre me towards a statement such as the one Cousin John had made about Herod, perhaps they would be rid of me in a similar fashion.

"Is it lawful for a man to divorce his wife for any and every reason?" they asked.[44]

Now the late Hillel the Elder, and another respected and very elderly rabbi, Shammai[45], who is almost eighty now, had opposing views on many things. On divorce, Hillel had maintained that any displeasure was grounds enough, whereas Shammai maintained that it must be for gross indecency only. This wouldn't have been the case for adultery; like the woman the Pharisees had brought to me, the law punished that by death[46]. Anyway, the topic was one that the Pharisees also hotly debated amongst themselves.

"What did Moses have to say?" I asked in reply.

"Moses permitted a man to write a certificate of divorce and send her away."[47]

So they knew the answer to their own question then, at least taking Hillel's more liberal view, as implied by it. However, the hardness of their uncompassionate hearts saddened me. My Father and I hate divorce, as the prophet Malachi recognised[48] when talking about Judah's unfaithfulness. We went out of our way to create Eve for Adam, a perfect match, and thus initiated the perfect framework of marriage

---

[42] Matthew 19:1(-2); Mark 10:1; John 10:40(-42)
[43] Matthew 19:3(-12); Mark 10:2(-12)
[44] Matthew 19:13 (NIV)
[45] "Shammai." Shammai *~50BC, †~30AD.
[46] Deuteronomy 22:22
[47] Mark 10:4 (NIV); Deuteronomy 24:1
[48] Malachi 2:10-16

for men and women to live, to love, and to raise children. We even made sexual union an intensely pleasurable affair, physically and emotionally, certainly compared with, say, the redback spider on that large island you call Australia, whose female specimens more usually than not eat their smaller male counterparts after mating[49]. But the pleasure, especially psychologically, is a poor second-best if taken outside the framework we gave it. We gave our children the good gift of marriage; it needs to be worked at and jealously guarded.

"Haven't you read," I said, ignoring divorce certificates for a moment, "that in the beginning God created them 'male and female', and said, 'For this reason a man will leave his father and his mother and be united with his wife, and the two will become one flesh'?[50] So they are no longer two, but one. Therefore what God has joined together, let man not separate."

Still not satisfied, the Pharisees persisted. "Why the certificate of divorce then?"

"Moses permitted you to divorce your wives because your hearts were hard. But it was not this way from the beginning. I tell you that anyone who divorces their spouse – except for marital unfaithfulness – and marries another, commits adultery."[51]

When we were back at the house, my disciples made the comment that if that was how things were between husbands and wives, you were better off staying single! Did they share the common interpretation of the law that divorce was permissible, even just because they didn't fancy each other anymore? Were they still fixated with points of law, instead of looking at what we created and intended?

"It's not for everyone," I acknowledged, "only those who are called to it. There are some who renounce marriage for the sake of the kingdom. Let them do so."

Celibacy is not for everybody, and after all, my Father and I decided that it was good for Adam to have a partner. Those who burn

---

[49] Wikipedia ("Spider")
[50] Matthew 19:5 (NIV); Mark 10:7-8 (NIV); Genesis 1:27, 2:24
[51] Based on Matthew 19:8-9

with passion are better off marrying.[52] But those able to live without that often become effective workers in our kingdom.

Soon after this, a weary-looking, dust-covered messenger approached me and, having ascertained my identity, delivered his news. My generous friends Martha and Mary in Bethany had sent word that their brother, my dear friend Lazarus, was sick.[53] Lazarus and I had first met while praying at the temple during a visit to Jerusalem for a Passover some years ago. We got talking in one of the outer courts, and Lazarus invited me back to his house in nearby Bethany, where he introduced me to his sisters. Perhaps he was hoping to find a suitable husband for one of them. They were from a reasonably well off family[54] that had made its money trading in spices with the caravans that travelled along the trade route from the east that you now call the Silk Road.

"His illness is not terminal," I told the messenger and my disciples. "It will serve to bring glory to God and thus to God's Son."

My Father and I often use our children's circumstances to show them aspects of our character that they would otherwise miss. I cared deeply for my friends, for Lazarus' well-being, and about the anxiety of his sisters. Developing trust in God through the most desperate of situations is something King David wrote about in his shepherd song[55] and is a mysterious gift to our children who are open to see us amidst their woes. (For I am never on the sidelines when you are suffering; I am always in the thick of it with you.[56])

I dispatched the messenger with the return news that I would follow shortly. In fact we stayed for a further two days before heading off.[57]

Amongst the other people present were some who had brought babies to me, for me to bless them.[58] There is nothing better you can do than to bring your loved ones to me in prayer. As I said about the

---

[52] cf. 1 Corinthians 7:7-9
[53] John 11:1-6
[54] cf. John 12:1-5
[55] Psalm 23:4
[56] Isaiah 63:9
[57] John 11:6
[58] Matthew 19:13-15

persistent widow, don't give up praying for them. My disciples, however, were presently more bothered that people were interrupting their tuition, and were rebuking them. When I saw it, my hackles rose as my spirit sank. Would they never get it?

"Let those little ones come to me, don't stop them!" I countermanded. "It's people like them who will enter God's kingdom. Indeed, no-one will unless they receive it like a child."

I took the children in my arms and blessed them, their trusting smiles an oasis in the desert of adult hard-heartedness and misunderstanding.

The next day I decided it was time to head back to Judea and to Bethany.[59] My disciples expressed concern that the leading Jews had tried to stone me a little while previously, at the Feast of Dedication, and now I was planning to go back so near to Jerusalem!

"Are there not twelve hours of daylight?"[60] I objected. "If you walk for as long as it's still light and you can see where you're going, you won't stumble. But if you walk after nightfall without light, you will stumble."

As in Jerusalem when bringing sight to the man born blind,[61] I was indicating to my disciples that my time here was gradually coming to a close, but until that point we still had work to do.

"Our friend Lazarus has fallen asleep; but I am going there to wake him up,"[62] I told them, using a common euphemism for death.[63] My disciples took my words literally and persisted in trying to put me off going near Jerusalem by saying that if he was asleep, Lazarus would get better again. So I told them plainly what my Spirit had shown me: "Lazarus is dead, and for your sake I am glad I was not there, so that you may believe. But let us go to him."[64]

Thomas, whose name in Hebrew means 'twin', as does his Greek nickname Didymus, resigned himself to my decision and announced to

---

[59] John 11:7(-16)
[60] John 11:9 (NIV)
[61] John 9:5; see page 173
[62] John 11:11 (NIV)
[63] NIV footnote for John 11:11
[64] John 11:15 (NIV)

the others, "We might as well go and die with him." His words were a penetrating reminder of what lay ahead for me, and remained with me for the rest of the day.

As we set off on our way west across the River Jordan, a young man ran up and fell on his knees before me.[65] He wore fine robes and was well manicured. A member of the local gentry.

"Good teacher," he enquired, "what must I do to inherit eternal life?"[66]

"Who says I'm good?" I asked him. "Only God is good," I added, drawing his thought processes towards considering my identity and away from his perceived need to have to do something to earn the life I came to give. "You know the commandments: 'Do not murder, do not commit adultery, do not steal, do not give false testimony, do not defraud, honour your father and mother,' and, 'Love your neighbour as yourself.'"[67]

"Teacher," he declared, at a loss (and having lost the "good"; he still didn't get my identity, then), "I've kept all of those since my youth. What do I still lack?"

I looked at the man, feeling pity and love for his wandering soul. He had much and yet nothing; dissatisfaction cast a dark cloud across the bright blue sky of his wellbeing, and he knew it. There was more to life than his riches, but what was it?

"You're lacking one thing," I answered. "Go and sell all your possessions, and invest the money in heavenly treasure by giving it to the poor. Then come and follow me."

At this, the young ruler's eyes misted over, and he walked off gloomily, for he was very wealthy. I too was sad, lost in thought as I watched him disappear. Then I turned back to my disciples and, as we resumed our journey, told them how difficult it is for the rich to enter the kingdom of God. As we passed a caravan of traders in cloth, I amazed my disciples even more with the seemingly impossible statement

---

[65] Matthew 19:16(-30); Mark 10:17(-31); Luke 18:18(-30)
[66] Mark 10:17 (NIV); Luke 18:18 (NIV)
[67] Mark 10:19 (NIV); Luke 18:20 (NIV); Exodus 20:12-16; Deuteronomy 5:16-21; Leviticus 19:18

that the traders' camels would more easily fit through a needle's eye than the rich would squeeze through the gate into God's kingdom.

"So who can possibly be saved?" they asked each other.

I watched them struggle with this concept for a moment, then replied, "It isn't possible for man, but with God everything's possible."

Contrary to the rich young man, my disciples had left all they had to follow me. Now Peter piped up, a little reproachfully, "We've left everything behind. What's in it for us?"

"You have," I agreed, "and because of that, when everything is restored and the Son of Man is enthroned in glory, each of you will be enthroned to judge the twelve tribes of Israel."

When I return to this world at the end of time, the Twelve, albeit with a replacement[68] for the one who will soon betray me, will have a part in judging the nation, not least for its rejection of me. But Peter was somewhat missing the point, which is that eternal life is given by grace. It cannot be earned by any amount of sacrificing or 'doing'. But I do appreciate what my disciples have given up, and assured all my listeners that such sacrifice was not in vain.

"Anyone who leaves family or property for me and the gospel will get it back a hundred times over in this age, and, in the next, inherit eternal life. But many at the front will end up at the back; many at the back will be brought to the front."

The family is very important in my culture, and so it is a wrench for someone to break from their family. What I have said previously[69] about leaving one's family was intended to indicate the level of commitment required to follow me. It is a very real commitment in your time for many people of other faiths who come to believe in me; they not only lose family support, but maybe employment and their home, or even worse. Even those from your modern gang cultures who turn to me realise that they can no longer live the life they did with the support, however questionable, that they once had.

Yet all these things will be made up for many times over when they are given up on my account. Those who have given up the security of a

---

[68] cf. Acts 1:15-26 (v20: Psalm 109:8)
[69] See page 186

job to serve me elsewhere, learn to trust my ample provision through the gifts of fellow believers. Close and present ties to family and friends, lost when someone leaves to serve me on a far-flung mission field, are replaced by new friendships and people to care for.

I was not done with teaching on feelings of superiority when it came to the kingdom. I knew that there could be problems with those who have given up much early on in their lives and seemingly done everything right, when they see someone being accepted who has done everything wrong but repents at the end. People here regularly stand around in the market or some other central place, hoping that a landowner or wealthy farmer will come and hire them for the day to work on his fields or harvesting his crops. You in your time might see this exact same thing in parts of the African continent; in your country you might call that place an agency. At any rate, the illustration I gave was familiar to the people listening.[70]

"The kingdom of heaven is like a landowner who went out first thing of a morning to hire people to work in his vineyard. He agreed the usual daily wage of a denarius with them, and they trooped off to work. At the third, and again at the sixth and ninth hours, and even at the eleventh hour, he went back to the marketplace, found people still standing about doing nothing, and told them to go and work in his vineyard too, promising them a fair wage. At sunset, he instructed his foreman to pay the wages, starting with the last workers hired. When they saw those hired at the eleventh hour receiving a denarius, those who had worked all day naturally expected to receive more and grumbled against the landowner when they didn't."

My disciples were murmuring similar thoughts as they listened to my story. They were straining to link it with the kingdom of heaven.

"The landowner confronted one of the servants: 'Friend, I am not being unfair to you. Did you not agree to work for a denarius? Now accept your pay and go. Don't I have the right to pay you all the same, if I so desire? Or do you resent my generosity?' So again," I concluded,

---

[70] Matthew 20:1-16

"the last in will be brought to the front; the first at the front will be sent to the back."

This was a new way of thinking for an audience used to the concept of having to earn your way into the kingdom in some way. You might take offence at some of those who will enter my kingdom, but there is only one entry requirement: accept the invitation! And that can be done right up to death's door. But why miss out on life now by waiting?

Bethany lies around a day's journey away, about twenty miles from Bethabara. Travelling during the cooler winter is more pleasant than in the stifling heat of the summer, so despite the frequent pauses along the way, we made good time.

On our arrival at the edge of the village,[71] we met some Jews from nearby Jerusalem who informed us that Lazarus had already been in a tomb for four days. Many Jews here believe that the soul remains near the body of a deceased for three days after death in the hope of returning to it,[72] so in their minds all hope for Lazarus was gone.

Someone went to bring word to Lazarus' sisters that I was here. Martha soon came running out to meet me. "Lord," she said, "if you had been here, my brother would not have died.[73] But I'm sure that even now God will give you anything you ask for."

Her grief-stricken eyes looked into mine imploringly, provoking a knot of emotion in my throat. The slightest hint of a reproach had preceded her simple declaration of faith in me.

"Your brother will rise again,"[74] I managed.

"I know he will rise again with everyone else on the last day, in the resurrection," she replied, almost matter-of-factly, taking my statement as one of customary consolation, though with a suggestion of unfulfilled expectation that I would do something sooner.

"*I am* the resurrection and the life,"[75] I stated, using once again the scriptural name for my heavenly Father, and making clear that I do

---

[71] John 11:17-19,30(17-44)
[72] NIV footnote for John 11:17
[73] John 11:21 (NIV)
[74] John 11:23 (NIV)
[75] John 11:25 (NIV, emphasis added)

not only bring life but *am* life, just as my Father has endowed me.[76] "Believe in me and you will never die. Do you believe me, Martha?"

"Yes, Lord," she declared, "I believe that you are the Messiah, God's Son, who has come into the world." I was as moved by her profession of faith and understanding as I had been by Peter's declaration of whom he believed me to be.

Martha, though, suddenly jumped up, seemingly remembering something, and disappeared. She returned a few minutes later with her sister Mary, followed by the crowd of Jews, who had come to their house from Jerusalem to mourn with them. Mary fell at my feet and repeated her sister's combination of belief and gentle recrimination.

"Lord, if you had been here, my brother would not have died."[77]

She was weeping, as were Martha and the Jews that had accompanied her to the edge of the village. Their grief compounded my own: grief for my friend Lazarus and his distraught sisters; sadness and pressure that had mounted up over months of rejection by my own people, even my family, and especially the Pharisees; and apprehension at what was imminent, which would finally be precipitated after what would happen here.

"Where have you laid him?" I whispered.

"Come and see," they replied,[78] as the emotion finally overcame me and I too wept. Some of the Jews commented about how much I must have loved my friend, though even then I could make out haunting comments that, having opened the eyes of the blind, surely I could have kept Lazarus from dying. Yes I could, but I am here to glorify my Father. Lazarus could have recovered unspectacularly, but only my Father's power could possibly raise him from the dead. And that, I hoped, would give my disciples hope in the days to come.

We arrived at the tomb, a small cave with a circular stone laid across the entrance. As I ordered them to remove the stone, Martha protested.

---

[76] John 5:26
[77] John 11:32 (NIV)
[78] John 11:34 (NIV)

"But Lord, it's going to stink; he's already been in there for four days!"

"Did I not tell you," I chided her gently, "that if you believed, you would see the glory of God?"

Some of the people from the village took away the stone. I looked up to heaven and, for the benefit of those present so that they might believe he sent me, prayed aloud to my Father, thanking him for hearing me. Then I called out into the darkness of the cave.

"Lazarus, come out!"

The people's faces expressed a mixture of fascination and disbelief. In their world, this was not possible. Yet the expected odours did not assault their nostrils, and tension increased with the first shuffling noises that came from within. Eventually, Lazarus appeared in the mouth of the cave, taking the tiny footsteps that his burial cloths allowed.

Gasps of amazement echoed round the crowd; people were riveted to the spot, unable or unwilling to move forward to help him. In the end, I had to tell them to free him from his burial attire. We hugged and laughed for a long time.

Many of the Jews who had visited the sisters in order to console them now put their faith in me, after seeing Lazarus emerge from his grave.[79] But some of them, as I knew they would, went to the Pharisees to report what I had done. It was after this that the temple authorities took the formal decision that I must die and started plotting how to kill me.

But for that it was not yet time. My sacrifice was to be a Passover sacrifice, and the Passover Feast was several weeks away yet. The next day we left the three overjoyed siblings rejoicing in each other's company and headed out to the edge of the desert, to a village called Ephraim, some twelve miles and a morning's walk north of Jerusalem. The village was named after the second of Joseph's sons, who received his grandfather Jacob's blessing over his older brother Manasseh[80].

---

[79] John 11:45(-54)
[80] Genesis 41:52, 48:14

Joshua allotted the area around Jericho to the tribe of Ephraim when he split the land between the twelve tribes of Israel.[81]

For now, it was refuge enough.

---

[81] Joshua 16(-17)

25

Last Rites

From Ephraim we made our way back across the hills towards the Jordan. People still followed; others would join us even now. Leaving the river, we turned westwards towards Jericho, beyond which lay Jerusalem.

Talking about the eleventh hour on our way to Bethany had focussed my thoughts on my own impending destiny. My disciples had a good idea by now that I was going to die in Jerusalem, though the significance of it was still lost on them,[1] and despite Lazarus returning to life, they were afraid of what lay ahead for me and could not see beyond it. I took them aside and quietly pressed the point home again.[2]

"We're heading for Jerusalem, where all the prophecies about the Son of Man will be fulfilled. He will be betrayed to the temple authorities, who will condemn him to death and turn him over to the Gentiles. He will endure mocking, insults, being spat upon and flogging, before they finally crucify him. But on the third day he will be raised to life!"

Despondency knotted my stomach as I could see on their faces that they hadn't got a clue what I was talking about. At the same time, I

---

[1] cf. John 20:9; Luke 18:34, 24:12,45
[2] Matthew 20:17-19; Mark 10:32-34; Luke 18:31-34

knew that our Spirit had to hide it from them; it was too much for them to cope with just yet.

A further display of their lack of understanding was not long in forthcoming. Zebedee's wife, who had joined our wandering group, appeared at the front of the moving throng of people with her two sons, James and John, and had a favour to ask.[3]

"Grant that these two may sit either side of you in your kingdom!" she requested, the two men nodding in agreement.

"You don't know what you're asking," I said to them. "Can you drink the cup I drink or be baptised with the baptism I am baptised with?"[4]

The 'cup' has long been a symbol of God's wrath against sinful rebellion and his judgement of it.[5] I was not sure that James and John had understood the implications of my question. The baptism I am to undergo is the sacrifice I will soon make for that sin.[6]

"We can," they replied confidently.

"You will indeed," I told them prophetically, "but to sit at my right or left is not for me to grant. These places belong to those for whom my Father has prepared them."

James and John must have reported this conversation to the other ten further back, because the next time I saw them all they were grumbling at the pair indignantly. Gathering them together, I walked ahead a bit with them and told them about true greatness, reminding them what the prophet Isaiah had written about me.[7]

"You know how the world's rulers lord it over their subjects, and how officials exert authority over people. By contrast, any of you who aspire to leadership must practise serving the others, while anyone wanting to make top dog must become everybody else's slave! For even the Son of Man came to serve, not be served, and to give his life as a ransom for many."

---

3 Matthew 20:20(-28); Mark 10:35(-45)
4 Mark 10:38 (NIV)
5 Psalm 75:8; Isaiah 51:17-23; Jeremiah 25:15-28, 49:12, 51:7
6 Luke 12:50; cf. Romans 6:3-4
7 Isaiah 42:1; 52:13-53:12

It was late afternoon when we reached Jericho,[8] or New Jericho to be more precise, which Herod the Great built as a winter residence[9]. It's noticeably warmer some six hundred cubits below sea level than in Jerusalem, two thousand cubits higher up in the Judean mountains, just fifteen miles to the southwest.

When you come from the direction of the Jordan, you come to the largely ruinous old Jericho first, which was the first city captured from the Moabites under Joshua when Israel entered the Promised Land[10]. On the seventh day of the Israelites marching round it, accompanied by trumpet blasts and tumultuous shouting, its walls had collapsed. Five furlongs further along the road towards Jerusalem, you enter Herod's new city.

It was here that we came across a couple of blind men, sitting at the roadside begging. We were quite a large crowd by now, made up of people who had followed us around for a while, but also of pilgrims making their way to Jerusalem for the Passover and looking for somewhere to stay the night as we were.

When the blind men heard the crowd going by, they asked some of the passers-by what was happening. When they found out that I was amongst them, the two men called out at the top of their voices. "Jesus, Son of David, have mercy on us!"

I could hear the people ahead of us rebuking them and telling them to be quiet, but they shouted out all the more.

"Son of David, have mercy on us!"[11]

Why would people want to keep them away from me? By this point, I was drawing level with them, touched by their plight and by their expectant faith. I ordered those near them to bring them over.

"What do you want me to do for you?"[12] I asked them.

One of them, who was called Bartimaeus (that is, the Son of Timaeus), spoke for both of them and said, "Lord, we want to see."

Simple, expectant faith. It always moves me.

---

8   Matthew 20:29(-34); Mark 10:46(-52); Luke 18:35(-43)
9   Alden (pp 1118-1120); Hultgren (p95)
10   Joshua 6
11   Matthew 20:30 (NIV)
12   Matthew 20:32 (NIV)

"Receive your sight," I proclaimed to them both, touching their eyes. "Your faith has healed you." Both were able to see again immediately, and praised God as they followed me. All the people who saw it also praised God; by everything I do, I am here to bring glory to my Father's name. It was good to see – if you'll excuse the pun – and buoyed me up by briefly taking my mind off events soon to unfold.

As we made our way through the town, looking out for somewhere to stay, word had spread that I was around, and people lined the streets wanting to see me. My Spirit alerted me to a small fellow by the name of Zacchaeus, who was a chief tax collector and correspondingly wealthy. Being vertically challenged, he couldn't see over the crowds, and climbed a sycamore-fig tree in order to get a better view.

It was this that I stopped in front of now, puzzling my disciples, even more so when I looked up into the tree and started talking to it. We were supposed to be finding a hostel!

"Zacchaeus, come down here now! I have to stay at your house tonight!"

My disciples were as surprised as everyone else was to see Zacchaeus scramble down the tree, but their faces soon brightened. I was obviously on the ball after all.

Zacchaeus led the way through the crowded streets, and I couldn't help overhearing people who saw us muttering amongst themselves that I was going to be the guest of a 'sinner'. Zacchaeus, however, welcomed us warmly into his house. Equally aware of his shortcomings and suddenly prepared to admit them, he declared that he would give half of his wealth to the poor, there and then. Furthermore, he promised to pay back anyone he had cheated four times over.

"Today salvation has come to this house,"[13] I declared to him, delighted, and making sure everyone could hear, continued, "for this man, too, is a son of Abraham. For the Son of Man came to seek and to save those who were lost." That remains my mission, with little time remaining, right to the end.

---

[13] Luke 19:9 (NIV)

Zacchaeus owned a spacious house that held many guests besides my disciples and me. Many of them recognised me as Messiah and assumed like most that the kingdom of God was going to appear in all its conquering glory as soon as I reached Jerusalem.[14] I am here to overcome death, but not yet to put aside humankind's kingdoms. So I started telling them a story to illustrate that there would be a delay before the end times, and about people using what they have been given in the meantime.

"A certain nobleman was about to travel to the far-off centre of an empire to have himself crowned, before returning as king."

Now I realise that might seem strange to you, but my listeners were used to the idea – all the Herods did it when they went to the emperor in Rome to be appointed ruler over my people, the Jews.[15]

"Before he went, the man summoned ten servants, gave them a mina each, and told them to invest it until he came back. Now his subjects already hated him and sent a delegation to the emperor saying that they didn't want him as their king."

This scenario had also happened for real, within living memory, when the people declared their dislike of Archelaus, a son of Herod the Great.[16] He successfully sought approval, of course, and did return with the due authority. I was hoping that my listeners would understand a warning about rejecting me.

"The nobleman did return home as king, however, and promptly sent for his servants to find out what profits they had made with his money."

Now a mina is worth a hundred drachmas, or some three months' wages. So the first servant in my story was pleased to report that his mina had earned ten more.

"'Well done!' the king enthused. 'You're a good servant. You have proved yourself trustworthy with relatively little, so I'm appointing you governor of ten cities.'"

---

[14] Luke 19:11(-27)
[15] NIV footnote to Luke 19:12
[16] Josephus (Wars of the Jews II.6.1, Antiquities of the Jews XVII.9.3)

The second man in the story replied similarly, having earned five more minas, and so was given authority over five cities. However, the third had hidden his mina in a piece of cloth, and presented it back to the king saying, "I was afraid of you, because you're a harsh man, taking out what you haven't put in and reaping what you haven't sown."

This is a common view of God in my world, and in yours. The sinner regards God as demanding more than one can give and therefore as being 'unjust'. However, on the day of reckoning, that person remains accountable. I continued the story with the king saying that the servant should at least have put the money on deposit to gain interest, and ordered that his mina be taken from him and given to the one with ten.

"When the others protested that he already had ten minas, the king continued, 'I tell you, the rich will get richer, but the poor will get poorer. Now as for those enemies of mine who didn't want me as their king – bring them here and kill them in front of me.'"

With that warning hanging in the air, our host dismissed his remaining guests and those outside listening in, and we turned in for the night.

The following morning we set off early, avoiding some of the crowds of pilgrims, and arrived in Bethany six days before the Passover.[17] Time enough for the preparations we needed to make. Lazarus was there too; it was good to see him again looking so well.

That evening Martha and Mary took us round to the house of a man still known as Simon the Leper, though I had healed him of his affliction some time previously. He had wanted to invite us round for a meal as an expression of thanks. Such an event would have been unthinkable for him not so long ago. Simon had engaged the help of Martha, and she served up a feast of a supper. We were all relaxed and enjoying each other's company. I did notice, though, that Mary seemed to have something on her mind. It was usually Martha who did the worrying.

---

[17] John 12:1(-11); using John's order over: Matthew 26:6-13; Mark 14:3-9

At the end of the meal, as we were still reclining at table, Mary reappeared and approached me, kneeling down by my feet. She was holding a jar of what turned out to be pure nard, a hugely expensive perfumed oil used on festive occasions – and for burial. I knew instinctively what Mary was doing, just as she had realised what lay ahead for me. She broke the neck of the jar, spilling its contents over my feet, then wiped my feet with her hair. The rich fragrance filled the whole house. This was an act of love and humility – only a lowly servant would ever wash a visitor's feet – given while she could still show me her devotion, and as a symbolic preparation for my burial.

Judas Iscariot interrupted my reverie. "Why wasn't this perfume sold and the money given to the poor?" he objected. "It was worth a year's wages!"[18]

Now the rest of the Twelve know as well as I do that Judas isn't always straight in his handling of our kitty, and sometimes helps himself from it[19]. The others question me on this occasionally but soon have to admit their own faults. I still hope that good example and patience will persuade him to change this aspect of his character; equally, I know that he has a predestined role to play in my mission here, tragic though that will be. In the end, his greed and his fundamentalist impatience will get the better of him. His idea of a Messiah is a Roman-conquering one, not the servant-hearted one I have shown them.

You may wonder why I would choose someone like Judas, with 'known faults'. But then, as I had told the Pharisees at Matthew's house, I came to heal the sick, not the healthy; sinners, not the righteous. I call everyone to follow me; those who choose to are not perfect, but realise they are far from it and are prepared to work towards becoming so. Some just take longer than others do.

So the rest of the Twelve weren't too surprised at Judas' outburst.

"Leave her alone!" I replied in Mary's defence. "She has done a beautiful thing for me in anointing me for my burial. You will always have the poor with you, but you will not always have me. I tell you the

---

18 John 12:5 (NIV)
19 John 12:6

truth, wherever this gospel is preached throughout the world, what she has done will also be told, in memory of her."

You will not always have me... That moment is coming very soon now. Father, help me to stay strong!

Out of the corner of my eye, I noticed Judas Iscariot slipping out of the room.

26

Love the Lord Your God

The temple courts are getting busier now. More and more pilgrims are arriving in the city, getting ready for the Passover Feast at the end of the week. The Pharisees who asked me about my authority are conferring with each other, displeased that I outwitted them in the trick question stakes. Before they can come up with another one, I use the opportunity to challenge and teach them some more.

"What's your opinion?" I ask them.[1] "A man with two sons asked the first to spend the day working in his vineyard; he refused, but later changed his mind and went. Then the man approached his other son with the same request; he agreed readily, but when it came to it, didn't bother. Which of the two did what his father wanted?"

They're looking at each other with a hint of shoulders shrugging, reluctant to state the obvious. "The first," they answer hesitantly, wondering what's coming next.

"I tell you the truth, there are tax collectors and prostitutes getting into the kingdom of God ahead of you."

Indignation is colouring their cheeks. Don't they realise that they act like that second son, rich in words but devoid of action? I want them to respond like the first. In fact, I would like them to respond like the second but do like the first! I spell it out to them.

---

[1] Matthew 21:28(-32)

"For John came to show you the right way to live, but you didn't believe him, while tax collectors and prostitutes did. And even after seeing this, you refused to believe him and repent."

I so want them to accept our good news, to relinquish their insistence on a load of rules, and align their hearts with ours. Outwardly, they do what my Father said through the law, but they ignore the spirit of the law. The tax collectors and prostitutes I have come across, on the other hand, have evidently acted against what my Father has ordered, yet on hearing the good news amended their ways and now do what he wants.

"Listen to another parable," I tell them.[2] I have to make them understand that they have a duty of account towards my heavenly Father for the people in their spiritual care, and that they're currently not doing a very good job of it.

"A landowner planted a vineyard, built a wall round it, dug a pit for the winepress, and erected a watchtower in the middle. Then he rented it out to tenant farmers and went away on a long journey. When harvest time came around, he sent a servant to collect his share of the grapes. However, the tenants beat him and sent him away empty-handed. This happened several times, the tenants treating the servants worse each time. Finally, the landowner sent his son, thinking that the tenants would respect him. Instead, they dragged him out and killed him, thinking that if they killed the heir of the vineyard, it would become theirs."

The Pharisees are starting to shift uneasily. My words no doubt remind them of Isaiah's song of the vineyard[3]. They understand well enough that I'm talking about prophets and myself here, and realise their role as tenants is not being cast in a favourable light. That's only because they won't see the light!

"So what's the vineyard owner going to do with those tenants?" I ask firmly. "He's going to come and kill them and give the vineyard to others who will give him what is his."

"Surely not!" someone at the front of the crowd interjects.

---

2   Matthew 21:33(-46); Mark 12:1-12; Luke 20:9-19
3   Isaiah 5:1-7

"Then what does the Scripture mean: 'The stone the builders rejected has become the capstone; this was the Lord's doing, and it is wonderful to see.'⁴?"

The Pharisees know what it means; they've been rejecting the capstone all along and are looking more determined than ever to arrest me. But that is going to have to wait until the time is come. Right now, my disciples and I are going to go and buy some food. There's a stall by the Xystus that does a fantastic line in unleavened bread with garlic and herbs...

We've just left the stall, and now some Pharisees are approaching me, accompanied by several Herodians.⁵ I wonder how unleavened their intentions are.

"Teacher, we recognise you as a man of integrity and that you instruct people in the way of God truthfully and with impartial judgement."

Get on with it!

"So would you say that we should pay taxes to Caesar or not?"

Definitely leavened intentions then. My countrymen detest having to pay taxes to the Roman occupation, so it won't exactly enhance my popularity to endorse them. However, the Herodians support the resented occupiers and will cause trouble if I say anything against them.

"You hypocrites," I shout at them, "why are you trying to trap me? Show me the coin used for paying the tax."⁶

Fumbling inside billowing robes eventually produces a denarius.

"Whose head and inscription are on it?" I ask.

"Caesar's," they reply.

Emperor Tiberius. The inscription on his coins reads 'Tiberius Caesar Augustus, son of the *divine* Augustus'.⁷ Such claims of divinity are why these coins may not be used to pay the temple taxes. I take a side-swipe at this falsehood as I answer.

---

⁴ Psalm 118:22-23
⁵ Matthew 22:15-22; Mark 12:13-17; Luke 20:20-26
⁶ Matthew 22:18-19a (NIV)
⁷ NIV footnotes at Matthew 22:19,21; Smith, M.H. (*"Tiberius"*)

"Well then, give to Caesar what is his, but give to God what is God's."

Astonished silence. They don't know what to say, and before they embarrass themselves in front of the people any further, the Pharisees withdraw to the edge of the crowd.

A group of Sadducees, however, have just approached me and have come up with a conundrum of their own.[8] Sadducees do not adhere to the many rules of the oral law propagated by the Pharisees,[9] nor do they believe in the resurrection of the dead.

"Rabbi, the law of Moses states that if a man's brother dies and leaves a wife but no children, the man must marry the widow and have children for his brother.[10] The eldest of seven brothers we knew married a local girl but died childless. The second did his duty and married her, but he too died childless. In fact, it was the same with all seven brothers, before finally the woman died."

Smug faces exchange perceptible smiles.

"Now then, at the resurrection, whose wife will she be, since all of them were married to her?"[11]

I'm tempted to remark that the woman was a pretty bad cook! But they've got it all wrong and I tell them so. "You know neither Scripture nor the power of God. At the resurrection people will no longer marry or be given in marriage; they will be like the angels in heaven and will never die."

My Father and I instituted marriage for our children, certainly; but in the kingdom to come, the relationships of this age will pale in comparison to the relationship I shall have with my bride, the church.

I conclude by addressing the Sadducees' lack of belief in the life to come. "As for the resurrection, even the account of Moses and the burning bush[12] shows that the dead rise, for he calls the Lord 'the God of Abraham, Isaac and Jacob'. He's the God of the living, not of the dead!"

---

8 Matthew 22:23(-33); Mark 12:18(-27); Luke 20:27(-40)
9 Josephus (Antiquities of the Jews XIII.10.6)
10 Deuteronomy 25:5; cf. Genesis 38:8; "we knew": Matthew 22:25
11 Matthew 22:28 (NIV); Mark 12:23; Luke 20:33
12 Exodus 3:1-6

The Pharisees standing further back look vindicated again. For once, some of the teachers of the law amongst them agree with me. "Well said, teacher!" they reply, glowing with satisfaction that their rivals' view has been defeated.

Such a shame that they cannot find any more to agree with. One of them, seeing that I have silenced the Sadducees as well, is coming forward to have another go.[13] In all of this, unwittingly or not, they are seeking to find an imperfection in the sacrificial lamb. Can they find a fault? I look this man in the face; he appears to be genuine in his enquiry.

"Teacher, which is the most important commandment in the law, and why?"

The Pharisees and teachers of the law are constantly debating questions like, which of their over six hundred precepts is the most important. I'm reminded of a counterpart of this man whom I encountered at the Feast of Tabernacles last autumn. He quoted the Shema – those passages of the Torah worn by some on their foreheads – after enquiring about what to do to inherit eternal life. The answer now is the same.

"The most important one," I reply, quoting the same portion of Scripture, "is this: 'Hear, O Israel, the Lord our God, the Lord is one. You shall love the Lord your God with all that you are: heart, soul, mind and strength.' The second is this: 'Love your neighbour as yourself.'[14] These two are the most important and form the basis of all the law and the prophets. Everything hinges on them."

The man is pleased with my answer, affirming it by repeating what I just said, and adding that to do these things is more important than all the burnt offerings and sacrifices that will be going on here in a couple of days. This is quite a statement for a man in his position, who would normally defend every law in the rulebook, however trivial, including those on making sacrifices. He's absolutely right, and I tell him so.

"You are not far from the kingdom of God!"[15]

I hope that he will make it all the way.

---

13 Matthew 22:34-40; Mark 12:28(-31); Luke 10:25-37
14 Deuteronomy 6:4-5; Leviticus 19:18
15 Mark 12:34

I look round at the Pharisees and teachers of the law. None of them seems anxious to ask me any further questions. So I pose one myself.[16] "Whose son do you say the Messiah is?"

"Our ancestor David's," they reply, without hesitation.

"Then how come David, inspired by the Holy Spirit, calls him 'Lord'? One of his Psalms declares, 'The Lord said to my Lord: "Sit here on my right while I set about fashioning a footstool for your feet from your enemies."'[17] If David calls him 'Lord', how can he be his son?"[18]

No reply is forthcoming. Now none at all seems willing to ask me anything. The crowd loves it. It won't make me popular with the Pharisees, but I feel the need to warn the people and my disciples again against following their example.[19]

"The teachers of the law and the Pharisees are the legitimate successors of Moses. So you should follow anything they say."

The subjects of my exhortation are looking on approvingly.

"But beware of doing anything they do, 'cause practising what they preach just isn't in their repertoire. They burden people with heavy loads that they are unwilling to lift a finger to move. Everything they do is for show: their fancy phylacteries and long-tasselled, flowing robes, their love of the best seats at a feast, and of others showing respect."

The looks of approval have darkened into reproachful glares. I address them with more of the same, as I did at Capernaum.

"Woe to you, teachers of the law and Pharisees, you hypocrites! You do not enter the kingdom of heaven and prevent anyone else from doing so. Anyone you convert becomes twice as bad as you are! You won't swear by the temple or the altar, but you swear by objects in and on them, as if they were more important. You tithe your garden herbs, but do nothing about justice and mercy."

I remember all the prophets my Father and I sent to our chosen people, and how they were treated just like the vineyard owner's servants. Like that man's son, I am going to experience worse.

---

16 Matthew 22:41(-46); Mark 12:35(-37); Luke 20:41(-44)
17 Psalm 110:1
18 Matthew 22:45 (NIV)
19 Matthew 23:1-36; Mark 12:38-40; Luke 20:45-47 (cf. 11:37-54)

"I send you prophets," I continue, "but you kill and crucify them, or flog them in your synagogues, and chase them out of town."

Apprehension is surging up through my whole being. My Father's city, Jerusalem, has rejected so many prophets and is in the process of rejecting me too. I cry out aloud to ears that refuse to listen.

"I've wanted so much to be able to protect your children, as a hen gathers her chicks under her wings, but you wouldn't come to me. Now, your house will be deserted, and you won't see me again until you say, 'Blessed is he who comes in the name of the Lord.' [20]"

One day, I shall come again and all will sing the same words.[21]

These are the last words I shall speak to my people in public. I have done all I can. If they reject me – which they will – my presence will depart from the temple[22] and they will not see me again until I return, when all will utter the words that were on their lips just a few days ago when I entered the city on the colt.

My thoughts are in turmoil, and I withdraw to a corner of the Women's Court where I sit down in the shadows opposite the offering boxes. I briefly lose myself in thought, absent-mindedly watching people place their offerings in the trumpet-shaped receptacles.

Many rich people are making a song and dance about the large gifts they are making. But right now I can see a poor widow, dressed in black, stooping, making her way to an urn. Some of my disciples have discovered me and are torn between coming over straightaway and sharing their discovery with the others first. I signal them towards me and wait until all have caught up.

"You see that poor widow? I tell you, she gave more than all those others. They gave from spare abundance, but the little she put in was everything she had to live on."

My disciples exchange glances, each attempting to assimilate my remarks. At least they are still willing to listen to me, trying to learn even if they don't immediately understand. I have just the rest of today and tomorrow to teach them. Father, help me! Help them!

---

[20] Psalm 118:26
[21] Isaiah 45:23; cf. Romans 14:11; Philippians 2:10
[22] cf. Ezekiel 10:18 (ch. 8-11)

We make our way towards the exit,[23] picking our way past a team of builders working on an unfinished section of pavement. As we round the south-eastern corner of the main temple building, some of my disciples seem to be preoccupied with admiring the huge stones at the base of the walls and the decoratively carved ones higher up. The largest stones are colossal, some twenty-five cubits long, twelve wide and eight high.[24] The buildings are indeed magnificent, but history yet to be made isn't going to be kind to them.[25]

"You see all these great buildings?" I ask them. "The time will come when not one of their stones will be left on another; they will all be torn down."

My disciples cannot imagine it. No-one can, and we walk in silence until we reach the Mount of Olives, across the Kidron valley from the temple. There we sit down and take in the view of the city. After a short while, Peter, James, John and Andrew gather round, almost conspiratorially, with a burning question.

"When is all this going to happen; how will we recognise it?"

I know that in the future many will come claiming to be me, and that the end times are near. My disciples shouldn't be deceived. "Don't follow these people," I instruct them. "All over the place wars, earthquakes and famines will only signal the beginning, like the onset of birth pains."

Their faces are falling with uncertainty.

"Don't be afraid when you see these things."

I warn them that they will find themselves in front of the authorities because of me, but even that will serve to preach the good news to the nations. Alarm is now joining their uncertainty.

"Do not worry about what to say. Just say whatever the Holy Spirit gives you at the time."

I prepare them for the emotional turmoil of family and friends betraying them, and that many will hate them because of me.

"But everyone that remains faithful throughout will live."

---

[23] Matthew 24:1(-35); Mark 13:1(-31); Luke 21:5-38
[24] Josephus (Antiquities of the Jews XV.11.3)
[25] The temple was destroyed in AD70

I remind them of Daniel's prophecies[26] about an abomination that causes desolation and brings the end of sacrifices and offerings. The first fulfilment of that came with Antiochus Epiphanes, who erected a pagan altar to Zeus over the temple altar, provoking the Maccabean revolt and the Hanukkah celebration I have already mentioned.[27] Another abomination is about to happen, though it is the purpose for which I have come, to make the sacrifice for sin once and for all. Daniel's prophecy will be fulfilled again when, as I have just told my disciples, the temple is destroyed and worship there ends.

In the days before my final return, when the final abomination happens, the evil one will set himself up in my Father's temple,[28] and all people in Jerusalem should flee the coming destruction. It will be terrible for those who cannot flee. Even the sun, moon and stars will display signs that the time is come. On the day I return to reclaim the city, all will see me arrive like lightning.

I warn my disciples again. "Do not listen to the false prophets who will appear at that time. I've let you know all this in advance so you can stay alert. When you see these things, you will know that the end times are near, just as you know that the summer is near when leaves appear on the fig-trees."

I tell them that some will doubtless live to witness these things, certainly the destruction of the temple.

"Heaven and earth will pass away, but my words will never pass away."[29]

They are shocked yet uncomprehending. I underline the fact that no-one knows when these things will happen.

"Not even the angels in heaven, nor the Son, know what day or time any of this will happen, but only the Father.[30] When the Son of Man comes, it will be like in the days of Noah. Up to the flood, people were carrying on with normal life, oblivious to the imminent danger

---

[26] Daniel 9:27, 11:31, 12:11
[27] NIV footnote at Matthew 24:15; see page 196
[28] cf. 2 Thessalonians 2:4
[29] Matthew 24:35 (NIV)
[30] Matthew 24:36(-51); Mark 13:32(-37); cf. Luke 17:20-37 and 12:35-48

until the flood swept them away. That's exactly how it will be when the Son of Man comes."

I am encouraged to see that this illustration has connected with them. They realise that I have to go, be killed even; but return? I give them another angle on the same theme, so that they might remember these things and be prepared for when I come.

"If the homeowner knows when a thief is going to come, he will keep a lookout and prevent his house from being broken into. In a similar way, you must remain ready, for the Son of Man will return when you least expect him. If a master puts a servant in charge of the other servants in his household, that servant is wise to look after them such that when his master returns, he finds all in order and puts the servant in charge of everything he owns. If the master returns to find him mistreating the other servants, he will have him cast out with the hypocrites to where there is weeping and gnashing of teeth."

We have been sitting here for a while; it's getting late, and dark. Since the weekend, we have been staying overnight on the Mount of Olives,[31] and going to the temple by day. In two days (tomorrow night as you would reckon it) we will eat an early Passover meal together. My disciples look tired; I too am weary, but I must press on, teach them, encourage them, reassure them, and prepare them for their own ministry as much as I can while... I still have time. I notice that our pole lamp – a stick bound with oil-soaked rags – is slowly extinguishing, but that gives me a spark of an idea.

"When the kingdom of heaven comes," I pick up again,[32] talking of my return as bridegroom to collect my bride, the church, "it will be like ten virgins who took their pole lamps[33] and went out to meet the bridegroom. Five of them, who were foolish, took their lamps but no spare oil. The other five, who were wise, took some jars of oil as well. The bridegroom took so long to get there that the girls all became drowsy and fell asleep. At midnight, they were woken by an announcement of the imminent arrival of the bridegroom, and set about

---

[31] Luke 21:37
[32] Matthew 25:1(-13)
[33] NIV footnote and Barnes (on Matthew 25:1)

trimming their lamps. The foolish ones asked the wise ones for some extra oil, for their lamps were going out, but they refused, saying that they may not have enough spare. 'Go and buy your own!' While the foolish ones were off buying oil, the bridegroom arrived and was greeted by the wise virgins, who accompanied him inside to the banquet. The door was closed behind them. The others came back and begged to be let in, but the bridegroom said, 'I really don't know who you are!'"

My disciples have made a connection and are now pretending to be wide awake; and despite the fact that one of them is feverishly hunting around in his bag for the jar of oil, I think they are slowly getting the message.

"So stay alert," I finish, "for you don't know when all this will happen." Then, "Tad, forget the lamp!"

Thaddaeus looks up at me, embarrassed. Nervous smiles from the rest. They are feeling the same unease as I am.

"It's like this too," I say, breaking the tension, and using an illustration similar to the one I shared with Zacchaeus and his guests.[34] "A man, about to go on a journey, called his servants and entrusted his property to them, according to their ability. To one he gave five talents of money, enough to buy a decent second-hand camel.[35] To another he gave two talents, and to a third, one talent. The first two put their money to work and doubled it. The third, however, dug a hole in the ground and hid the money entrusted to him."

I continue the story as before, describing the master's return and his praise of the first two servants, to whom he entrusted much more again, and whom he invited to share in his happiness. The third servant was berated for not at least ensuring that his talent earned interest, and was thrown out.

When my Father and I created the world, we chose from an infinite palette of colours, textures, shapes, sizes, and other characteristics. We entrust all our children with multifarious talents from the same pot of creativity. But they only reach their potential when they are put into

---

[34] See page 216
[35] NIV text note at Matthew 25:15: a talent was worth several hundred pounds

service. I need the disciples to use what I have given them after I'm gone. What are you doing with the talents I've given you?

Time for a bedtime story before that lamp finally runs out of oil. I want to cement what I have just told them; they need to understand both for themselves and to be able to tell it further, that there will come a time of final judgement, where everybody will be accepted or rejected.

"When the Son of Man comes with all the angels," I start, "he will sit on his throne in heavenly glory, with the nations gathered before him. He will separate the people into two groups, just as a shepherd separates the sheep to his right and the goats to his left."

Did I explain the thing about my left and my right? From early times, the Israelites have associated the right hand with blessing, and the left with poor luck at best, otherwise darkness. That's why Joseph was put out when his aged father Israel put his right hand on his younger grandson, Ephraim, to bless him, and his left on Manasseh, who, as the eldest, should have received the main blessing.[36] In the words of the Teacher who wrote the book you know as Ecclesiastes, "The heart of the wise inclines to the right, the heart of the fool to the left."[37] God's left hand is seen as a place of judgement and justice, as one of the psalmists hints at.[38]

When the Scriptures talk about God's right hand, as they do often, they are describing a place of blessing, redemption and power, and even exaltation. Moses sang about God's "right hand ... majestic in power" after the Israelites had crossed the Yam Suph, which means 'Sea of Reeds' and which you know as the 'Red Sea'.[39] King David, in one of his psalms, wrote about the Lord answering "with the saving power of his right hand", while the sons of Korah talked in one of theirs about His right hand being "filled with righteousness".[40]

King David, in another of his psalms, prophesied about my heavenly Father telling me to sit at His right hand.[41] Soon, I will take up

---

[36] Genesis 48:13-20
[37] Ecclesiastes 10:2
[38] cf. Psalm 111:7
[39] Exodus 15:6; NIV text note at 13:18
[40] Psalm 20:6, 48:10
[41] Psalm 110:1

this place of glory and power again, but first I have to bring glory to my Father by fulfilling the purpose he sent me here for. When I speak about separating the sheep to my right hand, I am talking about sharing the place of glory that is mine at my Father's right hand, the place of power where I, as the Word that spoke creation into existence, speak redemption into being.

I go on with my story, hoping to show my disciples how to put their faith into servant-hearted action in the everyday situations of life.

"Then the King will welcome those on his right into his kingdom, saying, 'For you fed me when I was hungry, gave me a drink when I was thirsty, looked after me when I was a stranger or needed clothes or was sick, and visited me in prison.' The righteous will ask, 'Lord, when did we see you in any such need and look after you?'"

My disciples are looking as quizzical as the enquirers in my story.

"The king will reply, 'Really, whatever you did for one of the least of these children of mine, you did for me.'"

"You mean, if we help someone, we, like, help you?" asks Matthew.

"Exactly right," I reply, delighted at his understanding.

"What about the ones on the left?" Andrew wants to know.

"The king will banish the ones on his left into the eternal fire prepared for the devil and his angels, saying, 'You gave me nothing to eat when I was hungry, nor water when I needed a drink. You didn't look after me as a stranger or when I needed clothes or was sick, nor visit me in prison.'"

I continue with those on the left asking the same question: "Where did we see you in need, and not attend to you?" The answer is similar: "Anything you failed to do for even the lowliest of my children, you failed to do for me."

"The king will consign them to eternal punishment," I conclude, "but he will usher the righteous into eternal life."

Faith that doesn't serve me by serving those around – one's neighbour – is empty. I look round at my disciples in the fading light. Their faces betray consideration of the things they perhaps haven't done. I think they have got it! What are the things you can do for others, for me?

Tad extinguishes the flickering lamp and we settle down to rest. I won't be sleeping tomorrow night.

27

Last Supper

It's been a bright and sunny spring day, but now the sun has set, and the Day of Preparation for the Passover has arrived.[1] People now often call this the first day of the Feast of Unleavened Bread, which officially is the seven-day Feast that immediately follows the Passover. Either way, at the end of today – tomorrow afternoon in your reckoning – the Passover Lamb is slain. That is how my Father and I ordered things as Moses was preparing the Israelites for the exodus from Egypt.[2] Tomorrow evening is when we Jews eat the Passover meal, but by then...

My disciples and I will eat supper together later tonight. It's a night when people go round the whole house, making sure that any leaven – anything with yeast in it – is removed,[3] symbolising the removal of sin from our lives.[4] As yet unsuspecting, my disciples come to me now and ask what we're doing for the Feast.[5]

"Where do you want us to make preparations for you to eat the Passover?"[6]

---

[1] See 'Dating the Crucifixion' note, page 305; see also 'The Last Supper' note, page 304
[2] Exodus 12:1-6; Leviticus 23:4-5; Numbers 28:16
[3] Exodus 12:15-20, 13:3-10, 23:15, 34:18; Leviticus 23:6-8; Numbers 28:17-25
[4] cf. Luke 12:1; 1 Corinthians 5:6-8
[5] Matthew 26:17(-30); Mark 14:12(-26); Luke 22:7(-38); John 13:1(-14:31)
[6] Matthew 26:17 (NIV); Mark 14:12

I assign Peter and John the task. "Go into the city and follow the man you meet carrying a jar of water. Say to the owner of the house he enters, 'The Teacher asks, "Where is the room you have for us to eat the Passover?"' Make preparations in the large upstairs room he will show you."

My similar instructions for finding the colt at the beginning of the week[7] provoked glances between them that indicated I was sending them on a wild-goose chase. Now they just take me at my word and depart with an affirmative nod. The host is expecting us; my Spirit has just told me that his servant is collecting water in a jar right now. They won't have much trouble finding him, for that's normally a job that our womenfolk do.[8] The rest of us spend a couple of hours relaxing a little, chatting a lot, and, in my case, reflecting on the hours to come and having quiet communion with my Father. The others can sense my growing unease as we make our way into the city.

Peter and John have done a good job of preparing tonight's meal that for us will be our last Passover Seder together, if a day early.[9] We all recline at the low table, looking forward to food and fellowship, which start with a recital of the Kiddush blessing over the first cup of wine, the Cup of Sanctification, remembering the promise my Father God made to the Israelites to lead them out of Egypt.[10] The Urchatz ritual washing of hands follows, then we each dip a sprig of hyssop into salted water that reminds us of our people's tears shed as slaves in Egypt. They used hyssop to daub the lamb's blood on doorposts and lintel before the Passover.

I sit more upright to unwrap the three matzot – flat loaves of unleavened bread – from their tri-compartmental linen cover, and break the middle matzah in two, wrapping the larger piece, the afikomen, in a linen napkin. We put that aside to eat instead of the usual olive-sized morsel of the Paschal Lamb at the end of the meal. The afikomen, as its

---

[7]   Matthew 21:1-7; Mark 11:1-7; Luke 19:28-35
[8]   Genesis 24:11
[9]   See 'The Last Supper' note, page 304
[10] The four promises / cups: Exodus 6:6-7

Greek-derived name suggests, looks forward to the promised 'one who will come'.[11]

The matzot represent, among other things, our patriarchs: Abraham, Isaac and Jacob. A facet of our Jewish nature is that we would never inflict on anyone else something we would not take upon ourselves, as my Father's word commands and Hillel taught.[12] So when my Father God tested Abraham's faith by asking him to sacrifice his son Isaac,[13] and also when he later ordered the slaughter of Egypt's firstborn,[14] he was also implying that he would be prepared to sacrifice his own son – me! I must indeed be broken, wrapped up and hidden for a while.

"I've wanted so much to eat this Passover with you before I suffer," I tell my disciples as I settle back into my place,[15] "because I won't be eating it again until it is fulfilled in God's kingdom."

The Passover will find its ultimate fulfilment in my impending sacrifice when redemption will be won. I wonder whether they understand.

We move on to the Maggid section of the Seder and remember those ten plagues visited upon the Egyptians, who were so desperate by the night of the Passover that they gave our ancestors all the gold and silver we had told them to ask for as they were leaving, materials that later went towards building the tabernacle.[16] We drink the second Seder cup, the Cup of Deliverance.

Before eating the Matzah bread, we perform the netilat yadayim ceremonial cleansing of our hands. As the bowl of water goes round, I become aware that some of my disciples have started a discussion about which of them should be considered the greatest. This needs nipping in the bud. I get up, groaning inwardly that they still don't understand many of the kingdom values I have been trying all this time to instil into them. I will show them what greatness in my kingdom means, by

---

[11] See 'Afikomen' note, page 305
[12] Exodus 23:9; Leviticus 19:18; Talmud – Shabbath 31a; cf. page 148
[13] Genesis 22:1-19
[14] Exodus 11:1,5, 12:12,29-30
[15] Luke 22:15
[16] Exodus 11:2, 12:35, 26, 27

performing – as their master – the menial task that normally the lowliest of servants would undertake.

I grab a towel, and consternation spreads across their features as I remove my outer garment and wrap the towel around my waist.[17] Contrition replaces it as they realise what I am going to do in the light of their previous discussion. Taking the bowl of water, I start washing my disciples' feet. They accept this without a word, until I reach Peter.

"Lord, are you seriously going to wash my feet?"

"You won't understand it until later," I tell him.

"There's no way you're ever going to do that!"

Why does this man, this rock of mine, still have such a problem with his pride? "Unless you let me wash you, you'll be cut off from me," I tell him gently but firmly.

"In that case, Lord," Peter says, "wash my hands and head as well!"

That's not quite what I meant, Peter, but you're getting closer. He's all or nothing sometimes, is my Peter, but his heart is definitely in the right place.

"If you've had a bath, you only need to wash your feet; the rest of you is still clean. You lot are clean," I add cryptically, addressing the group, "though not all of you."

They look puzzled at that, but I leave it for now as I dry my hands and put my outer garment back on.

"Do you understand what I just did for you?" I ask them. "You call me 'Teacher' and 'Lord', and rightly so, for that is what I am. I did that to set you an example to follow; serve each other in the same way. Gentile kings lord it over their subjects, but the greatest among you should be like servants, as I am among you."

I voice my appreciation for the way my disciples have stood by me the past three years, and confirm to them again their place in my kingdom and role of judging the twelve tribes of Israel. They look as burdened with all this information as I feel to impart it.

---

[17] John 13:4(-17)

We've eaten the matzah and some bitter herbs – horseradish that brings tears to our eyes and reminds us of the affliction of our people. Now we're eating the 'Hillel sandwich', a combination of both, introduced by the rabbi when he had disagreed with other sages whether they should be eaten separately or together[18] – we do both! Judas and I dip our matzah into the same bowl of horseradish.

The household servants bring in the main meal. It smells good – tastes good too – but I am unable to relax much. My thoughts are circling around events imminent. I need to prepare my disciples for what is going to happen, and that the end is very close, while encouraging them that it is only going to be a temporary end. A new beginning in fact!

After the meal, we continue with the Seder as I speak the traditional Ha-Motzi blessing: "Blessed are you, Lord, our God, King of the Universe who brings forth bread from the earth."[19] Having given thanks to my heavenly Father for it, I break up the afikomen into pieces for them. The one who will come... The Paschal Lamb.

"This is my body, given for you;" I declare, "do this in remembrance of me."[20]

At the end of supper, I continue by taking the third cup of wine, the Cup of Redemption, which remembers my Father's promise to redeem our people with an outstretched arm.[21] I give thanks for it using words from the Kiddush: "Blessed are you, Lord, our God, King of the Universe who creates the fruit of the vine."[22] I declare to my disciples, "This cup is the new covenant in my blood,[23] which is poured out for you and for many for the forgiveness of sins. I tell you the truth: I won't be drinking from the vine again before God's kingdom comes." The fourth and final Cup of Restoration will come soon enough, but not until I have outstretched my arms.

---

[18] Talmud – Pesachim 115a; cf. Exodus 12:8; Numbers 9:11
[19] Rich ("Ha-Motzi")
[20] Luke 22:19 (NIV); 1 Corinthians 11:24 (NIV); Matthew 26:26-29; Mark 14:22-25
[21] Exodus 6:6 (cf. Deuteronomy 4:34; Psalms 136:12; Jeremiah 32:21)
[22] Rich ("Kiddush")
[23] Luke 22:20 (NIV); 1 Corinthians 11:25 (NIV)

We sing some of the 'Egyptian Hallel', the Psalms of praise[24] that remind us about my Father saving our ancestors and leading them out of Egypt, and teaching us to trust him for our future. *Give thanks to the Lord, for he is good; his steadfast love is everlasting. The Lord is with me so I will not be afraid. What can anyone do to me?*

It will soon be time for me to leave this world and return to my Father in heaven. I feel a growing sadness. In my human state, I am going to terribly miss these guys and the wider circle of those who have accompanied me. We have been through a lot together, and I know that as I show them the extent of my love, they will face a tough test, as everything they have lived for these past few years will appear to unravel before them. I feel sad that one of them has to betray me. All my disciples have hang-ups of some form or another, areas that the refining nature of my Spirit hasn't been allowed near yet. Judas hasn't let me deal with his inherent greed, nor got over his conquering-Messiah expectations. I am sad that he should have to play his tragic part in tonight's events. What are the things *you* haven't let me deal with yet?

The others can see my discomfort and I pre-empt their question. "Yes, one of you is going to betray me – despite eating with me." They are crestfallen, staring at one another and at a loss to know which one. In a confused babble of individual questions, they enquire who would do such a thing. Peter was just leaning over to John, whispering to him; and now John is leaning back against me, asking who I mean.

"The one dipping bread into the dish with me," I reply.

John stares past me across at Judas, uncomprehending, and then leans back towards Peter, whom I will address in a moment. First, I must give a last instruction to Judas.

I dip my piece of bread into the bowl with him. "Go and do quickly what you have to do."

My remark goes over the heads of the others; they imagine that, as Judas holds the kitty, I've told him to go and buy something for the Feast, or give alms to the poor sat at the temple entrance.

---

24 Psalms 113-118 (quotes from 118:1,6); Matthew 26:30; Mark 14:26

Judas stares at me, a gamut of emotions briefly rooting him to the spot. He utters no words and, after this short hiatus, gets up from the table and makes his way out. Through the momentarily open door, I see that it is already dark. That is how I am feeling as I watch Judas depart.

Turning back to the others, I know that I have done everything here that my Father wants me to do. Everything I told John's disciples to go and tell him about has been done. Judas' departure now will initiate the final chain of events that I came for, becoming the Passover sacrifice for all eternity. It has also purged our group of the evil within,[25] figuratively removing the leaven from the house, and I can give my remaining disciples some last valuable teaching.

"The time is now here for the Son of Man to be glorified, and God will be glorified in him, imminently. My children, I am with you only a little longer. You will look for me, but, as I told the Jews,[26] you cannot come where I am going."[27]

My disciples are as puzzled as my listeners at the Feast of Tabernacles were. I try to direct their thoughts to something positive.

"I'm giving you a new commandment: love each other, just as I have loved you. If they see you doing that, people will recognise you as my disciples."

The commandment to love is in itself not new; my Father and I had Moses write it into our law[28] as our Spirit prompted him. But as I have shown you, many have forgotten the spirit of the law and I want my followers to know that they should love each other in word and deed, for my glory, not because it is a law they feel obliged to follow.

Simon Peter is still mulling over a question, and no doubt speaks for the others too. "Lord, where is it you're actually going?"

"You can't follow me there for now, though you will later. Simon, Satan intends to test you,[29] but I have prayed that your faith may not falter. When you have returned, build up your brothers in theirs."

---

[25] Morris (p.630)
[26] John 7:34
[27] John 13:31-38
[28] Leviticus 19:18,34
[29] Luke 22:31-32

This shocks Peter, and with some characteristic bluster he asks why he cannot follow where I am going and claims he would even be prepared to die while doing so.

"Are you really willing to die following me?" I respond sadly, inclining my head slightly and looking him in the eye. "Seriously, three times you're going to deny knowing me before you hear the cockerel!"

Peter is having none of it. "Even if I have to die with you, I will never disown you."[30] The others chime in with similar confidence.

I look round at each of them.[31] "You will all desert me," I inform them, "for Scripture says, 'I will strike the shepherd and the sheep will be scattered.'[32] But don't let doubts trouble you," I continue. "Believe in me as you believe in God." It is important to me to tell them this, given what they will soon witness. I help them to look beyond any imminent troubles. "My Father's house has more than enough room for you, and I'm making my way to prepare a place for you there. Then I will return and take you to be with me where I am. You know the way to where I am going."

Peter remains silent, still moodily digesting what I told him. Thomas takes up the baton instead. "Lord, we don't even know where you're going, so how are we supposed to know the way?"

"*I am* the way, the truth, and the life. No-one comes to the Father except through me.[33] If you had really known me up to now, you would have known my Father too. But now you do, and you have seen him!"

Philip is still not convinced. "Lord, show us the Father and that will suffice."

"Don't you know me, Philip, even after so long? Anyone who has seen me has seen the Father.[34] My words are the Father's, who lives in me, doing His work. I am in him and he is in me, and if you don't believe that because I say so, then at least believe it because of the miracles. And listen, anyone with serious faith in me will achieve even greater things

---

[30] Matthew 26:35 (NIV); Mark 14:31 (NIV)
[31] John 14:1(-31)
[32] Zechariah 13:7; Matthew 26:31; Mark 14:27
[33] John 14:6 (NIV, emphasis added)
[34] Based on John 14:9 (NIV)

than what you've seen me do, because I am going to the Father and will do whatever you ask in my name to bring glory to him."

I can sense the cogs of their minds turning, trying to process the truth I have just presented. They can remember me sending them out and what they achieved. But they are also struggling to get their heads round my now undisguised and imminent departure. I encourage them by explaining the remaining facet of my Father's and my nature, our Spirit.

"I will ask the Father, who will give you another, constant companion, the Spirit of truth. The world doesn't know him and so won't recognise or accept him, but you do, because he is in you as I am, and you are in me as I am in my Father. Whoever loves me will obey my commands and be loved by my Father, and I too will love him and show myself to him."

Now Judas (the Thaddaeus one) is puzzled. "But, Lord, why do you intend to show yourself to us and not to the world?"[35]

I restate what I have just told them and add, "My Father will send you the Holy Spirit, who will help you understand everything I have told you. I am returning to my Father, but I leave you my peace, so do not be afraid."

My disciples *are* afraid; they sense that their world is about to implode. I too am afraid; I know what is about to befall me. Still, I need to encourage my disciples, as well as warn them of opposition to come and the need to be prepared.

"When I sent you out without purse, bag or sandals," I remind them, "did you lack anything?"

"No," they reply in unison.

"But now if you have a purse and bag, take them; and if you don't have a sword, sell your coat and buy one."

A means of self-defence is common in these parts, both against highway robbers and wild animals, but when I tell my disciples to be ready to defend themselves, I am alluding to the level of opposition that they will encounter;[36] also to how I am about to be treated.

---

[35] John 14:22 (NIV)
[36] Gill (on Luke 22:36)

"Isaiah's prophecy that, 'He was counted among the transgressors,'[37] is about to find its predestined fulfilment in me."

A couple of my disciples have been fumbling amongst the collection of objects in the corner, and now produce two swords. They have been taking me a little bit literally. "That's enough," I say, dismissing the subject. "Come on, let's go."[38]

---

[37] Isaiah 53:12
[38] Luke 22:38; John 14:31

28

Gethsemane

It doesn't take long to put on sandals and cloaks and, after thanking our host for his help, we head off into the night. This isn't going to be like our other nights spent on the Mount of Olives.[1] I tell my disciples as much as possible on the way there.

"*I am* the true vine," I start, using my Father God's name again, "and my Father is the gardener."[2]

I am alluding to the image of the vine the Scriptures often use for my people, Israel. Moses, Asaph, Isaiah, Jeremiah and Ezekiel all compared Israel's wickedness with a vine that produced bad fruit.[3] The vine's subsequent destruction symbolised Israel's consequential judgement under the old covenant of the law. Under the new covenant, I am the true vine. Just as grapes are crushed to produce wine, so I will be crushed and my blood, figuratively, will be the Passover wine of the new covenant, shed for the forgiveness of sins. That is what I instructed my disciples to commemorate at supper just now.

Thinking of Judas, and wondering whether my disciples would make the connection, I continue. "He cuts off every branch in me that yields no fruit, but prunes every branch that does yield fruit to make it even more productive."

---

[1] Luke 21:37; 22:39
[2] Based on John 15:1 (NIV); see also verses 2-17
[3] Deuteronomy 32:32-33; Psalm 80:8-16; Isaiah 5:1-7; Jeremiah 2:21; Ezekiel 15

Pruning promotes new, strong growth, but it can be painful. Sometimes we ask you to give up a ministry, something you love and may have been very fruitful at, in order to lead you to another field of mission. Until you can see the latter, letting go of the first can be harrowing. I know; I've just done it! And what's coming in the next few hours will crush me completely, but only this way can I win for you and for all an even greater prize. Keep trusting us if you're going through a time of pruning; better is to come!

To keep trusting, you have to keep rooted. I tell my disciples, "You have already been pruned and cleansed by my words to you. Remain in me and I will remain in you. A branch can only ever bear fruit if it remains in the vine. In the same way, you will only bear fruit if you remain in me. That will bring my Father glory and show that you are my disciples." I am encouraged that they appear to understand the need to remain rooted in me, and repeat my words at the meal about remaining in my love and obeying my commands, adding a directive. "Laying down one's life for others is the greatest love anyone can express. So love one another as I have loved you."

My talk of laying down lives brings home to them – and me – the events that are almost upon us. All of us can sense their inevitability now. As we pass the temple, my Father's house, I think about the authorities within it, who claim allegiance to him but reject me, whom he sent. My disciples too will experience the same opposition, the same lack of love that I am about to endure.

"If the world seems to hate you," I tell them,[4] "remember that it hated me first; but whoever hates me, hates my Father too. Had I not spoken to them these past few years and given them miraculous signs, they would not be guilty of sin. Now they have no excuse for it. They hate me without reason and thus fulfil what their law says."[5]

My disciples are looking downcast again; I need to build them up, and take up the thread of what I told them earlier.[6]

---

4   John 15:18(-16:4)
5   Psalms 35:19; 69:4; 109:3
6   John 14:16; testify: cf. 1 John 5:6-8

"When I send you the Counsellor, the Father's Spirit of truth, he himself will testify about me. You too must bear witness about everything you have seen me do from the start."[7]

They might not believe it yet, but it won't be long before they are testifying about me[8]. However, they will encounter opposition.

"I've told you all this so you don't go astray," I tell them. "They will expel you from the synagogue, and some will even think they are offering a service to God by killing you. They will commit such things because they know neither the Father nor me. I'm telling you this only now so that when it happens you will remember my warning; up to now I was with you."

They are bewildered about what I have just described. I reassure them that I have to return to my Father so that our Spirit can come to them.[9] Grief and incomprehension prevent them from asking where I am going; Peter started to earlier, but soon became sidetracked with his claims of loyalty.

"The Counsellor will convict the world of its sin of rejecting me," I continue, "and prove my righteousness by revealing that I am going to the Father, where the world will no longer see me; and that I have brought judgement on the prince of this world. He, the Spirit of truth, will lead you into all truth, speaking what he hears, and bringing glory to me as he shows you what is mine – everything that belongs to the Father! Soon you will see me no more, then a little while later you will see me again."

Now they are asking each other what I mean by all this 'going to the Father' and 'in a little while'. I can see that they want to ask and yet can't bring themselves to do so. The less fit among them are also puffing laboriously up the side of the Mount of Olives from the Kidron river below.

"It is true that you will weep and mourn, but your grief will turn to joy when you see me again, and no-one will take that from you – just like a woman after giving birth immediately forgets the pain she has

---

[7] John 15:27; cf. Luke 1:2, 24:48

[8] cf. Acts 2:14ff; 4:1ff

[9] John 16:5(-33)

endured. Then I will no longer speak figuratively but will tell you about my Father in cleartext. You will ask him for things in my name, and he will fulfil them because he loves you for loving me and believing I came from God."

Their faces are bright as they reply, "Now we get you! Now it's clear that you know everything and that you really did come from God."

"At last you believe!" I exclaim excitedly, and then, more subdued, remind them that they will be scattered. "But you will desert me and only my Father will remain with me. I have told you all this so that you may have peace in me despite all the troubles you will have in this world. For I have overcome the world!"

We have reached the garden, an olive grove not very far up the Mount of Olives, from where you look up towards the eastern city wall and the Temple Mount.[10] This place, called Gethsemane, which means 'oil press',[11] has been a favourite haunt of mine for many a visit to Jerusalem. The cave here offers shelter from the cold, damp nights; its olive press is only used in the autumn and winter months.[12] Gethsemane is a quiet spot where I have often brought my disciples and where I can withdraw and pray to my Father. That is what I need to do now.

"Sit here," I tell my disciples, "while I go over there and pray. Pray that you will not fall into temptation.[13]" I pause a moment, and motion to Peter, James and John to come with me. We walk about a stone's throw towards the far end of the garden, and as we do so, the reality of the next few hours overtakes me.

The prophecies of Isaiah course through my mind: despised and rejected by men; pierced, crushed, oppressed, afflicted; led like a lamb; cut off.[14] Cut off from the world. Cut off from my Father, just like my ancestor King David when he made the same journey across the Kidron valley and climbed this same hill.[15] He was fleeing from his son Absalom

---

[10] Matthew 26:36(-46); Mark 14:32(-42); Luke 22:39(-46); John 18:1
[11] NIV footnote at Matthew 26:36
[12] See 'Gethsemane' note, page 305
[13] Luke 22:40 (NIV)
[14] Isaiah 53
[15] 2 Samuel 15:23-30; Schlenker ("Gethsemane")

and, recognising that it belonged there, instructed Zadok the priest to return with the ark to the city, thus cutting himself off from the symbol of God's presence. I am about to relinquish my heavenly power totally and submit to human authority. Cut off from my Father in heaven.

My three closest followers are shocked to see me so overwhelmed with sorrow as I tell them to stay and keep watch with me.

I go on a few steps and drop to the ground, my emotions exhausting me. "Abba[16] – Dad," I pray, "if it is possible – and everything is possible for you – please take this cup of suffering from me. Yet not my will, but your will be done."

I feel the presence of the devil, the tempter, prowling around me, willing me to throw in the towel because he knows I am on course to defeat him. *You don't need to go through all this pain; take the easy way out; why not let the people continue bringing their own sacrifices? Those who want to will believe in you anyway!*

But I also feel my Father's presence welling up in me as the Spirit encourages me to look beyond the hours to come. The price will be paid, the old covenant will be rescinded and replaced with the new, a covenant of love where grace makes the sacrifice, and acceptance of that gift brings our children into our presence.

"Father, the time has come. Glorify your Son, that your Son may glorify you.[17] For you gave me authority to grant eternal life to everyone you have given me, so that they might know you, the one true God, and me, the Messiah you have sent them. I have given glory to you by completing the work you gave me to do. So now, Father, glorify me with yourself, as we were before we created the world."

I know I can defeat Satan; I know my Father in heaven will stand by me, that our Spirit will work through me. But I wonder how my disciples will cope without me. I return to the three and find them already asleep.[18] "Simon," I say to Peter, "are you asleep? Couldn't you guys keep watch with me for even an hour?"

The others are stirring again.

---

16 Aramaic for Father, 'Dad' (NIV textnote at Mark 14:36)
17 John 17:1 (NIV); see also verses 2-5
18 Matthew 26:40; Mark 14:37; Luke 22:46

"Stay awake and pray, that you may resist temptation," I reprimand them, then add more gently, "Your spirit is willing, but your flesh is weak."

Distraught, I return to the same spot and drop to my knees again to pray. "Abba, if it's impossible to avoid drinking this cup then your will be done."

But it's not impossible! You don't need to drink it! I can feel the devil attacking again. *You have the power; use it!*

I have the power... but power for what? If I don't go through with this, I will not have made the sacrifice and achieved what I came for. My Father in heaven has empowered me to do this; I have to drink this cup to the last dregs. I force the devil's voice from my consciousness.

My thoughts turn to my disciples, and I pray for them.[19] "Father, I have made your name known to those you gave me from this world, and now they believe that you sent me and that all I have comes from you. They are yours, Father, so as I return home to you and leave them here, protect them from the evil one by the power of your name, that they may be one as we are one. As I consecrate myself now to complete what you sent me into the world to achieve, so may that truly sanctify them as I send them out in my place."

I return to Peter, James and John and find them asleep once more.[20] Exhausted from sorrow, they can't keep their eyes open. The three stir again and don't know what to say. I raise my hand in a gesture that says it's okay, and walk away a few steps again. I desperately want their company, while at the same time longing that I could already return to my Father. I have stomach cramps from the anguish that I am feeling, muscles tightening involuntarily and beyond my control. It's the early hours of the morning now, but I am sweating profusely, and mop my brow. In the moonlight, I can see that my sweat is mingled with blood.[21]

The believers... I have to pray for the people that believed me as I went round teaching and healing. And what about those whom my disciples will reach, and who will believe – how are they going to fare?

---

19 John 17:6-19
20 Matthew 26:43; Mark 14:40
21 Luke 22:44

"Father, I don't pray only for my disciples, but for all who through their words come to faith in me.[22] May they be united too, and live in us in such a way that the world may believe that you sent me, and that you love them as much as you love me. And so may they partake in the glory you gave me before we created the world, as they come to know you through me."

I return to my disciples and, finding them asleep for a third time,[23] admonish them with urgency. The hour I have always known was coming has arrived, announced by the hustle of many footsteps and the rattling of chains and weapons. "Are you lot asleep?" I ask them. "It's time... Look, here comes the traitor to betray the Son of Man into the hands of sinners. Get up, let's go!"

We collect the bleary-eyed rest of the group and move towards the detachment of sword-bearing soldiers and a collection of officials from the chief priests and Pharisees, armed with clubs.[24] Judas is walking purposefully at their head, no longer with us. He is here to betray me, and approaches me now with long strides. I anticipate his signal.

"Judas, would you betray the Son of Man with a kiss?"

He hesitates for the briefest of moments, an embarrassed flicker of doubt appearing momentarily and suppressed just as quickly. He is unable to look me in the eye. "Hello, Rabbi!" he exclaims nervously in a mock-friendly voice, and leans forward to kiss my cheek.

I reply by recalling the instruction I gave him at the meal. "Friend, do what you came here to do."

Judas retreats and immediately those at the front of the mob step forward. They pause as I challenge them.

"Who are you looking for?" I ask, knowing full well what their answer will be.

"Jesus of Nazareth."

"*I am* he," I declare, using the form of God's holy name that even the soldiers understand.

---

[22] John 17:20(-26)
[23] Matthew 26:45; Mark 14:41
[24] Matthew 26:47-56; Mark 14:43-52; Luke 22:47-53; John 18:2-11

Caught off guard, they draw back, tripping over themselves and each other, and fall in a heap. I repeat my question, and they repeat their reply.

"Like I said, it's me: Jesus! If it's me you're after, then let these men go." I must not lose any more of my disciples, for it is my Father's will that they perpetuate my teaching.[25]

The mob is recovering; they are rightly interpreting my request as intended acquiescence.

My disciples are becoming restless, their rising tension betraying comprehension of what is about to happen. "Lord, should we use our swords?"

In their agitated state, they are not thinking straight. Two swords, they said we had, and that against all this lot. Peter, characteristically, is neither thinking about that nor waiting for an answer from me. He brushes past me, sword drawn, and strikes out wildly at the nearest adversary. The man's right ear lands on the ground next to him as his hand goes up instinctively to protect what is no longer there. As blood trickles through his fingers, pain and realisation combine to cause a piercing scream to emanate from deep within.

"Put your sword away!"[26] I command Peter.

He looks at me, desperate, almost pleading, what are we supposed to do then?

"All who live by the sword shall die by the sword,[27]" I tell him, and reminding him of how we helped Elisha of old,[28] continue, "Do you not think that my Father would send legions of angels to help me, were I to ask him? But that would not fulfil the Scriptures that say it has to happen this way. I have to drink the cup the Father has given me."

I turn back towards the crowd. They are frozen in a febrile mixture of fear and horror. Peter's victim is still holding the side of his head, moaning incessantly. He draws away as I reach out to him, and I have to take a step forward. He lowers his bloodied hand as I pray silently to

---

[25] cf. John 6:37-40 and 18:9
[26] John 18:11 (NIV)
[27] cf. Genesis 9:5-6 and Exodus 21:12
[28] 2 Kings 6:17

my Father for a last infusing of his authority, before I finally submit to theirs, and touch the cowering man with restorative power. Realising with incredulity that his pain has ceased, he raises his hand tentatively, hardly daring to explore the side of his head. He peers down at the ground, trying in vain to locate his ear, and then gazes up into my eyes with a mixture of gratitude and uncertainty. His earache has vanished! *Who are you?* I manage a weak smile.

Looking beyond him, I address the crowd. "Do you take me for a rebel leader, that you have come armed to the teeth to capture me? I sat teaching in the temple courts every day and you didn't lay a finger on me. But now is your moment – when darkness reigns and the writings of the prophets are fulfilled."

This seems to serve as a reminder of their mission and galvanises them into action. Brushing past the still-dazed man, the nearest two soldiers grab hold of me and roughly pull my arms behind my back, chaining them together. My disciples have already deserted me and are running away as fast as they are able. As the mob leads me down the path, I notice over to my left that some of them are trying to apprehend not one of my disciples but young John Mark, whose parents' house we ate supper in earlier.[29] He is dressed only in a linen cloth, and it seems that Judas led the soldiers to the house first. Mark must have wanted to warn us that they were heading this way, but has himself come under attack. However, he has wrenched himself out of the smooth garment and the firm but slippery grip of his accosters, leaving the cloth behind as he sprints away. The soldiers' commander, no doubt already annoyed at having to turn out so early, is cursing under his breath. But now we're heading towards the gate, he yells at them to, "Forget it!" He has apprehended the suspect he was told to arrest. Just following orders.

Abba, Father, help me through the next few hours...

---

[29] See 'Mark' note, page 310

29

Innocent Pronounced Guilty

We're just reaching the city wall, and the first hints of daylight are straining over the horizon behind us. Passing through the Eastern Gate, two of my capturers frogmarch me along the outer ramparts of the temple. With an air of finality, the soldiers' hobnailed caligae[1] are echoing off the walls that line this narrow alleyway. I feel frightened, yet determined, accepting the fate that is mine, anticipating both the agony to come and the victory beyond.

Skirting round the front of the temple, we're bearing towards the Upper City, which sprawls over Mount Zion, the highest part of the city.[2] The Roman commander dismisses all but a handful of his soldiers, sending them back to the Antonia fortress at the other end of the temple. Looks like we're heading to the high priest, Caiaphas, whose residence is situated part-way up the hillside and faces the temple.

Right now, though, we've arrived at his father-in-law, Annas[3], in a separate part of the building complex. Our then Roman procurator, Valerius Gratus, deposed Annas about twenty years ago, but the Jews

---

1 Cleland, Davies, Llewellyn-Jones ("Caliga")
2 Israel MoFA ("Mount Zion")
3 John 18:12-14

consider the office of high priest as being for life[4] and resent Roman interference in religious affairs, so Annas still wields much influence.[5]

The remaining Roman soldiers stay out in the courtyard, handing me over to the temple guards who were part of the arrest party. We make our way indoors. Annas questions me about my teaching and my disciples. He is – as many Sadducees are – brusque in the extreme.[6] That alone would make them unpopular with ordinary people, but they also apply the Torah much more rigidly than do the Pharisees, whose oral traditions and many rules they reject.[7]

"I have always spoken openly," I reply, with resigned irritation, "teaching where the Jews meet – in local synagogues or here, down at the temple. I said nothing in secret. Why question me? Ask those who heard me. I'm sure they'll know what I said."

Without warning, the official standing nearest me lashes out towards me. My shoulders attempt to raise my arms in a reflex movement of protection, but with my hands still tied behind me, I am helpless, and my assailant lands a stinging blow cross the side of my face. I stagger backwards a step as he voices his accusation.

"Is that how you answer the high priest?" he snarls.

I shake my head in an attempt to clear it. Trembling with a mixture of pain and anger tempered with sorrow, I reply calmly. "If I said something untrue, state it in evidence. Otherwise, why did you strike me?"

The man fumes in awkward silence and behind him Annas stands up.

Annas might have influence, but he has no power, and after an hour or so[8] has tired of interrogating me. "Enough!" he declares, and orders the commander to take me across the courtyard to his son-in-law.

---

4 Numbers 18:7, 25:10-13, 35:25,28;
5 cf. Luke 3:2, John 18:13; Acts 4:6; Elwell ("*Annas*"); Josephus (Antiquities of the Jews XVIII.2.2)
6 Josephus (Antiquities of the Jews XVIII.1.4; Wars of the Jews II.9.14)
7 Josephus (Antiquities of the Jews XIII.10.6)
8 cf. Luke 22:59

Most of the soldiers are hanging around in the middle of the paved courtyard, staving off the cool of the night by warming themselves around a fire, and eyeing up the young servant girls serving them fresh flat bread with a hot broth. A heated argument is taking place on the far side, and I stop abruptly as I recognise Peter, remonstrating with a couple of bystanders. Alerted by the gradually brightening sky, a cockerel in the garden beyond the courtyard wall crows the first of its morning alarm calls, and Peter looks up. For a moment, our gazes meet, before a hand strikes my back and pushes me forward.

"Get moving!"

I stumble forwards, simultaneously warmed by the fact that Peter is here and distraught that he has been denying me as I warned him he would. Before entering through the doorway of Caiaphas' house, I glance back towards Peter. He is cradling his head in his hands as he blunders out through the gateway.

In the meantime, Caiaphas has managed to summons the whole Sanhedrin council, as well as a motley assortment of 'witnesses', with whose evidence they are hoping to incriminate me.[9] One after another, they come forward and make their claims. I am being forced to stand, still bound with my hands tied behind my back.

The Sanhedrin uncovers not a shred of incriminating evidence from any of their witnesses. *Your lamb shall be without blemish.*[10] Finally, however, two witnesses come forward and give similar, though inconsistent, versions of what I am supposed to have said. "We heard this fellow say he could destroy God's temple and rebuild it in three days."

Which is not exactly what I said,[11] but the council have already seen a chink of light. By law, the word of one witness does not suffice; two or more are required,[12] and now they have them. Their oral laws may require that the witnesses give non-contradictory evidence, but they also prohibit capital charges being tried either at night or on the eve of

---

[9] Matthew 26:57-68; Mark 14:53-65; John 18:19-24
[10] Exodus 12:5a (KJV; RSV; ASV; ESV, 2001)
[11] cf. John 2:19
[12] Deuteronomy 19:15

a Sabbath.[13] On that basis, these proceedings are already illegal. But that doesn't count anymore; they are out to indict me.

Satan bounces into my thoughts. *Tell them you didn't mean it like that. Tell them you meant yourself; get them debating about resurrection again like you did before. You don't need to put yourself through any more of this!*

No, Satan, I will not stand in their way, and you will not stand in mine.

Caiaphas gets to his feet, anxious to force a conclusion. "Haven't you got anything to say? What do you say to these men's testimony against you?"

I look through him to a point he cannot see, and think of King David's words: "Though they plot evil against you and devise wicked schemes, they cannot succeed."[14]

Caiaphas steps right up close, his face in mine, threatening. "Swear by the living God: are you the Messiah, the Son of God?"

Time to tell it straight. "You said it," I reply, looking round the chamber and sealing my own fate. "But in the prophet's words[15], one day all of you will see the Son of Man seated at the right hand of the Almighty and returning on the clouds of heaven."

Caiaphas' cheeks have reddened alarmingly and he loosens the clothing around his neck so savagely that the fine material tears. This action is a typical sign of being distraught, though not one the high priest is supposed to perform.[16] "That's blasphemy!" he thunders. "We don't require any further witnesses! You heard him; what do you reckon?"

To a man, they apply the prescribed Levitical law to the supposed crime.[17] "He deserves to die!"

The council members standing nearest to me spit in my face, showing utter contempt.[18] Caiaphas has no wish for this unseemliness

---

[13] Mishnah Sanhedrin 5.1; 4.1
[14] Psalm 21:11 (NIV)
[15] Daniel 7:13
[16] Leviticus 21:10
[17] Leviticus 24:16
[18] cf. Numbers 12:14 and Deuteronomy 25:9

to sully his house and orders the guards to take me back outside while they decide how to proceed. The guards push me out into the courtyard, where the Roman soldiers are still warming themselves by the fire, bored. One of the guards deftly removes a headscarf from one of the servant girls, earning a slap in the face. Ordinarily she would be taking a large risk by her reaction, but her chided superior chooses to ignore the rebuke and continues in his original intention of blindfolding me with the strip of material.

They start slapping me, taunting. "Come on, Christ, if you're a prophet, tell us who hit you!" Derisive laughter echoes around the courtyard as they hurl insult after insult at me.

I did not spare myself from mocking and spitting. Because the Sovereign Lord helps me, I will not be disgraced. That's why I have set my face like flint, knowing that I will not be put to shame. My vindicator is near.[19] Isaiah's words echo round my thoughts as I remain silent.

Eventually they tire of their game, rip the blindfold from my head and throw it in the direction of the servant girl.

"'ere, darlin', 'ave this back."

She stoops to retrieve her headscarf, glaring at them.

Before any further exchange can take place, Caiaphas appears, followed by the animated council members. "We're going to Pilate," he informs the commander sullenly, who passes on the implied order to his men. Two of them get hold of me again and push me towards the gate.

Pilate. I've already told you[20] about his brutal repression of the aqueduct riots. When he first arrived here about five years ago, he was ignorant of Jewish sensitivities and had his soldiers bring up ensigns bearing effigies of Caesar from his summer residence in Caesarea.[21] Under the 'graven images' laws[22], we do not permit such images. The people revolted and, anxious to quell the disturbance, Pilate threatened them with death. When the people lay down and bared their necks ready

---

[19] Isaiah 50:6-8
[20] See page 180
[21] Josephus (Antiquities of the Jews XVIII.3.1; The Wars of the Jews II.9.2-3)
[22] Exodus 20:4-5; Deuteronomy 4:15-18, 5:8

for the sword, he was greatly surprised and gave orders for the removal of the images.

For his Roman superiors, Pilate is probably a good leader of what they see as a troublesome province, though they won't tolerate any instability. For us Jews, while he does try to give us some autonomy, when we step over his line he is tyrannous. Caiaphas, therefore, will be very reluctant to defer to Pilate, but he is compelled to, for only Pilate has the authority to impose the death penalty that he wants discharged.

We are making our way to the Praetorium, the governor's official residence at Herod's Palace, which occupies a large area of the Upper City, stretching along the western city wall above the Hinnom Valley.[23] This is home to Herod's three landmark towers, named after his friend Hippicus, his brother Phasaelus, and his wife Mariamne.

Caiaphas is leading the way, council members strung out behind. The soldiers have ceased taunting me for now, concentrating more on the uphill march to the palace.

As we catch up, Caiaphas is in discussion with the young palace soldiers, who have recently relieved the night guard. "We cannot enter the palace," Caiaphas is saying, "for we must not be ceremonially defiled before tonight's Passover meal.[24] Bring Pilate out here."

"Who are you to demand the governor to do anything?" the bellicose guard retorts.

The commander, who has been up for much of the night, is anxious to terminate his involvement in the proceedings. He is going to have to be patient yet. "The High Priest and the Sanhedrin..." he starts explaining to the guard, then thinks better of it. "Go and inform the governor that they are here with their prisoner as arranged."

The guards exchange glances before one of them disappears. While Caiaphas and members of the Sanhedrin wait outside the gate, the soldiers push me inside the generously-proportioned courtyard with its gardens, channels of flowing water, and walkways. A semi-circular portico faces the gate, set at the midpoint of a covered walkway that runs the length of the two hundred cubit long area between the two

---

[23] Josephus (Antiquities of the Jews XV.9.3)
[24] John 18:28(-40); Matthew 27:11-26; Mark 15:1-15; Luke 23:1-25

main palace structures. It is mirrored on the other side of the courtyard, which is overshadowed by the city wall.[25]

Pilate, accompanied by the guard and a few officials, appears from one of the residential buildings and walks with long strides towards us. He is about fifty, starting to thin on top, and does not look impressed as he looks me up and down and casts his eye over the Sanhedrin. He is wearing an expression that says, surely this dishevelled figure can't be what he was woken in the middle of the night to supply a detachment of soldiers for. Now it's barely light and they're back already.

"Is this it?" he demands of Caiaphas, jerking his thumb towards me.

"This man has brought instability to our nation," Caiaphas replies, unfazed. "He opposes paying taxes to Caesar and claims to be the Messiah, our anointed king."

Caiaphas' specious charges are cunning. Pilate will have little interest in a charge of blasphemy, but anything that could appear to threaten the local status quo with regard to Rome will get his attention.

He turns to me. "Well, are you the King of the Jews?" he asks mockingly.

"Yes, I am," I reply, to an audible gasp from outside the gates.

Pilate turns back to Caiaphas. "What actual charges are you bringing against him?" he wants to know.

Caiaphas answers evasively. "We wouldn't have handed him over to you if he weren't a criminal."

"Go and try him yourselves under your own law," Pilate replies, becoming impatient.

Your own law. In the Sanhedrin's law, the punishment for blasphemy is stoning, going right back to the time of Moses[26]. They would probably condemn me to the same punishment on the grounds of being a 'wizard' or a 'sorcerer'[27] as well.

"But we are not permitted to execute anyone," Caiaphas retorts, confirming the judgement that he and the Sanhedrin have already

---

25 Josephus (The Wars of the Jews 5.4.4); models at the Israel Museum, Jerusalem
26 John 18:31; Leviticus 24:13-16,23; Mishnah Sanhedrin 6.1
27 Mishnah Sanhedrin 7.5

reached. They proceed to accuse me before Pilate, whose knowledge of Jewish religion and law is struggling to keep up with their charges.

Eventually he has heard enough. "Wait here while I try him myself," he orders, and motions to his guards to bring me to his palace building.

We traverse one half of the imposing courtyard and enter his even more impressively decorated palace.

"Are you the king of the Jews?"[28] he starts, repeating his original question.

This time I reply with a question of my own. "Did you come up with that yourself, or have you been talking to others about me?"

"Do I look like a Jew?!" he replies, irritated. "It was your people and chief priests who brought you to me for trial. Why? What have you done?"

"Mine is not an earthly kingdom," I tell him quietly. "If it were, my subjects would fight to prevent the Jews arresting me. But my kingdom is not of this world."

"So you are a king, then," protests Pilate.

"'King' is your word," I inform him. "Actually, I was born and came into the world to testify to the truth. All who are committed to the truth listen to my voice."

"Huh, truth," Pilate responds, "what is truth?"

If only he knew.

Pilate stands up, and I follow him with the bemused guards back to the gate. He goes out and addresses the waiting Sanhedrin. "I don't find this man guilty of anything,"[29] he announces to them.

But they insist, "He's been stirring up the people with his teaching all over Judea, starting in Galilee and right the way down to here."

"He's a Galilean?" I hear Pilate ask them. "Well in that case, he is under Herod's jurisdiction,[30] and Herod happens to be staying here for the Passover, over at the Hasmonean Palace." Herod Antipas, the tetrarch of Galilee who imprisoned and later beheaded Cousin John.

---

28 Matthew 27:11 (NIV); Mark 15:2 (NIV); Luke 23:3 (NIV); John 18:33 (NIV)
29 John 18:38 (GOD'S WORD)
30 Luke 23:7(-12)

"Take him there," Pilate continues, throwing a glance in my direction, "and have Herod deal with him."

The Hasmonean Palace is situated lower down the slopes of the Upper City, about halfway to the temple complex. It is considerably smaller though no less ornate than Herod the Great's palace. Before heading down the hill, we stop momentarily by the three towers to use the latrines, which drain into a sewer that runs under the street through the Jaffa gate, along the wall, and out into the Hinnom valley at a spot aptly named Bethso[31]. There the Essenes have their latrines, outside the city walls, in strict accordance with the Torah.[32] One of my guards has the propriety to unbind my hands. He assumes correctly that I do not pose an immediate security risk, and I am thankful.

Like Pilate, Herod Antipas is around fifty, a little portly. Unlike Pilate, he is a Jew, or at least viewed like his family as half-Jewish,[33] so Caiaphas and his cohort have no qualms about entering his palace with me.

In contrast to Pilate, when Herod realises who has been brought to him, he seems particularly pleased, despite the early hour. "I've been wanting to meet you for ages," he enthuses. I cannot say I share his eagerness right now. "People have told me all about the miracles you do. Healing the sick and even raising the dead, eh? I've heard you do a nice little line in wine. Perhaps you would you care to show me?"

Perhaps not.

He answers my silence with more questions.

The members of the Sanhedrin are trying to hurry proceedings along by vehemently accusing me. I ignore all of them.

Presently they begin mocking me, Herod starting the entertainment for his troops, who need little encouragement to join in. "What sort of miracle maker are you? Call yourself a king? You don't even talk!" Herod summons one of his soldiers, who leaves the room and reappears moments later carrying an old but otherwise elegant scarlet robe, one of their outer cloaks. The others remove my outer

---

[31] Strong's #1004 (beth=place); #6674 (tso=filthy) or #6627 (tseah=dung)
[32] Josephus (The Wars of the Jews V.4.2); cf. Deuteronomy 23:12; Pixner
[33] Josephus (Antiquities of the Jews XIV.15.2)

garment and wrap the robe around me. Guffaws of laughter chase each other round the palace courtyard. "Hail, O king!"

Some of them taunt me by striking me in the face. My eyes close reflexively with each stinging blow, but I remain silent and in control. The devil is still prowling round in a desperate attempt to throw me off course. What is happening to me is his usual modus operandi, but even he knows the Scriptures, and just as Isaiah prophesied, he realises the end-result of all this is going to spell his defeat.

He was oppressed and afflicted, yet, like a lamb led to slaughter, did not protest. My righteous servant will pronounce many righteous, taking upon himself all their wrongdoing.[34]

Herod has no doubt boosted his popularity with his men but, apart from some diversionary merriment, remains dissatisfied. I am not going to give him the hoped-for entertainment. Now he is bored, and I imagine his main concern is getting on with his breakfast.

"Take him back to Pilate," he orders Caiaphas and the council members. "No point keeping him here; there's nothing to sentence him for."

Caiaphas, with the Sanhedrin, and I, sandwiched between two of Pilate's soldiers, process back up the hill towards Herod the Great's palace, Pilate's official Jerusalem residence. I notice one of the soldiers is carrying my cloak. We arrive at the palace in just a few minutes.

Pilate looks no more pleased to see me again than the first time round. Indeed, alarm spreads across his features as he surveys the sizeable crowd that is now filling the open square facing his gates. People have started the day's business – for most, making their Passover preparations – and many have recognised the Sanhedrin and also me. Curious to find out what is happening, they have gathered around us.

Pilate addresses the gathering, gesturing towards me. "You brought this man to me and accused him of inciting the people to rebellion. Both Herod and I have examined him and found no evidence to support your charges against him. He has done nothing to deserve

---

[34] Isaiah 53:7a,11b

the death penalty. Therefore I will punish him then release him, as it is customary to do at the Passover."

"No, release Barabbas," comes the unanimous reply. We too heard earlier in the week of this man's arrest for insurrection and murder. That the crowd is shouting for him can only be the persuasive influence of the Sanhedrin. His name soon becomes a chant.

"But what shall I do with this Jesus, whom you call the Christ?" Pilate shouts over the din.

"Crucify him!"

"Why?" Pilate asks, mystified. "What crime is he supposed to have committed?"

"Crucify him! Crucify him!"

My thoughts wander, shutting out the noise. I am feeling very alone. Some of those people were shouting hosanna just a few days ago. What has made them turn so completely? How can the temple authorities pronounce me guilty when Pilate declares me innocent? I realise that it has to happen like this, and I know that my Father in heaven is standing by me, giving me strength. *He who vindicates me is near.*[35] My Father in heaven will enable me to complete the work I came to do.

There are times you feel overwhelmed, I know, but I have been there before you and am there with you, even now.

Crucify him! The chanting pierces my thoughts and sends a shudder through my whole body. Crucifixion is a potent symbol of the brutality that is at odds with my Father's will. It results from the sin that took hold after he and I had created a perfect world, and it is about to be unleashed on me.

Pilate will not withstand the pressure much longer. He does not wish to condemn me – so much is obvious – but politically he cannot afford to have to explain another disturbance to his Roman superiors. He starts to buckle – as he must. He whirls round, all but sweeping the guards and me inside with him.

---

[35] Isaiah 50:8

We march towards one end of the courtyard, where Pilate's soldiers reside. As we do so, a servant sprints up to Pilate from his residence at the other end of the courtyard.

"What is it?"

"Your wife ordered me to give this to you, sir."

Pilate reads the delivered note, then, hand covering his face, massages his temples as though trying to exorcise a splitting headache. While he paces up and down indecisively, his soldiers start teasing me and pushing me around.

"You, a king?" they taunt.

A few of them use their daggers to cut some of the briars growing in a corner formed by one of the defensive towers in the city wall. They twist these carefully together, fashioning a crown, and swearing prolifically each time the thorns thwart their caution. Using a hand-shield for protection, one of them rams it down over my head. The thorns bore into my skull, causing me to wince in pain, and my eyes to water. Someone thrusts a stick into my hand, to act as a staff.

"Hail, O king!" they laugh, bowing down in mock deference. "Long live the King of the Jews!"

Father, uphold me!

Pilate leaves them to their game for a while and then appears to come to a decision. Desperation shows in his eyes. He sends one of the soldiers to fetch a flagrum.

"Tie him up there," he orders two others, pointing at one of the pillars of the portico. Knowing instinctively what is coming, the guards rip off the cloak that Herod's soldiers adorned me with, and remove my tunic, push me to my knees against the pillar, and tie my hands together the other side of it. Drops of blood are starting to run down my face from the thorns.

Pilate himself[36] takes the whip, pauses briefly, as if unsure of himself. For a moment, I see the sharp splinters of bone, chips of stone, and lumps of lead pressed into the leather strands that make up the whip, resting on the floor beside me.

---

[36] from the third person singular, aorist active indicative tense in the Greek

In a split second they are flicked away and brought down across my back. I gasp in shock and my muscles contract involuntarily, but I cannot move away from the source of the torture. Another whoosh of air pre-empts the next attack, and I cry out in pain.

Whoosh. I scream in agony, though even that is muted because I am tied too tightly to the pillar and cannot take a deep enough breath to fully express the pain that I feel.

Whoosh. I am panting already – short, shallow breaths, as though I were running uphill.

Whoosh. My chest is tight, my head becoming light from shock and the pain.

Pilate pauses for a moment and hands the whip to the soldier nearest to him. "You, carry on."

Whoosh. The soldier doesn't hesitate – *whoosh* – and seems to possess a stronger conviction than his master.

Whoosh. Each lash rips into my increasingly torn flesh, and my eyes are watering freely with the smarting pain.

Whoosh. A line of a Psalm courses through my fading awareness. *Ploughmen plough long furrows into my back, but the Lord is righteous and will free me from the wicked.*[37]

Whoosh. I start to drift in and out of consciousness as the blows rain down.

Whoosh. A misplaced blow causes the ends of the flagrum to catapult round the side of my waist, tormenting a fresh set of nerve endings.

Whoosh.

Fighting to stay conscious.

Whoosh.

Father…

Whoosh…

Finally, Pilate gives the order to stop. "That's enough!" I hear at last, distant. "Untie him!"

---

[37] cf. Psalm 129:3-4

I collapse backwards as they unbind me, and a new inferno of pain causes me to scream out as my raw back makes contact with the ground. I roll onto my side in an attempt to escape the agony, but to little avail. Two of the soldiers drag me to my feet, stretching the broken skin across my back, which they torture even more as they redress me in my tunic and the scarlet robe.

Pilate orders us back to the gate. My shaking legs can barely support me as I stumble forwards. Every step causes the coarse material of my tunic to rub abrasively against the wounds.

"Here is the man," Pilate is saying as I reach the gate. "I have punished him for you and will now release him."

But the crowd is not satisfied with my beating. There is only one punishment acceptable to them now, and full of venom they shout it out.

"CRUCIFY, CRUCIFY!"

"You take him then and crucify him yourselves," Pilate concedes. "As for me, I find no grounds for charging him. He's innocent."

Caiaphas contradicts him with characteristic polemic. "We have a law," he says, "and by that law he ought to die, because he made himself out to be the Son of God."

The colour drains from Pilate's face, and he orders his soldiers to take me inside again. I shuffle back through the gateway between two of them.

"Where are you from?" Pilate asks, but I remain silent. "Aren't you going to speak to me?" he continues after a few moments. "Don't you realise I have the authority to free you or, alternatively, to crucify you?"

"You would have no authority over me," I gasp through clenched teeth, "were it not given you from above; it's the ones handing me over to you that are heaping the greater guilt on themselves."

This statement does not quell Pilate's discomfort. He steps back outside, trying to reason with the crowd.

I hear one of them shouting above the general hubbub. "If you release this man, you are no friend of Caesar, for anyone claiming to be a king is opposed to Caesar."

At this, Pilate reappears, orders a servant to fetch a bowl of water and a titulus board. He has given up. He takes me outside, and climbs the steps to his judgement seat, which we call 'Gabbatha', a raised section of stone pavement, to address the crowd once more.

"Look, here's your king," he announces.

"Away with him. Crucify him!"

"You want me to crucify your king?" Pilate asks in one last attempt to avert what even he recognises as a travesty of justice.

"Caesar is the only king we have," one of the chief priests answers.

"Then go and crucify him," Pilate replies in capitulation, more concerned with quelling any possible uprising. "But I," he states defiantly, washing his hands in the water that has been placed before him, "am innocent of this man's blood. It's your responsibility."

"So be it," they answer belligerently.

Pilate dictates the text of the supposed crime to his servant, who chalks it on the wooden board in Aramaic, Latin and Greek[38]: "Jesus of Nazareth, the King of the Jews."

When the chief priests see it, they complain to Pilate. "Don't write, 'The King of the Jews'," they protest. "Write, 'This man *claimed* to be King of the Jews.'"

"What I have written, I have written,"[39] Pilate states bluntly, hurling to one side the towel he was flexing around his hands. He snatches the sign from his servant and thrusts it into the hands of a young soldier, then climbs down from the raised platform and strides back through his gateway. His soldiers push me in after him.

"Take that robe off him," Pilate orders the commander brusquely, "and take him down to the fort. Load a crossbeam onto him, then take him up to Golgotha with the other two we sentenced yesterday, Gestas and Dysmas[40]. Let me know when you're done."

Pilate's soldiers rip the red robe from my back, causing another lightning bolt of pain to shoot through me as the congealed blood is pulled away from the wounds. Another has tossed me my own cloak,

[38] John 19:20(-22)
[39] John 19:22 (NIV)
[40] Gospel of Nicodemus IX.5; see 'Non-Canonical Gospels' note, page 300

and I am struggling to put it on, overcoming every instinct not to move my upper body.

Pilate heads off towards his residence. In contrast to Herod, I suspect he won't be worrying about breakfast too much.

30

Guilty Pronounced Innocent

Fort Antonia is located at the north end of the temple area, slightly higher up Mount Moriah,[1] and was built to protect the Temple Mount and the lower city, the City of David, against attacks from that direction. Two of its four squat towers butt up against the temple wall. The garrison houses many of the Roman soldiers stationed in the city. Here they store their armaments as well as their stock of capital punishment equipment.

"Here's another one," the commander of Pilate's troops greets the centurion on duty in the garrison with. "Got to be done straightaway." He looks glad to finally be handing over responsibility for me.

"I've just sent two up,"[2] the centurion replies, "but there's always room for another one." He turns round and gives the necessary orders to three of his soldiers. "Go and fetch another crossbeam and a set of tools."

Two of them return carrying a heavy eight-by-four cedar beam, which must weigh some fifty or sixty pounds.[3] It has a central cross-halving joint cut out, flanked by two iron hoops hammered into the wood. The rough-cut surface is pockmarked with nail holes and covered

---

1 Various sources, e.g. models in Israel Museum, Jerusalem
2 cf. Luke 23:32
3 See 'The Wooden Cross' note, page 308

in dark stains at each end. They drop it alongside me and it lands with a solid thunk.

"Get down!" one of them orders.

I obey silently, and awkwardly lie face-down while they lay the patibulum across my shoulders.[4] The pressure it exerts on my wrecked back is excruciating. The soldiers slide leather straps under my arms and pull them tightly over the wood. My shoulders are on fire.

"Get up!" the soldier commands. I have only just managed to struggle to my hands and knees, and already the soldiers are becoming impatient. They grab each end of the wooden beam and yank me to my feet. It won't be the last time. The searing pain and resultant shock make me come over faint, and I'm struggling to remain upright.

Blast them away, get your angels to help you!

Away from me, Satan! Father, help me!

We descend the stone staircase from the fort into Tyropoean Street. My sight is blurring, partly from the dizziness I am feeling, partly from the trauma-induced sweat collecting on my forehead and forming itself into occasional rivulets as it overcomes the force of gravity. These are stinging the wounds from the thorns as they pass on their downward journey.

I misjudge the last step and stumble forwards under the weight of the wood. It judders across my raw shoulders like a rasp catching on rotten wood, with my tunic somewhere in-between. My head is throbbing. The two soldiers flanking me yank me upright again, and I stumble on.

We skirt round the corner of the temple, below the large staircase that exits the outer court towards the upper city, and make our way past the Huldah gates.

"It's Jesus," I hear someone say with a gasp. I look up but cannot distinguish who has recognised me. At the moment, it is all I can do to stay on my feet. But when we reach the eastern wall and the narrow alleyway which leads to the eastern gate and the Jericho road, even that

---

[4] John 19:17(-27); Matthew 27:32-44; Mark 15:21-32; Luke 23:26-43

becomes too much for my battered frame, and I fall spread-eagled to the ground. I barely notice the impact.

Hands are fumbling with the straps around my arms, and relief of sorts courses through my body as the solid wooden beam is taken off my back.

I thought your angels were supposed to lift you up before you tripped over anything!

And I thought I'd told you not to put the Lord your God to the test.

"Get up!" A kick against my thigh accompanies the command and helps push the devil out of my mind.

Through half-closed eyes I notice a few hardy blades of grass straining into existence between the flagstones. I strain myself upwards on leaden arms that are unwilling to take any weight. Looking at me from a doorway is a little girl. She smiles coyly and hides behind the leg of the adult standing next to her. I am glad she does not understand what she is witness to. I look up a little further to her mother, recognising in them both the mother and daughter I saw just four days ago when I entered Jerusalem along this same street. The mother gasps in horror as she realises the state I am in and the fate that awaits me outside the city. She instinctively puts a hand over her daughter's eyes, as tears well up in her own.

As I consider this, I hear the centurion issue an order. At first I mistake it for being aimed at me.

"You, come over here."

I look round and see a man of north-African origin, I guess, coming towards us from the direction of the city gate.

"Carry that," the centurion orders him, pointing at the patibulum. The man glances at me in a brief moment of sympathy, and obeys. As he does so, the noise of wailing penetrates my consciousness. I glance round and realise that a large number of people are following me, the women bemoaning the events that are unfolding before them now.

Future events in many of their lifetimes will cause them much greater woe.[5]

"Daughters of Jerusalem," I tell them, "do not weep for me; weep for yourselves and for your children.[6] For a time is coming when you will consider women who have never borne children as blessed." I remember a sentence from the prophet Hosea and add, "At that time 'they will say to the mountains, "Fall on us!" and to the hills, "Cover us!"'[7] For if this is what people do to the life-giving, righteous branch of David's line, what will happen to the dead branches of a people who have deserted God?[8]"

As I already told my disciples, Jerusalem faces a destruction that none can contemplate; the centre of worship will be lost, and those who are able to flee will consider themselves lucky. What men are doing to me, who came to bring life, is nothing compared with what they will do to those who have no life, no truth, and no compassion left in them. *O Jerusalem…*

I struggle to my feet, and the procession moves forward again. We reach the eastern gate and cross the Kidron valley via the Miphkad causeway. The sacrifice is led outside the camp…

Screams pierce the air as we reach the spot above the bridge where I sat one evening during last year's Feast of Tabernacles[9]. One of the two malefactors Pilate mentioned is already hanging on a cross. The Roman soldiers have just nailed the second to another. Dread fills me.

At an order from the Roman centurion, the man carrying my patibulum drops it at the foot of the stipes between the other two unfortunates. He looks at me again, briefly, and with compassion. Two women approach nervously, proffering a cup. They help me raise it to my lips, but as I taste the wine mixed with myrrh that is supposed to numb the pain, I refuse it. Their action was well intended, and I am grateful for their comfort, but I am determined to stay conscious to the end. I have to see this through.

---

[5] Destruction of Jerusalem in AD70; see NIV footnote to Luke 23:28.
[6] Luke 23:28 (NIV)
[7] Hosea 10:8
[8] Jeremiah 23:5, 33:15; Isaiah 27:11; John 15:2,6
[9] See page 167

"Nail him onto it," the centurion commands two of his soldiers. Without a word, they remove my outer cloak and my leather belt. For them, it is another routine execution. I carefully raise my arms so they can remove my tunic. They show no compunction and tear the garment from me. The numbness that was setting in across my back disappears in an instant, as jagged nerve endings re-announce their presence with a vengeance. I gasp out in pain and shock.

The soldiers each grab an arm and drag me backwards to the ground, my shoulders grinding over the wood, and what is left of my back making contact with the dust. Grit bores into the wounds like a myriad of sharp teeth. The back of my head has hit the ground and the thorns around it are doing likewise with renewed vigour.

Father, help me! Help me complete this mission!

I feel a hand grab my arm and press it down hard against the wood. I close my eyes, feeling faint, part of me wanting to faint but finding no escape, part of me refusing to succumb. To my left I hear a metallic jangling, close to, amplified by a wooden container. The sound is familiar... nails. The soldier, having selected one from the box, holds it briefly against my left palm. I know what is coming but am unprepared for the agony as he brings his hammer down, driving the nail straight through my hand and deep into the wood. I scream out, and wonder at how man – that pinnacle of our creation – has become so cruel.

But he was pierced for our transgressions and crushed for our iniquities; he bore the punishment that brought us peace, and by his wounds we are healed.[10] Yes, Isaiah knew exactly what I would come to do.

"Father," I cry out, "forgive them, for they don't know what they're doing!" The soldiers hesitate, glance at each other for a moment, not sure what to make of this pronouncement. They are just following orders, after all, and anyway, what does a condemned prisoner have to say? Yes, they are following orders, but they are also unwittingly playing their part in fulfilling prophecy.

---

[10] Isaiah 53:5

The soldier on the other side resolutely snatches another nail from the box, and I close my eyes tightly, bracing myself for the inevitable. It soon comes, and I scream out in pain again. Someone pulls the sandals from my feet. The soldiers take hold of each end of the crossbeam and hoist me upwards. Much of my weight is hanging off the two nails now, and my feet scramble to keep up.

They slam me against the upright, causing a further explosion of pain. A third soldier helps his colleagues slot the patibulum into the corresponding notch on the upright stipes, and fixes it in position by what sounds like a long, wooden dowel being hammered through the two iron hoops. My feet are barely touching the ground now, and the agony in my hands is overwhelming. One of the soldiers grabs my legs under the knees, lifts them up slightly, then forces my feet sideways and downwards, one over the other, while another selects a longer nail and drives it through both into the upright beam.

Hammering above my head brings me back to consciousness. "King of the Jews," the soldier is reciting doubtfully, reading the Latin inscription of the titulus he has just affixed to the stipes. "You, a king?" he says mockingly, looking at me. "As if!"

He steps back and surveys me and my fellow crucified, satisfied with his morning's work. The other soldiers have packed away their tools, and they proceed to argue about who should keep my clothes. They have already profited from the two others, and are now drawing lots as to who gets what of mine, just as King David had experienced – and foretold. *They divide my garments amongst themselves and cast lots for my clothing.*[11]

It is difficult to breathe now; I can only take shallow breaths. Every so often it feels like I am suffocating and I am forced to push down on my feet in order to raise my body and take a proper breath. The pain in my feet is indescribable, and shoots up the nerves of my legs, which go into spasm with the effort. Indeed, my whole body is shuddering involuntarily. The two others are moaning regularly as they too try to breathe.

---

[11] Psalm 22:18

Again and again, observing my agonizing manoeuvres, people standing round make some or other sneering comment. "He saved others; why doesn't he save himself if he really is the Messiah?"

Even the chief priests are mocking me with similar remarks. "He could save others, but not himself! If we were to see this 'Christ', this 'King of Israel', come down off the cross now, then we might believe!"

Don't they read the scriptures? *Everyone who sees me mocks me; they hurl insults, and shake their heads at me, saying, "He trusts in the Lord; let the Lord rescue him. Let the Lord deliver him if he delights in him so much."* [12]

Go on, I hear the devil tempting me, *why don't you? Easy-peasy, get your angels down here and prove who you really are!*

But you, O Lord, are my strength; don't stay far away, come and help me quickly! [13]

It is now some time after the third hour, or gone what you know as 9am. On the nearby Bethany road, pilgrims coming from as far as Jericho and beyond the Jordan, and places I visited along that route, are passing by on their way into the city for the Passover. Some of them, recognising me, also hurl insults at me. "You who reckoned you were going to tear down the temple and build it again in three days, save yourself! Come down off that cross, if you are the Son of God!"

"Hey, Jesus," I suddenly hear from my left, "you're the Christ, aren't you?" I look across to the man; he's desperate, afraid. "Then save yourself and us!" [14]

"Shut up, Gestas," the other one retorts. [15] "Don't you fear God? We're all about to meet our maker, but we deserve our sentence, whereas this man has done nothing wrong."

Turning to me, the man who must be Dysmas pleads with me. "Jesus, remember me when you get into your kingdom, mate."

Do you remember the parable of the workers, hired throughout the day for the vineyard? [16] Dysmas has admitted his guilt, and turned

---

[12] Psalm 22:7-8
[13] Psalm 22:19
[14] Luke 23:39(-43)
[15] Gospel of Nicodemus X.2; see 'Non-Canonical Gospels' note, page 300
[16] See page 207

to me, even now. That's all it needs, wherever you are. Or, as Isaiah put it, "But whoever finds refuge in me will take possession of the land and of my holy mountain." [17] *Thank you, Father!*

"It's a fact," I assure him, "that today you will be with me in paradise."

A while has passed, and my shoulders are on fire now. One of them dislocated a little while ago when I flopped back down, sending a new sensation of never-experienced pain through my already ravaged body. I have just become aware of my mother standing close to my cross.[18] Emotion overcomes me as I consider what she is going through. Her tear-stained cheeks bear witness to her anguish. I imagine all those words she stored away in her heart coursing through her thoughts now, as she tries to make sense of events, clinging to faith in a God she cannot understand right now.

Clopas' wife, Mary, and Mary Magdalene are there trying to comfort her, lost in their own distress. A few paces away I spot my young disciple John, barely out of his teens, distraught, his youthful enthusiasm evaporated for now.

I raise myself up as best I can to address them.

"Mum," I say to my mother tenderly, and looking at John, "here is your son." She cups her hand to her mouth, sobbing.

I have to hold back my own emotions as I address John. "Here is your mother." He manages a silent nod, tears all spent, words not forthcoming. I know he will look out for my Mum, and she will take care of him.

It's around the sixth hour now, and the sun is at its highest. But my Father is at work – and at the same time abandoning me to take mankind's sin upon myself. For this moment in time, he must separate himself from me, for he is holy and nothing impure may enter his presence. The sky darkens as my Father aligns planets and slows the earth and time to black out the sun.

As physical darkness covers the land, so spiritual darkness closes in upon me. Now I am separate from my Father in heaven, and weighing

---

[17] Isaiah 57:13c; cf. Isaiah 2:2-4 and Micah 4:1-3
[18] John 19:26

upon me is everything in all time that separates mankind, including you, from him. Every evil deed presses down on my shoulders: every murder, every theft, every cruel or untrue word, every blackmail, every rape and abuse, every corner cut in the name of profit, every drug deal, every time the homeless or helpless are ignored, every case of greed, every disrespectful word or profanity and every time my Father's holy name is taken in vain. All these things become an intolerable burden, *my* burden, my cross.

Again, my Father showed Isaiah this moment centuries ago. *For he bore the sin of many, and made intercession for the transgressors.*[19]

Father, take this sacrifice and open the way to you once and for all!

After three hours of darkness, I have borne all, and can bear no more. I am alone, cut off from my Father from whose presence I am banished. Rejected by the very people I came to save and whose sin I bear. For this moment in time, I belong nowhere.

I have to summon all my remaining human strength to raise myself up to take a deep enough breath, and use one of David's psalms to cry out to my Father.

"Eloi, Eloi, lama sabachtani?" *My God, my God, why have you forsaken me?* [20]

"He's calling Elijah," I hear someone propose.

No, I am expressing the pain of separation, the spiritual oppression of sin, and the physical burden of my tightening chest and dehydration. My heart is pounding as it struggles to supply my weakened body with the meagre supply of oxygen provided by constricted lungs. Cramps and spasms set in hours ago as starved muscles could no longer fulfil their duty.

Another of David's psalms reminds me that my job is almost done. *All my bones are out of joint. My heart has become like molten wax within me. My strength has been sapped, dry as a shard of pottery, and my tongue is sticking to the roof of my mouth.*[21]

---

[19] Isaiah 53:12b
[20] Psalm 22:1; Matthew 27:46; Mark 15:34
[21] Psalm 22:14-15

"I am thirsty,"[22] I say after a moment, and someone uses a hyssop stalk to lift a sponge to my lips. Just as David also foretold: *They gave me vinegar for my thirst.*[23] I suck a few drops from the sponge. I barely notice the sour taste; it loosens my tongue and brings me a moment of comfort.

Again, I resolutely push myself up to declare to all triumphantly: "IT IS FINISHED!"

The Cup of Restoration has been emptied, fulfilling the fourth promise made by my Father and remembered at Passover: "I will take you as my own people, and I will be your God."[24] I have fulfilled the mission I came here for! The sacrifice is made, and though my Father has had to abandon me, I know it is only for this moment. Like the red heifer and the scapegoat of old,[25] I have removed sin from the camp, and made the sacrifice for all eternity.

It is almost the ninth hour now; the Passover lambs are about to be sacrificed. My Passover sacrifice means that the angel of death will 'pass over' those who sin but who accept me. Mankind's salvation is procured. It is finished!

My Father in heaven is on the move. I can feel a tremor rising from the deep. It is time. As the priests in the temple raise their knives, I push against the nail through my feet one last time, take as deep a breath as I can, and cry aloud, "FATHER, BADDACH EPHKID ROUEL."[26] *Into your hands I commit my Spirit.*[27] Now he can redeem me at last.

My body falls limp as my soul rises above it. Below, an earthquake shakes the city, rocks crack, tombs eject their occupants, and the lintel over the temple cracks and falls with a mighty crash, taking the sixty by thirty foot veil with it, tearing the hand-width thick material from top to bottom.[28] The symbolic barrier that separated people from God is removed. It is as if my Father has torn his outer garment, a normal gesture of mourning made by any father for a lost son. In doing so, he

---

[22] John 19:28

[23] Psalm 69:21b

[24] Exodus 6:7a (NIV)

[25] Red heifer: see page 168; scapegoat: Leviticus 16

[26] Gospel of Nicodemus 11:1; see 'Non-Canonical Gospels' note, page 300

[27] Luke 23:46 (NIV); Psalm 31:5

[28] Matthew 27:51; Mark 15:38; Mishnah Shekalim 8.5

and I have opened the way for all to come to us directly. *I am the way and the truth and the life; no-one comes to the Father except through me.*[29]

My soul hovers for a moment longer. The centurion, having seen all these things, has fallen to his knees in recognition of who his prisoner was. He pronounces the guilty innocent. Many of the onlookers are leaving, beating their breasts in contrition, but those who know me remain standing, unwilling to leave, trying to make sense of these strange happenings.[30]

The sky begins to lighten as the sun's rays burst through once again. Daylight returns, but I must go for a little while for I have an appointment to keep.

---

[29] John 14:6 (NIV)
[30] Luke 23:48-49

31

Descended to the Dead

I am making my way to a place that transcends any physical location or even time.[1] It is the place of reward or punishment postulated by the Pharisees. They hold that those who have lived a vicious, ungodly life are detained in an everlasting prison, which you know as 'hell'.[2]

However, up until now, hell has also harboured a separate place, a sort of holding bay, an interim paradise that houses the righteous who have died throughout the ages. Adam and Eve are there (despite their failure in the original Paradise, the Garden of Eden); and so is Noah with his family; likewise, the Patriarchs and the prophets, along with all those who trusted my Father during their earthly lifetimes.

The poor beggar Lazarus, whom I told you about, had arrived here to stay at Abraham's side,[3] but the rich man in that story had rejected our laws of compassion and dwelt – for ever – in that neighbouring chamber of hell called 'the pit'. All who die go to one of these places, even the righteous, for it is only now that I have paid the price that those who have already died can enter my Father's presence. Remember: *no-one comes to the Father except through me*.[4]

---

[1] Narrative based on non-canonical Gospel of Nicodemus (Acts of Pilate)
[2] Josephus (Antiquities of the Jews XVIII.1.3)
[3] Luke 16:22(19-26)
[4] John 14:6

And so I am on my way to plunder hell, claim those who have died in the faith and release them to eternal life in my Father's presence! My presence lights up this dark, forbidding place as I enter, and a wave of excitement echoes up out of the depths as the prophets of old recognise my arrival at last.

I announce myself in a voice of thunder with one of David's Psalms. "Remove your gates, O princes; be lifted up, you ancient doors, that the King of Glory may come in."[5]

I can hear Satan in discussion with Hell. Hell is nervous. "Go and fight this King of Glory, in case we that hold captivity be taken captive ourselves."

The assembled righteous repeat the order to open the gates.

"Who is this 'King of Glory'?" Hell asks, as if he didn't know.

King David himself answers emphatically. "The Lord, strong and mighty. The Lord, mighty in battle. *He* is the King of Glory!"

Hell and all his underlings quiver with terror. "Who are you, Jesus, that having been dead and lying in the tomb, you should be alive and appear here? The whole earth quaked when you died on the cross, yet now you are free and have come here to set our prisoners free."

Now it is time to execute the punishment Satan is due, that we warned him about in the Garden of Eden: "I will make you and the woman, and your offspring and hers, hostile to each other; he will crush your head, and you will strike his heel."[6] And so I, a woman's offspring, trample upon death, lay hold of Satan and deliver him, writhing in terror, to Hell.

Hell realises what Satan has done and berates him bitterly. "Prince Satan, father of all the wicked and ungodly, what have you done? You wanted to crucify the King of Glory and promised us great spoils from his death. Like a fool, you didn't know what you were doing. You crucified him who was innocent and now his radiant presence has put to flight the darkness of death. All the gains you made by the tree of transgression, you have lost on the tree of the cross. He has freed our prisoners and loosed those who were bound."

---

5   Psalm 24:7 (NIV); see also verses 8-9; Gospel of Nicodemus XXI.1(-3)
6   Genesis 3:15; Gospel of Nicodemus XXII.2; cf. Romans 16:20

"Satan the prince shall be in your power for all ages," I tell Hell, "in the place of Adam and his children, all my righteous ones."

"Come to me," I shout to my saints, "all you who bear my image and my likeness. You who were condemned by the tree, the devil, and death, come and witness the devil and death now condemned by the tree."

Adam and the saints break out in praise as I lead them from captivity[7] and hand them over to the archangel Michael, who leads them to the gates of the new Paradise. There they meet Enoch and Elijah, who were transported away long ago and never knew death;[8] and that thief, Dysmas, who turned to me with repentance from on his cross.

I watch them safely enter heaven together, but it is not my time to return to my Father just yet[9]. I have to return to my disciples. And for that, I need to go and pick up my body.

Descended to the dead... Where are *your* dead? Who in your family or community, or in the wider world, is lost, bound up? What could you do to free them?

---

[7] Gospel of Nicodemus XXIV.2; cf. Psalm 68:18
[8] Genesis 5:24; Hebrews 11:5; 2 Kings 2:1,11; Gospel of Nicodemus XXV-XXVI
[9] cf. John 20:17

32

Risen First Fruits

There is a simple reason why I cannot return to my Father in heaven just yet, but must come back.[1] How will people know that death is defeated if my burial was the last they saw of me?

However, there is a further reason. Today is the day after the Passover Sabbath, the Feast of Firstfruits. Before they entered the Promised Land, we gave the Israelites instructions through Moses concerning, amongst other things, the various feast days they were to celebrate. On the Feast of Firstfruits, they were to present to the priest a sheaf of the first grain harvested. The priest would wave this before the Lord so that he would accept the offering.[2]

While my crucifixion fulfilled both the sin offering of the red heifer and the sacrifice of the Passover lamb,[3] my resurrection represents the 'first fruits' of the harvest I told my disciples about at Jacob's well in Sychar. When people come to faith, they are 'born again', as I explained to Nicodemus; spiritually, they rise from death to life.[4]

Remember the seed analogy?[5] A seed contains life, yet it has to die and fall into the ground before it can burst into that life as the plant it

---

1   Luke 24:1-12
2   Leviticus 23:10-11
3   Hebrews 13:10-14; 1 Corinthians 5:7; 1 Peter 1:18-21
4   1 Corinthians 15:20-23; John 4:35-38, 3:3-8
5   See pages 19-20

was designed to be, and be fruitful.[6] Abraham's seed[7] died three days ago; today is 'bursting back to life' day!

My soul re-enters my body before dawn on this first day of the week. My Father has ensured that it has not decayed, just as David prophesied[8]. Just as an earthquake accompanied my death on the cross, so a violent aftershock rocks the region anew as my Father raises me back to life. With a grinding sound, the heavy stone is rolled along its channel from the entrance to my tomb, and the angel who has just performed this feat climbs up and sits on it. He has the appearance of lightning.[9]

As I stand up, I realise that my burial cloths are lying on the ledge undisturbed, resting there without having been unwound. My body is real enough but has taken on new properties, and as if to prove the point, I am whisked off and find myself on top of the Mount of Olives.

The rising sun banishes the last vestiges of the night. From a distance, I see that Mary Magdalene, Joanna, Mary the mother of James, and Salome are coming to my tomb, laden with spices to embalm me.[10] The angel tells them that I am no longer there. That appears to be particularly bad news for the guards posted outside.

The women leave their spices near the tomb and depart hurriedly. Mary Magdalene returns a little later with Peter and John. I stand up, wanting to shout out, but pause. No, I will re-introduce myself quietly, gradually.

John reaches the tomb first, surveys the soldiers, but is reluctant to enter. Peter soon catches up and with no hesitation goes into the tomb. John joins him briefly, then both emerge, scratching their heads in puzzlement. They talk with Mary and then head off back to town.

Another angel joins the first,[11] unnoticed by Mary, and the two disappear into the tomb. Mary, like all my disciples, was unable to comprehend my death, and now she is unwilling to accept that I am

---

6   John 12:24; 1 Corinthians 15:35-38
7   Galatians 3:16
8   Psalm 16:10
9   Matthew 28:2(-10); Mark 16:1-8; Luke 24:1-8; John 20:1-10
10 Matthew 28:1; Mark 16:1; Luke 24:1,10; John 20:1
11 cf. Matthew 28:2,5 and Mark 16:5, with Luke 24:4,5 and John 20:12

gone again. She ventures to the door of the tomb, stoops over and looks in.[12] I see her startle and step backwards, before hesitantly drawing closer again, as I make my way down towards her. She is talking to the angels as I arrive at the tomb.

Mary hears my footsteps and turns round, but in her grief she doesn't recognise me.

"Why are you weeping?" I ask her. "Who are you looking for?"

"Sir," she blubbers, "if it was you that removed him, tell me where you have put him and I will fetch him."

Since I healed her, Mary has been a close follower, one of the several faithful women who supported my disciples and me as we travelled from place to place. They opened their homes to us, cooked meals, mended our clothes. We have so often talked and laughed together, yet I am not surprised she does not recognise me. The angels cleaned my body before my return, and my Father has renewed the skin of my back. While the scars in my hands, feet and side are still present, I look vastly different from when she last saw me, hanging there on the cross, battered, bruised and bloodied. Anyway, why should she expect me to be alive again? Even the Twelve didn't comprehend that!

But now, with beating heart, I will gently – well, as gently as possible – surprise her. She may not recognise me in the flesh, but she will know my voice, for my sheep always do[13].

"Mary."

Mary gasps in disbelief and joy, and launches herself at me in a flying hug. "Rabboni!" she delights, in the Aramaic we usually speak with each other. *My master.*

"Don't cling on to me now," I tell her, pulling away and holding her at arm's length. "I'm not returning to the Father just yet. But go to my brothers and tell them that I will soon return to my Father and God – *our* Father and God."

Mary nods, hardly daring to believe that the encounter is real, insistent tears still moistening her eyes. She gathers up her skirt and runs off towards the city, almost skipping.

---

12 John 20:11(-18)
13 John 10:3-4

I spend the remainder of the morning up on the Mount of Olives, and strolling through Gethsemane, talking with my Father and working out how I will build my disciples back up. I must tie up some loose ends and commission them before I leave. Then I can return to my Father in heaven!

Early afternoon finds me walking along the road to Emmaus,[14] a few miles from Jerusalem. Ahead of me, two men are walking with the slow gait of people deep in discussion. I recognise them, as I catch them up, as belonging to my wider circle of disciples. One of them is Clopas, whose wife Mary was one of the women standing near my cross looking on.

"What are you talking about so intensely?" I ask them. They stand still and look at me with downcast faces, not recognising me any more than Mary did. Do I look so different?

"Are you the only visitor to Jerusalem," Clopas asks with surprise, "who doesn't know about what's been happening here these past few days?"

"What *has* been happening here?" I ask innocently.

"All this about Jesus of Nazareth," Clopas replies, "who was a mighty prophet in everything he said and did before God and people alike. Our religious rulers had him condemned to death and crucified. We had been hoping that he was the one intended to redeem Israel..." His voice trails off.

"Yes," the other continues, "and now it's the third day since it all took place. Jesus had talked about being raised again on the third day,[15] but by this morning we'd given up any hope. Then some of our women, having been up to the tomb first thing, came back with the amazing news that they hadn't found his body but had seen angels who told them he's alive! Some of our group went to the tomb and found it empty, as the women had reported, but they didn't see Jesus anywhere!"

"How little you understand," I admonish them gently, "and how reluctant you are to believe the words of the prophets! Didn't the Messiah have to endure these things before entering his glory?"

---

[14] Luke 24:13-35
[15] Luke 9:22

I wonder afresh that my people can't see the signs in my Father's Word. Time for a history lesson and a revelation! I begin to explain to them what the Scriptures say about me.

"Right at the beginning, the Lord warned the serpent – Satan – that Eve's offspring would crush him.[16] The arrival of sin in the world drove a wedge between the Lord and his created people. When things became so bad that he could no longer stand it, the Lord destroyed his creation and started again with Noah and his family and the animals they had taken onto the ark. After the flood, he promised Noah that he would never do that again, and made water droplets reflect light in such a way that he could set the rainbow in the sky as a sign of this covenant.[17] However, sin was still present in the world. When he had promised our ancestor Abraham countless descendants and given him a miracle son, the Lord tested Abraham by asking him to sacrifice that long-desired son. Abraham trusted in God's promise that he would bless all peoples through him and his descendants. God renewed that promise after providing a ram to sacrifice at the last second.[18] The sacrifice of Abraham's son, and God's provision of a substitute, formed a picture of what he was planning to do far in the future to atone for sin."

"So Jesus was the substitute for the sacrifices demanded by the law?" Clopas enquires, a light dawning.

"Yes."

"So the law is no longer valid?" asks his companion.

"No, the law still holds; sacrifice for sin must be made. Remember that an animal was sacrificed in order that God could make clothes for Adam and Eve, to cover up their nakedness and remove their sin.[19] Blood has always been shed to atone for sin. But that alone is not enough. Cain's sacrifice was not accepted because of his evil deeds; God detests the sacrifices of the wicked, as Solomon told us in his collection of proverbs. The priest Samuel told King Saul that obedience is better than sacrifice, just as God told us through His prophets Hosea and

---

[16] Genesis 3:15
[17] Genesis 9:8-17
[18] Genesis 12:1-3, 15:5-6, 22:18; cf. Galatians 3:16 and Acts 3:25-26
[19] Genesis 3:21

Micah.[20] People's hearts need to be right; that's much more important than any number of sacrifices. King David understood this too, after committing adultery with Bathsheba (before later becoming Solomon's father), and recorded it for us in one of his Psalms[21]."

Clopas' friend now speaks up, looking puzzled. "I thought that the promised Messiah was to come through King David."

"It was indeed King David's line that the Lord chose. As the people grew in number, the Lord narrowed down the path his blessing would take and showed us in advance how he would bring it about. He determined through Jacob, when Jacob gave his sons a final and prophetic blessing: that a ruler would come from Judah.[22] Later, Samuel anointed David, the youngest son of Jesse, from whose 'stump', as Isaiah later described it, a branch would shoot. Jeremiah described it as a righteous branch sprouting from David's line, a wise king in whose days Judah would be saved. He would be called 'The Lord our Righteousness'. The Lord assured David through the prophet Nathan that his house and his throne would endure forever.[23] So you are right; the Messiah had to come from David's line."

"But Jesus came from Nazareth," Clopas objects. "The prophet Micah said that the Messiah would come from Bethlehem."

"He did!" I affirm. "You'll remember the census that took place when you were a young lad."

"The one ordered by the last emperor, Augustus?"

"Yes. Well, everyone had to return to his family's hometown. Jesus was considered the son of Joseph, who belonged to the house and line of David, so Joseph went to Bethlehem. His mother Mary, too, was in fact a descendent of David. Thus Jesus was born in Bethlehem, just as the Scriptures foretold.[24]

"However, in different ways, the Scriptures also tell us that Jesus would come from Nazareth, which name derives from our word 'neser', or the branch that not just Isaiah and Jeremiah but also Zechariah

---

[20] Genesis 4:5-7; Proverbs 21:27; 1 Samuel 15:22; Hosea 6:6; Micah 6:6-8
[21] 2 Samuel 11:4; 12:1ff; Psalm 51:16-17
[22] Genesis 49:10; cf. Hebrews 7:14
[23] Isaiah 6:13, 11:1-10; Jeremiah 23:5, 33:15; 2 Samuel 7:16
[24] Micah 5:2; Matthew 2:1-6; Luke 2:1-7, 3:23

described[25]. In addition, David in his Psalms and Isaiah both prophesied that the Messiah would be scorned and hated for no reason, just like people from the backwater Nazareth are regarded today, and just like Jesus has been treated by many.[26]"

"But why did Jesus have to die if he was the Messiah?" Clopas wants to know.

"Remember, the law demands a sacrifice. God has stepped in to make that sacrifice through his Son Jesus. Isaiah and Zechariah both talked about the Messiah being 'pierced', and our rabbis also hold this to mean that the Messiah had to die.[27] Isaiah even described[28] in detail how he would suffer – beaten and spat upon, rejected, treated like a criminal and crucified. King David, too, showed remarkable foreknowledge of what would happen – that the Messiah would be betrayed by a friend, the victim of false witness, pierced, bones out of joint yet (like the Passover lamb) none broken, and even that lots would be cast for his clothes.[29]"

The sun is low in the sky now, and we are approaching Emmaus.

"So you see, this Jesus is the one to redeem Israel, just as you hoped. He had to die, but King David also assured us that the Lord would not abandon him to the grave. Jesus himself said that he would die but on the third day rise again.[30] The way he has chosen to redeem us might be different from what you imagined, but read the Prophets with your eyes and hearts open, and you will see that he has fulfilled all that they wrote!"

As we reach what appears to be their house, Clopas and his companion are glowing with excitement.[31]

"It's been good to share with you," I tell them. "I must get on to where I am going."

"Stay with us," Clopas insists, his companion nodding agreement vigorously. "It's getting dark and the day is almost done."

---

25 NIV footnote at Matthew 2:23; Zechariah 3:8, 6:12
26 Psalm 22:6-7, 35:19, 69:4; cf. John 1:46 and 15:23
27 Isaiah 53:5-9; Zechariah 12:10, 13:6; Talmud – Sukkah 52a
28 Isaiah 50:6, 52:14, 52:13-53:12
29 Psalm 41:9, 35:11, 12:16, 22:14, 34:20 (Exodus 12:46), 22:18
30 Psalm 16:10; Matthew 16:21, 20:19; Mark 8:31, 10:34
31 cf. Luke 24:32

We enter their house, and my hosts prepare a simple meal of bread and wine, much like the one I ate with the Twelve just a few nights ago. They invite me to give thanks for it, and I use the same words of the Ha-Motzi blessing: "Blessed are you, Lord, our God, King of the Universe who brings forth bread from the earth."[32]

Having broken the bread, I begin to give it to them, but it is time to go and I disappear from their sight.

My resurrected body no longer binds me to any one location as before; it is simultaneously physical and immaterial. Later the same evening, I use this new property to appear to my disciples behind locked doors.[33] They are still afraid, still shell-shocked from the Feast where everything seemed to end. My materialising amongst them is outside their comprehension and well beyond their comfort zone.

"Shalom," I reassure them, failing to quell their terror. "What's troubling you? Why are you so full of doubt? Come, see my hands and feet, and my side." They still look like they've seen a ghost. "It's me: Jesus! Touch me and see for yourselves that I'm real flesh and bones, not a ghost!"

Peter, just like on the lake, needs to see for himself. His confidence falters a little as he stands in front of me, then takes my hand in his and studies it closely. His head rises slowly, his eyes meet mine, and his pursed lips relax and widen into a broad grin that soon becomes infectious laughter. "It's really you!" He hugs me, and the others jump up excitedly and do likewise, overjoyed. Thomas, however, is missing.

They still don't know quite what to make of me. "Have you got anything for me to eat?" I enquire, stating the obvious really, as they are in the middle of a meal.

They pass me a piece of broiled fish, and watch me eat it, mesmerised. *Hmm... tastes good.* Even better is the piece of honeycomb I chew on afterwards.[34]

32 Rich ("Ha-Motzi")
33 Mark 16:14(-18); Luke 24:36(-44); John 20:19(-23)
34 Luke 24:42 (e.g. King James Bible, after some Greek and Latin texts)

"Peace be with you," I repeat. "As the Father has sent me, I am sending you."[35] Breathing on them symbolically, I continue, "Receive the Holy Spirit. If you forgive anyone his sins, they are forgiven; if you do not forgive them, they are not forgiven." As I told Peter after his declaration of who I am, what I mean is that my disciples should preach and pronounce forgiveness, and warn of there being no forgiveness for those who do not respond to the message.

A week passes before I see my disciples again, this time with Thomas.[36] I enter the room in the same manner as previously, and again seek to quell their fright.

"Shalom."

My Spirit has already shown me that Thomas has struggled to believe the reports of his fellow apostles. I turn to him. He is studying me with incredulity, jaw wide open, with no commentary forthcoming.

"Thomas, look at my hands and place your finger in my side. Stop doubting and believe."

Thomas' doubts are transformed in an instant, banished, and feeling no further need to check out my wounds, he falls to his knees. "My Lord! My God!" he declares.

"You believe in me now, having seen me," I tell him, without reproof. "Blessed are those who have not seen and yet believe."[37] Then, as we finish the meal, I instruct all of them, "Meet me in Galilee, at the lake where you keep your boats, the day after the next Sabbath."

It is easy to believe in me in the presence of tangible evidence. Faith, though, is to believe in that which you cannot see; accepting the evidence presented, allowing other people's experience to become your own. In a sense, what to do with the evidence has been the challenge ever since my meeting with Thomas.[38]

---

35 John 20:21 (NIV)
36 John 20:26(24-29)
37 John 20:29 (NIV)
38 See Smith, Graeme

33

Last Words

A week later, Lake Galilee is glistening in the spring sunshine, which is accentuating the colours of the verdant shoots of fresh growth along the lakeside. Seven of my disciples have been out fishing all night[1] and are just rounding the headland at one end of the bay, where the beach serves as a fishing harbour. I have spent the past hour making a fire for a barbecue.

"You haven't caught anything, have you, lads?" I ask somewhat obliquely, knowing that their efforts have been in vain.

They don't recognise me despite our prearrangement. "No," they answer despondently. Just as well I caught some myself then, enough to get breakfast going anyway. Even the words I speak next don't remind them of when I first called them on this very beach.[2]

"Try throwing your net to starboard and you will catch some," I suggest, prodding the glowing firewood and turning the frying fish.

A pause. Then, "It's the Lord!" I hear John shouting to Peter.

Peter, without hesitation, nor considering helping the others haul in the bulging net, wraps his outer garment around himself and jumps into the water. He swims and wades the hundred yards to the shore ahead of the others paddling in the boat.

---

[1] John 21:1-14
[2] Luke 5:4-11

"Master!" Peter exclaims, thankfully sparing me a wet hug and instead clasping both my hands in his. He eyes the fish and bread that I have prepared.

"Bring some of the fish you have just caught,"[3] I tell him.

Peter returns to the water's edge and helps the others drag the unexpected catch of large fish ashore. They express surprise that the net hasn't torn. None of them dare ask who I am; they know it is me.

"Come and have some breakfast," I invite them with a grin, and distribute the bread and already-cooked fish amongst them. We put more on the fire.

At the end of the meal, I take Peter aside while the others set about loading the fish – a hundred and fifty-three of them including the ones we've eaten – into baskets, and cleaning the nets.[4] We sit on a large, flat-topped rock near the water's edge.

"Simon, Son of John," I ask him earnestly, using his original name, "do you really love me more than the others do?"

Peter needs my reassurance. He knows he failed me when, humanly, I most needed his support. For all his confident bluster about remaining faithful even should the others fall away, he did not possess the courage to admit he was my follower, and disowned me – three times, just as I had told him.[5] But that is not Peter's heart, and I desire to confirm to him the words I spoke over him after his confession of faith in me.[6]

"Yes, Lord," Peter replies a little awkwardly, "you know that I love you."

"Feed my lambs," I tell him.

I still intend to use Peter to help build my church, even though he might no longer feel worthy. Do you sometimes find it difficult to admit to being my follower? Does some past mistake make you feel unworthy, not good enough to serve me?

"Simon, Son of John," I ask again, "do you really love me?"

---

3   John 21:10 (NIV)
4   John 21:15(-23)
5   Matthew 26:33-34,75; John 13:38
6   Matthew 16:16-18

"Yes, Lord," he answers for the second time, "you know that I do."

"Shepherd my sheep for me."

I want Peter to be sure of my calling. You too.

"Simon, Son of John," I persist, "do you love me?"

The others throw a surreptitious glance towards us. They can hear the exchange. Peter's face drops; he is hurt because he knows that I am alluding to his failure.

"Lord, you know everything," he states solemnly. "You know that I love you!"

Indeed I do. In stating this a third time, Peter has, as it were, made good his three denials and cancelled them out. His faith, not his denials, shows his true character. His confidence is restored.

"Then tend my sheep," I repeat, then proceed to prepare him for what his future ministry will entail. "I assure you, up till now you got yourself ready and went where you liked; but when you grow old, you will stretch out your hands and someone else will get you ready and lead you to a place you don't want to go."

Peter will no longer fear reprisals or even death, as he did in Caiaphas' courtyard; he will preach boldly, whatever the cost. He will follow me more closely than he might like, as I indicated to him at our last supper together.[7]

"Follow me!" I challenge him in conclusion, repeating the invitation I gave him and the others when I first met them here.

As we jump down from the rock, Peter turns and notices John starting to follow us. "Lord, what about him?" Peter wants to know, a touch of the rivalry creeping in that they all displayed at our supper together before my arrest.[8]

"Whether it's my will that he remain until I return is no concern of yours. Your job is to follow me."

---

[7] John 21:19, 13:36b; 2 Peter 1:14
[8] Luke 22:24

Wondering about what I ask others to do does not achieve what I ask you to do. Each is called differently and equipped according to their calling with the gifts my Spirit bestows.[9]

The Eleven and I spend a few short weeks in Galilee, talking, fishing, and climbing the mountain above Capernaum like we used to do.[10] I continue to teach my disciples and help them to understand the Scriptures that have previously remained a mystery to them.

Finally, I must prepare them for my ultimate departure.[11] "While I was still with you, I told you that everything written about me in the law of Moses, the Prophets, and the Psalms must be fulfilled: the Christ will suffer and rise from the dead on the third day, and repentance and forgiveness will be preached in his name to all nations, beginning at Jerusalem.[12] Having witnessed all this, you are now to tell people about it."

Simon the Zealot is hoping that Daniel's prophecy is about to come true and that the Romans will be overthrown.[13] "Lord, are you going to restore Israel now and reunite Judea with the kingdom?"

"The dates my Father has picked are not for you to know," I inform him. "Come," I tell them all, "let's make our way back to Jerusalem to celebrate the harvest at the Feast of Weeks. I am going to send you what my Father has promised, the Spirit I told you about on that fateful evening; but stay in the city until you have been empowered from on high. John baptised with water, but in a few days you will be baptised with the Holy Spirit.[14]"

Jerusalem is still relatively quiet when we arrive. The main thrust of pilgrims will arrive next week. Forty days have passed since my resurrection; we hold the Feast of Weeks, or Pentecost, fifty days after the Passover Sabbath.[15]

Evening has come, and I am leading my disciples one last time, up through Gethsemane and to the top of the Mount of Olives, near

---

9   1 Corinthians 12:8-11,27-31
10   Matthew 28:16
11   Luke 24:45-49
12   Psalm 22; Isaiah 53, 2:3
13   Acts 1:6; Daniel 7:27
14   John 14:16-18; Acts 1:4-5, 2:1ff
15   Acts 1:3; Leviticus 23:15-16; Deuteronomy 16:9-10

Bethany.[16] My human side wants to put off this moment; equally, I am excited, both at the prospect of returning to my Father, and at what my disciples are going to achieve once I am gone. They too know that it is time for me to leave them again, this time permanently, as far as my bodily form goes. Gone is the angst they felt at that last supper, however; now they are joyfully worshipping me.

"All authority in heaven and on earth has been given to me," I declare to them as we reach the summit. "Therefore go and make disciples of all nations, baptising them in the name of the Father and of the Son and of the Holy Spirit, and teaching them to obey everything I have commanded you. And surely I am with you always, to the very end of the age."[17]

As I lift up my hands to bless them, two angels dressed in white descend with a cloud that envelopes me. The angels stay to encourage my disciples, while I am transported in the cloud back to my Father in heaven, and to a choral reception committee the likes of which has not been since the angelic choir that announced my birth to the shepherds.[18]

"Holy, holy, holy is the Lord God Almighty, who was, and is, and is to come. You are worthy, our Lord and God, to receive glory and honour and power, for you created all things, and by your will they were created and have their being. Worthy is the Lamb, who was slain, to receive power and wealth and wisdom and strength and honour and glory and praise!"[19]

Home at last! I take my place as high priest, seated at my Father's right hand, entry to His presence bought with my own blood for all who will follow.[20]

One day I will return the same way that my disciples have just watched me depart.[21] On that day, I, the bright Morning Star,[22] will usher in the end of the age. Death and Hades, already defeated by my cross and resurrection, will be cast into the fiery lake of burning sulphur,

---

[16] Luke 24:50(-52)
[17] Matthew 28:18-20 (NIV)
[18] Luke 2:13-15
[19] Revelation 4:8,11, 5:11-12 (NIV)
[20] Mark 16:19; Hebrews 4:14, 9:11-12
[21] Luke 24:51; Acts 1:9-11
[22] Numbers 24:17; Revelation 22:16

along with anyone whose name has not been written in the book of life.[23]

On that day, I, the Lion of Judah, will return in judgement.[24] But God will make his dwelling with humanity in a New Jerusalem, my bride. You will be God's people, and he will be with you. He will wipe every tear from your eyes. There will be no more death or mourning or crying or pain, for the old order of things will have passed away.[25]

Until then, I shall be with you, just as I have promised my disciples. I shall continue to speak with my children, and even those who are not my children. In a few years, for example, I shall meet with a guy named Saul on the road to Damascus;[26] that will be a life-changing experience for him and a turning point in the life of my body, the Church!

My Spirit now lives in you and helps you to continue my work of healing, bringing hope, pronouncing forgiveness, sharing the good news of my Father's love, such good works as we created you to do, and prepared in advance for you.[27] Are you up for doing them?

I, the Alpha and Omega, the Beginning and the End, am making all things new![28]

---

[23] Revelation 20:14-15
[24] Genesis 49:8-10; Micah 5:8; Revelation 5:5
[25] Based on Revelation 21:4 (NIV); see also verses 1-3
[26] Acts 9:1-18
[27] Romans 8:11; 1 Corinthians 3:16; 6:19; Ephesians 2:10
[28] Revelation 21:5-6

Epilogue

Fast forward a couple of days. My millennial days.

A phone rings, causing a gentle glow to illuminate the room. Though set to discreet, the movement of its tiny vibration mechanism is amplified by the hard surface it rests on, announcing the presence of the phone almost as stridently as any ringtone. A groping hand reaches out and grabs the intrusive device.

It's the middle of the night and you are already puzzled; the call must be important. Bewilderment turns to mild alarm as you recognise the name – but it's not in your contact list!

———

You awake with a start, uncertain, relieved, curious.
Surely he wouldn't...? No, of course not.
You check your phone anyway. *One missed call.*
Select.
Private number.
Go back.
One message received.
Hesitant and with beating heart, you fumble again for the Select button.
So he did...?
"It's me: Jesus. Come and follow me!"

Notes

This section elaborates in more detail than was possible in individual footnotes. Most website sources here and in the bibliography were originally retrieved 2010-2011 but checked late 2014 just before publication of this book. Any no longer available have been updated where possible or marked 'NLA'.

1. Literary and Language Sources

This book's narrative has its foundation in the Bible, working specifically from the NIV (Study Bible) version of the Holy Scriptures. Other literary sources have provided background information.

1.1. The Mishnah

The following is the briefest of summaries of information about the Mishnah found at *en.wikipedia.org/wiki/Mishnah, -/Tanakh, -/Talmud*. It seeks to place this quoted source in context.

The Mishnah was compiled in ~220AD by Judah haNasi, and represents the first redaction of Jewish oral traditions from Pharisaic times (536BC - 70AD). It is held as authoritative second only to the Tanakh (the Hebrew Scriptures, which form the basis of the Christian Old Testament). The Mishnah comprises six main sections, or orders, containing a total of sixty-three tractates and dealing with various aspects of worship, festivals, dietary laws and daily life. These are split into chapter and verse, which are included in any citations made.

Later rabbinic commentaries on the Mishnah, related Tannaitic writings, and the Tanakh, were redacted as the Gemara and coupled with the Mishnah to form the Talmud. The process of Gemara proceeded in the two major centres of Jewish scholarship, Israel and Babylonia. Correspondingly, two bodies of analysis developed. The Jerusalem Talmud was compiled in the fourth century; the Babylonian Talmud was compiled around 500AD, although it continued to be edited later. The word 'Talmud', when used without qualification, usually refers to the Babylonian Talmud.

While the Mishnah was compiled long after Jesus' earthly life, it reflects the thinking and oral tradition already prevalent at the time, and it is quoted as a source where no direct statement in the Old Testament exists. It has contributed much to the details of Jerusalem in the Passion Week narrative.

The (partial) text may be found at

- *www.sacred-texts.com/jud/talmud.htm*
- *www.come-and-hear.com/tcontents.html*
- *www.halakhah.com/talmud*

PDF files of all tractates may be found at *www.halakhah.com*

1.2. Non-Canonical Gospels

The Old Testament 'apocryphal' writings are reasonably well-known, a selection being printed in some Bible translations. However, there are many writings that did not make it into the 'canon' of the New Testament, which was more-or-less fixed by the fifth century but still being discussed at the ecumenical Council of Trent in 1546, and not agreed by Catholics and Protestants until 1700. This briefest of summaries originated from the much fuller description in the Catholic Encyclopedia, 1908, online at *www.newadvent.org/cathen/03274a.htm*

Besides the four known Gospels of the New Testament, there are several additional gospels and other writings which did not make it into the NT canon, including the Gospels of Thomas, James, Mary Magdalene, Nicodemus, Bartholomew, Peter, Thomas, Philip and Judas. Alfred G. Green Jr. lists these writings at *www.aggreen.net/bible/noncanon.html*

The texts may be found at *wesley.nnu.edu/sermons-essays-books/ noncanonical-literature*

The Gospel of Nicodemus supplied the names of the malefactors crucified with Jesus, Gestas and Dysmas, as well as the basis of the chapter "Descended to the Dead".

1.3. Greek and Hebrew Sources

All Greek words referenced were retrieved from *www.biblehub.com*. The website includes a verse-by-verse analysis of the biblical text and Strong's classification of Greek and Hebrew expressions.

Also of use were:

- *www.teknia.net/greek-dictionary*
- *www.biblestudytools.com/lexicons/greek* – a lexicon of NT Greek
- *perseus.uchicago.edu/#Dictionaries* – a digital library for the classical world, including dictionaries

1.4. Pericope Adulterae

The *pericope adulterae* (John 7:53 – 8:11) is generally assumed not to have been part of the original Gospel of John (Morris, pp 882-883). There is a helpful discussion about this at:

- *net.bible.org/#!bible/John+7:49*

According to the above link, 'Manuscript 225' (dated 1192) uniquely places this *pericope* after John 7:36, on or before the last day of the Feast of Tabernacles (v.37). This would mean that Jesus' statement "I am the Light" follows on from "If anyone is thirsty...", both of which allude to elements of the Feast, and would be a logical enough solution.

The overnight implied by 8:2 would mean that "I am the Light" came after the end of the Feast (cf. 7:37), which seems less logical. However, Morris notes (p.435) that the crowd is no longer mentioned in chapter 8 (eight times in chapter 7), so it might well have come after everyone had gone home (7:53).

I have chosen the latter view (and the traditional placement of the *pericope adulterae*) for my narrative.

2. Chronological Issues

Chronological issues include combining the four Gospels into one narrative ('Gospel Harmony'), and deciding on the timing of specific events. Dating Jesus' birth and his crucifixion fall into this category. The latter is discussed under *'Dating the Crucifixion'*, below.

2.1. Gospel Harmony

Trying to reconcile the four Gospel accounts of Jesus' life and ministry into one narrative has doubtless been the subject of much study and debate over the centuries. The writers each recorded their own and others' memories with a particular audience in mind, and with varying degrees of accuracy of chronological order over thematic grouping.

There are many references to particular times or (being on the way to) places, while numerous others are more general (e.g. "One Sabbath"). There is also nothing to indicate that Jesus didn't use any given illustration or parable on more than one occasion. (How many preachers recycle sermons?!)

I initially attempted to create a combined chronology of the four Gospels myself, starting with the NIV Study Bible's outline of Matthew, filling in the paragraph headings, then matching the others to it. I then marked larger sections where all matching accounts at least more-or-less agreed in their order, and was pleased to find that much of it did, particularly through Passion Week. However, the earlier parts of Jesus' ministry are far more difficult to reconcile between the four accounts.

Having tried all this, I found a few chronologies online. There is obviously little that someone hasn't previously attempted... Some have very few verses of any of the Gospels out of sequence, but consequently numerous stories or statements occur more than once. The overall consensus seems to follow the view of much modern scholarship that Mark's Gospel was the first to be written, a view first proposed by Karl Lachmann in 1835 (Silva [pp. 1396-1402], and Burge [pp. 1988-1990], writing in the 1990 Marshall Pickering Encyclopaedia of the Bible). Matthew and Luke, it is assumed, based their accounts on both Mark (using 91% and 58% respectively) and, where they otherwise agree, on an unknown 'Q' document (from the German Quelle, source).

I therefore reordered my own chronology, mainly using the order of Mark. It is thought that much of Mark's account was based in part at least on the preaching and recollections of the Apostle Peter, of whom (the John) Mark (of Acts) appears to have been a disciple after the death of Jesus (see note on Mark).

As an example, Gordon Smith compiled a chronology using J B Phillips' NT translation and writings (see bibliography). His chronology assumes Mark as being in date order, as above. I initially followed this chronology (and *www.bible-history.com*) instead of the NIV Study Bible's time chart of Jesus' life for placing the healing of the ten lepers (Luke 17:11-19), which takes place on the Galilee/Samaria border, after Luke 9:51-52. Here, Jesus has set out for Jerusalem, sent messengers ahead into a Samarian village but encountered opposition there. However, parts of Matthew 18 correspond to Luke 15 and 18, then Matthew 19:1a has Jesus leaving Galilee. So I have aligned that with the lepers on the Samaria/Galilee border of Luke 17, which the NIV timeline has after the raising of Lazarus (John 11).

Whatever choice is settled on, something is going to be out of order, and while desiring maximum possible accuracy, in the end I decided that it doesn't really matter. Most important is that Jesus' teaching and signs are faithfully recorded, and the story of his love and sacrifice told, and that I have attempted to do.

Various chronologies may be found on (amongst others) the following online sites:

- *www.bible-history.com/Chart_Jesus_Chronology*
- *www.bibletimelines.org/FramedMinistry.html*
- *www.randallmarkstewart.com/page16.html*
- *www.lifeofchrist.com/life/harmony/default.asp*

2.2. Dating Jesus' Birth

I have found various attempts online at calculating the likely time of Jesus' birth. Some base their calculations on various snippets of historical information within the gospels, and from other sources, e.g. Michael Scheifler (*www.biblelight.net/sukkoth.htm*).

Bryan T. Huie (*www.herealittletherealittle.net*) uses details of Zechariah's temple service and priestly division, details of those divisions in 1 Chronicles 24, the time of Mary's visit to Elizabeth in Elizabeth's 6th month of pregnancy, and details of conception of both John and Jesus. These may indicate the 15th day of the 7th month, Tishri – the start of the Feast of Tabernacles. John 1:14 alludes to the Word making his dwelling (tabernacle) among us.

2.3. Jesus' First Disciples

I have used John's account of Jesus' first disciples (1:35-50) as portraying an 'initial meeting' with them, with the invitation to "Come and ... see." The narratives of Matthew (4:18-22), Mark (1:16-20) and Luke (5:1-11) are taken as describing their later, permanent calling.

The passage in John's gospel is described in the NIV Study Bible's outline as being "Jesus' Introduction to Some Future Disciples". The footnote for Luke 4:16 states that: "Probably all the events of Jn 1:19-4:42 occurred between Lk 4:13 and 4:14." This view is also held by Gordon Smith and others (see 'Gospel Harmony' note, above).

2.4. The Cleansing of the Temple

Using the chronology described above (also see NIV footnote quote for Luke 4:16 in 'Jesus' First Disciples'), there are two cleansings of the temple. After narrating the wedding at Cana and Jesus' turning water into wine, I have included the early-on cleansing of the temple related only by John (2:12-25) and what follows (though without the Pool of Bethesda healing), as well as recounting, more briefly, the later such occurrence in Holy Week related by Matthew (21:12-17) and Mark (11:15-19).

2.5. Sermon on the Mount

Having worked on chronology (see 'Gospel Harmony' note, above), I went back to writing, starting from the Sermon on the Mount (Matthew) or Plain (Luke). I soon realised I wasn't finished with timing issues.

Various discussions of these accounts found online seemed to indicate that Luke's placing the discourse after the twelve Apostles are chosen (it comes before in Matthew) is more likely. If so, the calling of Matthew (Levi in Mark) logically needs to come before the naming of the Twelve.

So, while retaining the overriding order of Mark, I have used Luke's sequence for this over that of Matthew.

Regarding whether the sermon took place on a mountain or a plain, the words τόπου πεδινοῦ in Luke 6:17 mean literally 'place level'. The NIV and, for example, RSV correctly use "a level place" instead of "the plain" found in the King James Version. Mountains may certainly contain level places, and as such there is no disagreement between the texts.

2.6. Three Days and Three Nights

Jesus, in Matthew 12, refuses to give any miraculous sign but that of Jonah, who spent "three days and three nights" in the belly of a large fish (Jonah 1:17). He indicates that this will be the time he spends "in the heart of the earth". However, we know from the Gospels that he was in the grave for only two nights, noting also the phrase "...will rise on the third day" in Luke 24:46.

We, using the expression "in three days" e.g. on a Friday afternoon, would expect to return on the third day from then, i.e. Monday. However, in usual Jewish reckoning of time (according to the NIV footnote to Matthew 12:40, also noted in Barnes' Notes on the Bible and Clarke's Commentary on the Bible, commentaries on the same verse), a part of one day was reckoned as a whole day. A modern comparison might be the French 'huit jours' or German 'in acht Tagen' (eight days), meaning a week, and the French 'une quinzaine' (a 'fifteen') for a fortnight (fourteen days). So in our example above, Friday would be regarded as the first day, and Sunday would therefore be the third.

For comparison, verses 5 and 12 from 2 Chronicles 10 talk of returning "in three days" and "three days later". The same prophetic timescale can be found in Genesis 42:17-18, where Joseph put his brothers in custody for three days, then "on the third day" freed them (except Simeon) to return home to fetch Benjamin. Similarly, where again, saving the people was at stake, Esther 4:16 and 5:1 use the same terms: "for three days" and "On the third day".

These are a selection of passages taken to argue for inclusive counting. There are those who use some of these same passages to argue for a literal interpretation! Other arguments are based on there being two Sabbaths in the week of Jesus' execution: one, a special Passover Sabbath (Exodus 12:16); one the normal weekly Sabbath. Some also link in with the OT feasts of Passover, Unleavened Bread, and Firstfruits. Most of these give Wednesday as the day of crucifixion.

It is possible that Jesus died before the three hours' darkness ended, figuratively adding an extra (part-) night where Jesus was dead if not buried.

Finally, it is perhaps worth noting that Jesus used this (for scholarship) contentious phrase only once, but said "after three days" or "on the third day" many times when referring to his resurrection.

3. Jesus' Passion and Crucifixion

3.1. The Anointing of Jesus

Jesus, in the narrative of John 12, links the anointing Mary has given him with his burial. All four gospels contain a story of the anointing of Jesus. However, Luke's account appears to describe a separate event. Differences in detail, as well as its earlier place in his narrative, point to there having been two separate anointing events, which is what I have assumed in this book.

Dr R.F. Wilson (*www.jesuswalk.com/lessons/7_36-50.htm*) points out that in Luke's version (7:36-50), the house is that of Simon the Pharisee, not Simon the Leper. Bethany is not mentioned. The woman doing the anointing in Luke is described as sinful, which is not how Mary is otherwise portrayed. She anoints Jesus' feet (as in John, actually), not his head, as in Matthew and Mark. Lastly, the criticism recorded is not about the waste of perfume/money but aimed at the woman's sinfulness. In response to this, Jesus tells Simon the parable about the two men owing money. This is not mentioned elsewhere.

J.P. Holding (*www.tektonics.org/af/femanoint.php*) points out that while John's account appears to indicate the location in Bethany as being Mary and Martha's house, this is not actually stated, only that Martha was serving and that Mary and Lazarus were also present. Simon the Leper, if still with leprosy, would have been 'unclean' and not able to serve, so would have needed someone else to do so. Thus John's account doesn't necessarily conflict with those of Matthew and Mark on that point.

Holding further argues that the anointing of an honoured guest's feet was an ordinary custom, and therefore quite likely to have occurred more than once for Jesus. The name Simon was also a common name; there were two disciples named Simon, and the historian Josephus is quoted as recording nineteen men called Simon in his writings.

3.2. The Last Supper

There is an apparent mismatch between the Synoptic and John's Gospels regarding whether the 'Last Supper' was the Passover Meal. Matthew, Mark and Luke record the disciples asking Jesus where they should make preparations for eating the Passover, on face value the Seder meal. John (18:28) would seem to indicate that the events of the trial and crucifixion took place on the Day of Preparation, i.e. before the actual Passover Meal (though the NIV footnote there contradicts that!)

Bryan T. Huie ('Was the Last Supper the Passover Meal?'), amongst others, argues that the Day of Preparation (14th Nisan) included the slaughter of the sacrificial lamb, which is not mentioned at all with regard to the 'Last Supper' meal. Part of the preparation, ordained in Exodus 12:14-20, involved the removal of all yeast from the house the evening before, a practice described by Hirsch ('Passover') and still enacted today. This would be one reason the disciples needed to prepare the room.

The phrase ἐπιθυμίᾳ ἐπεθύμησα in Luke 22:15 literally means 'with desire I desired'. It may be read as Jesus expressing having wanted to eat the Passover with his disciples but not being able to (knowing he would have been buried by the following evening when the meal would take place).

The Jewish day starts and ends at 18:00, or sundown. The night lasts twelve hours, until 06:00; the day until 18:00. (cf. "there was evening and morning" in Genesis 1.) The daytime is itself split at noon into a 'morning' and 'evening'. The phrase "between the evenings" of Exodus 12:6 most probably means 15:00, the ninth hour (of daytime), which is when Jesus died on the cross (e.g. Mark 15:34-37). This is the time when the sacrificial lambs are slaughtered. Huie points out that Josephus, in The Wars of the Jews VI.9.3, records that "the Passover lambs were slaughtered 'from the ninth hour until the eleventh'."

The narrative here therefore assumes that:

- the Last Supper was not the Passover meal itself but an early one; I modified the text after taking copious notes at a Passover Seder meal hosted for our parish by a Messianic Jewish couple in 2014; see also 'Afikomen', below.

- Jesus died in line with the time of sacrifice. He was, after all, the sacrificial lamb described by Isaiah (ch.53; cf. 1 Corinthians 5:7). Furthermore, by assuming that the disciples asked Jesus where to prepare it right at the start of the day the lambs were killed (i.e. just after 18:00 on Nisan 14), all accounts can have the Last Supper later that same evening.

Hoehner, using calendar differences, concludes that the Last Supper was a Passover meal – see the note 'Dating Jesus' Crucifixion', above.

At the apparent end of the supper, there is the comment, "Come now, let us leave" in John 14:31, which with the later statement in John 18:1 that "Jesus left with his disciples [to cross] the Kidron Valley [and enter] an olive grove", does not fit in with the other Gospels (Morris pp. 660-662, 740). The narrative here keeps the sense of John 14:31, but places Jesus' prayers in John 17 in the Garden of Gethsemane (after John 18:1).

3.3. Afikomen

Early in every modern *Seder* meal, the middle matzah (unleavened bread) of three matzot is removed from its pouch and broken in two. The larger piece, the afikomen, is wrapped in a linen cloth and hidden, for the children of the house to search for during the main meal. This hide and seek tradition almost certainly evolved much later than Jesus' time.

Which Greek word was borrowed by Hebrew for 'afikomen' is as disputed as the origin and interpretation of the modern tradition surrounding it. Any tradition at the time of Jesus will have changed after the destruction of the temple in AD70, after which lambs could no longer be slaughtered as prescribed.

Mishnah – Pesachim 10.8 declares that "It is unlawful to conclude the eating of the paschal sacrifice with a dessert." The word for 'dessert' is based on the Greek 'epikomoi '.

Other interpretations refer to 'epi komon' (a call to [go to] after-dinner entertainment [elsewhere; cf. the Mishnah in Talmud - Pesachim 199b]). These are discussed for example here:

- *www.jewishawareness.org/the-significance-of-the-afikomen*

- *www.hebrew-streams.org/works/judaism/afikoman.html#T4*

The late Jewish scholar David Daube (see bibliography) expanded on earlier work by Austrian scholar Robert Eisler and argued that the word 'afikomen' was derived from the Greek verb 'afikomenos' and meant 'that which, or he who, is coming'. Both saw Messianic overtones in the traditions that would have been practised at the time Jesus held the Last Supper.

I have tried to keep the link between Jesus and the afikomen that Messianic Jews make.

3.4. Gethsemane

Gethsemane literally means 'oil press' or 'press of oils'. Only John (18:1) mentions an olive grove; Matthew (26:36) and Mark (14:32) detail a 'place' called Gethsemane, while Luke (22:39) only talks of the Mount of Olives ("as usual"). A 'Garden of Gethsemane' is not mentioned as such.

There is a useful description of Gethsemane in Joan E. Taylor's article 'The Garden of Gethsemane: Not the Place of Jesus' Arrest', which appeared in Biblical Archaeology Review (BAR), Vol. 21, Issue 4, July/August 1995, pp.26-35. This is still available online, with an account login, at:

- *members.bib-arch.org/publication.asp?PubID=BSBA&Volume=21&Issue=4&ArticleID=1*

3.5. Dating the Crucifixion

Having looked at Jesus' birth in some detail, on reaching Passion Week, I found an even greater wealth of material and opinions about the date of Jesus' crucifixion, burial and resurrection. There are three parts to this: year, date and weekday. (Deciding on what the Last Supper was is an integral part of this debate – see that note, above.) I'll keep it as brief as possible, but be warned: others seem to have written whole books on the subject...

Hoehner's 'Chronological Aspects of the Life of Christ' provides a measured approach to the problem, starting with working out the day of the week and month, and using dates of reigns or tenure of office, determining the years that come into question. But I will start with the year here.

The year I have most often observed proposed is AD30, followed by AD33. This agrees with B.L. Cocherell's findings, whose study I have found helpful (see *www.bibleresearch.org/articles/a3pws.htm*). AD32 is proposed by some using Daniel's prophecy of 70 weeks. I would love to follow these theories through far more thoroughly, but working to a timescale dictated by living off savings while writing this, I am (probably) inclined to agree with the majority on this point. The year does not affect the narrative as the day does.

While some use the start of John's ministry in Luke 3:1-3 ("In the fifteenth year of ... Tiberius"; Tiberius became emperor in AD14) to point to an AD33 crucifixion, Cocherell quotes others when pointing out that Tiberius reigned as co-regent from AD12. "In the fifteenth year" would then mean Jesus' ministry probably started in AD27, with crucifixion in AD30. However, Kenneth F. Doig, in Ch.12 of his book 'New Testament Chronology' refutes this (see *www.nowoezone.com*). Only John's Gospel mentions three, possibly four Passover Feasts, giving a ministry time of Jesus generally put at three and a half years.

Some use timings from Acts and Paul's epistles. Cocherell mentions that King Herod Agrippa I died (in AD44) while Paul, Barnabus and Titus were in Jerusalem (Acts 12:23-25), linking this with Galatians 1:22 - 2:1, fourteen years after Paul's conversion (probably; some add the three years of Galatians 1:18). That would date Paul's conversion (in Acts 9), and perhaps therefore Jesus' crucifixion, in AD30 (or AD33). Timeline charts in the NIV Study Bible, however, place Paul's conversion in AD35.

Extra-biblical evidence does exist that would indicate the year. The darkness (Matthew 27:45; Mark 15:33; Luke 23:44) is mentioned by several early historians, notably Phlegon of Tralles. His Olympiades histories from around AD137 record "a great eclipse of the sun, greater than had ever been known before, for at the sixth hour the day was changed into night and the stars were seen in the heavens" in the fourth year of the 202nd Olympiad, which was AD33. Thallus, whose writings (~AD52) are lost but quoted by Julius Africanus (Chronography 18.1, ~AD221), also mentions an eclipse, which cause Julius Africanus refutes as an eclipse cannot happen with a full moon, which is when the Passover is celebrated. See *www.ccel.org/ccel/schaff/anf06.v.v.xviii.html*

A further method uses the mysterious events recorded in the Talmud (Yoma 39a,b) that took place over forty years before the destruction of the temple (in AD70). These are outlined for example here: *www.hope-of-israel.org/ 31adcruc.html*

Of course, the combination of date and weekday narrows the choice of year. The date of crucifixion is usually given as Nisan 14, to tie in with the slaughter of the sacrificial lamb in Exodus 12, where the phrase "between the evenings" (Exodus 12:6; Talmud – Pesachim 108a) seems widely accepted as ~15:00, the time of Jesus' death. (It is otherwise interpreted as between sundown and darkness, which would be "the next day".) Some propose Nisan 15, particularly so that the Last Supper is an actual Seder (the Passover meal). The section 'The Last Supper' looks at this in more detail.

The traditional weekday given is Friday, but Wednesday and Thursday are also proposed by several. Of course, where a fixed date falls depends on the year. Arguments here revolve around how to interpret "The Day of Preparation" in the Gospels: that of the normal weekly Sabbath, or of the Passover (and "Passover" can refer to the lamb, the Feast itself, or the whole week of the Feast of Unleavened Bread). John's "high Sabbath" (19:31) is also a matter of debate. The first and seventh days of the Feast of Preparation were also Sabbaths, so does the term refer to (1) the Feast-Sabbath, (2) the weekly Sabbath that fell within the Feast, or (3) the weekly Sabbath which was 'special' (NIV) because the Feast-Sabbath coincided with it?

Leon Morris lists (p.775) a number of events that could (or should) not have taken place on the Sabbath (whether weekly or first day of the Feast of Unleavened Bread). These include the trial and crucifixion, but also the small detail in Mark 15:21 that Simon from Cyrene was coming from the fields (NIV: "the country"); even if he had not been working there, then Sabbath rules would have prohibited him from walking so far. These things would seem to rule out Nisan 15 and point towards the Passover's Preparation Day (Nisan 14) as the date of crucifixion.

I was able to harmonise the apparent differences between the Synoptic Gospels and John (see 'The Last Supper' note) enough in my own mind to decide on Nisan 14 as the date (Jesus dies as the sacrificial lambs are slaughtered). I also accept the interpretations of 'Day of Preparation', 'High Sabbath' etc. such that I can accept Friday as the weekday.

This will not satisfy those who insist on a literal 72-hour interpretation of the "sign of Jonah" that Jesus gives in Matthew 12:40 and Luke 11:30. Admittedly, I would have liked to accommodate this. See 'Three Days and Three Nights' note, above.

My conclusion does have a twist. If Nisan 14 (when the lamb of Exodus 12 was slain) was a Friday, then (with inclusive counting of the "six days before the Passover" of John 12:1) Nisan 10 (when the lamb was selected, and when Jesus entered Jerusalem) must have been Palm *Monday!* This is not obvious from the narrative though. Using a different interpretation of "Preparation Day" and a separate extra Sabbath might have allowed for the 72 hours, and would have given us back Palm Sunday, but also made for a Good Wednesday or (my preference in this case) Good Thursday.

Hoehner (pp. 81-90) also promotes a 'Palm Monday – Good Friday' scenario (my description), but harmonises the Synoptic Gospels with John's Gospel by attributing their differences to the Galileans and Pharisees using a sunrise-to-sunrise day, while the Judeans and the Sadducees used a sunset-to-sunset day. In this reckoning, the Last Supper was a proper Passover meal.

Does it matter? Well, yes – I want a narrative that honours Jesus by being as historically and culturally accurate and therefore as widely academically acceptable as possible, and I believe that (in theology-speak) the Passover lamb was the type of which Jesus was the antitype, so I want the events to 'fit' in all aspects. But also no – any attempt at dating the events of Passion Week relies on some interpretation (long after the event) of one or other of many variables, when the most important thing is that Jesus did what he did.

3.6. Siting the Crucifixion

There is as much debate over the location of the crucifixion (and of the burial tomb) as about the date, with two main contenders. One is the present Church of the Holy Sepulchre, to the west of and outside the then city walls. The other is the skull-like rock formation (which some say did not exist at the time, e.g. E. Martin, see below) and Garden Tomb at the top of Mount Moriah, to the north of the city beyond the Damascus Gate and near the Damascus road (next to a modern-day bus station).

Of these, I am persuaded towards the latter, having read the exploration accounts of the late Ron Wyatt:

- *www.realdiscoveries.org/modules/articles/item.php?itemid=242*

- *www.wyattmuseum.com/ark_of_the_covenant_special.htm*

...and of Simon Brown:

- *www.realdiscoveries.com/article-item.php?cat=277&id=414*

The Garden Tomb site does have some problems. Some hold that the tombs there are not first century AD but from much earlier.

A third location, the Mount of Olives, was originally proposed by R.F. Hutchinson, writing in the Palestine Exploration Quarterly in 1870/1873. See:

- *www.vision.org/visionmedia/Bible.history/Golgotha.where.is.it/31293.aspx*

It was taken up by the late Ernest Martin in his book 'Secrets of Golgotha' (ASK Publications, 1988), and expounded upon by James Tabor in his book 'The Jesus Dynasty' (Simon & Schuster, 2006). See:

- *www.hope-of-israel.org/crucmessiah.html*

- *www.jamestabor.com/2012/07/24/locating-golgotha*

John W. Ritenbaugh has a useful three-part series of bible studies at:

- *www.cgg.org/index.cfm/fuseaction/Audio.details/ID/2026/Eden-Garden-and-Two-Trees-Part-1.htm (-2, -3)*

...or as PDFs at:

- *s3.amazonaws.com/cggpdf/ TFT07-06.pdf (-09, -12)*

The Mount of Olives is east of the temple and where the 'Red Heifer' sacrifice (Numbers 19:2-3,9) was burnt (Mishnah-Kodashim-Middot 1:3; 2:4). Since the priest could see the door of the hekal (inner temple) from there, the centurion may have observed the tearing of the temple curtain (cf. Matthew 27:51,54). The passers-by would have been travelling the Jericho road, which ran over a saddle between two of the three peaks of the Mount of Olives (cf. Matthew 27:39). There was the garden of Gethsemane lower down, and maybe other gardens, to fulfil there being a nearby tomb (John 19:41,42).

Hebrews 13:10-13, talking about an altar outside the camp, is used to support this thesis. This goes back to instructions given to Moses in Exodus 29:14 and Numbers 19, and to Ezekiel (43:21; note also v.1). The remaining bulk of the sacrificial bull was to be burnt "outside the camp" as a sin offering. See also Leviticus 4:12,21, 8:17, 9:11, 16:27. The parallel to Jesus' sin offering is striking, a comparison drawn in Hebrews 9:13-14.

Additionally, the non-canonical Gospel of Nicodemus (9:5) has Pilate telling Jesus that he shall be "hanged ... in the garden wherein [he was] taken".

3.7. The Wooden Cross

Writing about Jesus receiving the crossbeam (patibulum) made me wonder how much it would have weighed. I decided on an 8"x4" 7' beam, and initially chose Red, then (of course) the heavier Lebanon Cedar, widely available at the time. The latter's density of 560 kg/m3 would have given a weight of ~55lbs (~25kg).

I did also consider olive wood, having discovered that in 1968 the remains of a crucified man were found in an ossuary in a burial chamber in the northern portion of Jerusalem, dating from the first century AD. The 7" iron nail driven through Jehohanan ben Hagqol's foot was still in place. Between the head of the nail and the heel bone, remains of olive wood were found, probably a small plate used to prevent the nail pulling through the flesh. This would have been plentiful locally, and has an average density of 62 lbs/ft3 or 990 kg/m3, giving a weight of ~96 lbs (~43.6 kg). However, whether olive trees grow straight enough for beams is questionable. More importantly, they would not likely have used a crop tree.

Details of the archaeological find may be found at:

- *www.orlutheran.com/html/crucify.html*

- *www.bible-archaeology.info/crucifixion.htm*

- *www.centuryone.org/crucifixion2.html*

A list of woods may be found at:

- *www.wood-database.com/wood-identification*

Details of Lebanon Cedar were found in Exotic Hardwood's 2007 Timberline General Catalogue (NLA online) and again in the 2013-14 catalogue at:

- *www.exotichardwoods.co.uk/docs/2013TIMBERLINE-CATALOGUE.pdf*

The form of cross may well have been a 'T'-shape rather than the traditional cross (†) shape. I have followed tradition for its shape, but have Jesus carrying only the horizontal patibulum. At set places of execution, the upright stipes would have been fixed in the ground permanently.

3.8. Sacrificial Lambs at Passover

According to Josephus (War XV.9.3), the number of sacrificial lambs in later times, before the destruction of Jerusalem, amounted in a single year to 256,500.

4. Historical Sites

(See also the notes 'Sermon on the Mount' and 'Siting the Crucifixion', above.)

4.1. The Temple

Herod the Great reigned from 37 - 4 BC. Josephus (Ant. XV.11.1) states that he undertook to (re)build the temple in the eighteenth year of his reign, i.e. 20 or 19 BC. (This would date Jesus' clearing of the temple and the comment of forty-six years building work to Passover in AD 27 or 28; John 2:20.) The cloisters and outer courts took eight years to build (Josephus, Ant. XV.11.5), while the temple itself was built by a thousand priests in a year and a half (Ant. XV.11.6). The rest of the area would, presumably, have still been a building site when Jesus visited there as a twelve-year-old.

Temple dimensions are discussed in the NIV Study Bible footnotes at Matthew 4, which quote (in general terms) Josephus and the later Mishnah regarding historical evidence of the dimensions of Herod's temple. More exact references to the relevant sources are made by Prof. Barry D Smith (2010):

- Josephus (War V.5.1-8; 184-247; Ant. XV.11.5-7; 410-25)

- Mishnaic tractate Middot: (m. Mid.) – measurements in cubits throughout; see 'Measurements' note, below.

The 'holy of holies', the temple proper, faced east towards the sunrise, as the Garden of Eden and the tabernacle before it (Genesis 3:24; Exodus 26:22; 36:27; 38:13; Ezekiel 8:16).

The glory of the Lord departed eastwards from the temple in Ezekiel's vision (10:18-19). The Talmud talks about miracles of crimson ribbons turning white, and the westward of the candles in the candelabrum staying alight, signifying the presence of the glory of God (Shekinah; Shabbat 22b, Menachot 86b). Moshe Shulman (www.judaismsanswer.com/Yoma39.htm) argues against it, but could the Talmud statement in Yoma 39b, that these miracles stopped forty years before the destruction of the temple, indicate that God's presence departed (or at least His acceptance of the traditional Yom Kippur sacrifice ceased) at the time Jesus was condemned and sacrificed himself?

In the same year, the Sanhedrin moved from the Chamber of Hewn Stones to the 'Trading Place' (Middot 5.4; Shabbat 15a; Rosh-HaShana 31a). Was this due to earthquake damage? Edersheim, in 'The Life and Times of Jesus the Messiah' (Ch. 15 of the section 'The Cross and the Crown') discusses the possibility that the temple entrance lintel cracked as a result of the earthquake and fell, tearing the curtain in two. He quotes a letter from Jerome to Hedibia, referring to the 'Gospel of the Hebrews' (and regarding Matthew 27:51). For Edersheim, see Bibliography; for the 'Gospel of the Hebrews', see:

- www.earlychristianwritings.com/text/gospelhebrews-mrjames.html

4.2. Hezekiah's Tunnel

This one simply deserves its own note!

The tunnel mentioned in 2 Kings 20:20 and 2 Chronicles 32:2-4,30 was built approximately 2,700 years ago to secure the water supply for the City of David, the then Jerusalem, in case of invasion. It is five hundred metres long and links the Gihon Spring with the Pool of Siloam.

An inscription was discovered in 1880, now in Istanbul's Archaeological Museum, which describes the construction. Teams started at each end, and met in the middle of what is roughly an S-bend, though apparently at a right-angle. It is still a remarkable feat, and one for which we require laser technology (and some large drill bits), for example building the Channel Tunnel.

Water still flows through Hezekiah's tunnel today, and visitors may walk through it. My kind of sightseeing! See:

- *www.inplainsite.org/html/hezekiahs_tunnel.html*

- *en.wikipedia.org/wiki/Siloam_inscription, -/Siloam_tunnel*

4.3. Mayan Pyramids

I have not researched this sufficiently to be satisfied that all references are authoritative. For example, just prior to the publication of this book, the Wikipedia page was highlighted as needing "additional citations for verification".

The following are the pages I looked at:

- *en.wikipedia.org/wiki/Mesoamerican_pyramids*

- *www.reformation.org/mayan-calendar.html*

- *www.world-mysteries.com/chichen_architecture.htm*

- *www.webexhibits.org/calendars/calendar-mayan.html*

- *www.insteadofapes.com/Pyramids/index.html*

5. Miscellaneous

5.1. Addressing Women

In our English translations, Jesus appears to address his mother very abruptly at the Wedding at Cana. However, γύναι, "gunai" ("dear woman", as here, in the Greek vocative case) or γυνή, "gune" ("woman") was commonplace 1st-century usage (Hunt, 1998; W. H. Harris III, quoting Liddell-Scott-Jones p.363 s.v. gunhv).

5.2. Mark

It is traditionally held ("generally agreed", NIV introduction to Mark's Gospel) that the writer of Mark's Gospel is the John Mark of Acts (NIV footnotes at Acts 12:25, and intro to Mark). John Mark is a cousin (possibly nephew – Strong's 431, ἀνεψιὸς) of Barnabas (Colossians 4:10) and son of Mary, whose house was in Jerusalem and was where Peter fled (Acts 12:12). John Mark accompanied Paul and Barnabas to Cyprus (whence Barnabas came; Acts 4:36, 13:5), though left them in Pamphylian Perga (Acts 13:13), causing later disagreement between Paul and Barnabas (Acts 15:37-39). Paul later, however, described Mark as useful for ministry (2 Timothy 4:11), and they were together in Rome (Colossians 4:10; Philemon 24) during Paul's house arrest (Acts 28:16-31).

"Mark" was a spiritual son to Peter (1 Peter 5:13). If this is John Mark, and his parents' house was where the Last Supper was held (and also perhaps the Apostles' retreat in Acts 1:13), he may have known Peter from that point. Mark is documented by early church writers, notably Papias (Bishop of Hierapolis, ~AD140; quoted by Eusebius in Historia Ecclesia III.39.15, ~AD325; mentioned by Irenaeus in Book III.1.1). He is described as Peter's interpreter, and as writing down what he heard Peter preach.

Texts may be found at:

- *www.bible.org/article/introduction-gospel-mark*
- *www.earlychristianwritings.com/text/papias.html*
- *www.hypotyposeis.org/synoptic-problem/2004/10/external-evidence-papias.html*
- *www.earlychristianwritings.com/text/irenaeus-book3.html*

From the above texts it is difficult to conclude decisively that Mark the Evangelist is John Mark. *en.wikipedia.org/wiki/Seventy_Disciples* displays a list accredited to Hippolytus of Rome (~AD170 – ~AD236), a disciple of Irenaeus, discovered at a monastery on Mt. Athos in 1854. This lists Mark the Evangelist separately from John Mark (and another Mark), and therefore appears to contradict the usual opinion that Mark the Evangelist is either John Mark or the cousin of Barnabas. The same list may also be found at:

- *www.ccel.org/ccel/schaff/ anf05.iii.v.iii.html*

In favour of the link between Mark and John Mark is the odd episode in Mark 14:51-52. The young man fleeing naked (only mentioned by Mark) does not fit into the narrative except as a personal memory, a signature almost. It is quite possible, even likely, that the upper room of the Last Supper is John Mark's family home (see above), and it could be that Judas took the mob there first, before going to the garden he also knew of. John Mark would have dressed hurriedly in the linen cloth and gone to Gethsemane to warn Jesus. It is conjecture, but one that I have used in the narrative. Alfred Edersheim is one proponent of such a theory ('The Life and Times of Jesus the Messiah, The Cross and the Crown', Ch. 12 - Gethsemane).

The present narrative assumes that Evangelist Mark is John Mark, and the young man who fled naked.

5.3. Measurements

I started using metric units of distance, but was easily persuaded that to use measurements common to Jesus' time, i.e. Aramaic or Roman ones, would be more authentic. This information comes from the Wikipedia website:

- *en.wikipedia.org/wiki/Furlong*
- *en.wikipedia.org/wiki/Biblical_and_Talmudic_units_of_measurement*

A stadium or stade (plural stadia) is seen as equivalent to today's furlong, an eighth of a mile (mille, meaning one thousand), which equated to a thousand passus, double-step paces. A league consisted of three miles and was considered the distance a man could walk in one hour. (I have actually used miles throughout.)

For shorter measurements, the cubit is a traditional unit of length, based on the length of the forearm, as explained at *en.wikipedia.org/wiki/Cubit*. Surviving Egyptian cubit rods are between 20.6 to 20.8 inches (52.3 and 52.9 cm) in length, though *www.convert-me.com/en/convert/length* lists a cubit as being 18 Roman inches or 18.87 Imperial inches (47.93 cm) long. We may assume 18", about half a metre.

For units of volume see *www.jewishvirtuallibrary.org/jsource/judaica/ ejud_0002_0020_0_20697.html*

Bibliography

See note regarding website links on page 299.

AICE (American-Israeli Cooperative Enterprise). Jewish Virtual Library. Web.
www.jewishvirtuallibrary.org Hebrew: *…/jsource/Judaism/hebscripture.html*

Alden, Robert L. 'Jericho', Encyclopaedia of the Bible. 2. London: Marshall Pickering, 1990. Print.

Barnes, Albert. 'Notes on the Bible', 1834. eBook, Web.
www.sacred-texts.com/bib/cmt/barnes/index.htm

BBC (British Broadcasting Corporation). 'Richard Hammond builds a planet', BBC1, broadcast Sunday
3.11.2013. Web. *www.bbc.co.uk/programmes/b03hhqvp*

BibleWalks. 'Sea of Galilee', n.d. Web. *www.biblewalks.com/Sites/SeaofGalilee.html*

Bohlin, Sue. 'Jesus and Women', Christianity: The Best Thing That Ever Happened to Women. Probe
Ministries, 2005. *www.bible.org/article/christianity-best-thing-ever-happened-women*

Brown, Paradox. 'A Modern Guide to Demons and Fallen Angels'. Seekye1 Publishing, 2008. Print. Also
eBook, web. *www.paradoxbrown.com/index.html*

Burge, Gary M. 'Source Criticism', Encyclopaedia of the Bible. 2. London: Marshall Pickering, 1990.
Print.

Cleland, Liza; Davies, Glenys; Llewellyn-Jones, Lloyd. 'Greek and Roman dress from A to Z'. Abingdon
(UK) / New York (USA): Routledge, 2007. Print.

Daube, David. 'New Testament Judaism. Collected Works of David Daube, Vol. 2 (Studies in
Comparative Legal History)'. Univ of California at Berkeley, 2001. Print (ISBN 1882239040). Quoted
by the following: *www.jewsforjesus.org/publications/newsletter/april-2011/01*
Daube's research is also quoted by these, amongst others:
* *www.hebrew-streams.org/works/judaism/afikoman.html#T1*
* *www.jewishawareness.org/the-significance-of-the-afikomen*
* *www.cwi.org.uk/library/articles/TheMysteryoftheMiddleMatzah1.htm*

Deffinbaugh, Bob. 'The Good Samaritan', Luke: The Gospel of the Gentiles. Bible.org, posted 2/2/2009.
Web. *www.bible.org/seriespage/good-samaritan-luke-1025-37*

Edersheim, Alfred (1825-89). The Life and Times of Jesus the Messiah (1886). Web.
www.ccel.org/ccel/edersheim/lifetimes.html

Elwell, Walter A. Editor of Encyclopaedia of the Bible. 2. London: Marshall Pickering, 1990. Print. (Used
for entries where no author listed.)

Gill, John (Dr). 'Exposition of the Whole Bible'. 1746-63. Web.
* *www.hebrew-streams.org/works/judaism/afikoman.html#T1*
* *www.reformedreader.org/rbb/gill/gillindex.htm (an introduction)*
* *www.freegrace.net/gill (easily usable copy with index frame, NLA)*
* *biblehub.com/commentaries/gill*

Gottheil, Richard & Krauss Samuel. 'Xystus', JewishEncyclopedia.com. The 12-volume Jewish
Encyclopedia was originally published in New York by Funk and Wagnalls between 1901-1906,
according to *en.wikipedia.org/wiki/ Jewish_Encyclopedia*. Web.
www.jewishencyclopedia.com/articles/15044-xystus

Greenstone, Julius H; Jacobs, Joseph; Blau, Ludwig; Hirsch, Emil G. 'Phylacteries',
JewishEncyclopedia.com (see Gottheil, above). Web. *www.jewishencyclopedia.com/articles/12125-phylacteries*

Harris, W. Hall (III). 'Exegetical Commentary on John 2', Commentary on the Gospel of John. Bible.org, 2001. Web. *www.bible.org/seriespage/exegetical-commentary-john-2*

Hein, Avi. 'Via Maris', Jewish Virtual Library. Avi Hein, n.d. Web. *www.jewishvirtuallibrary.org/jsource/History/ViaMaris.html*

'Hillel.' The Columbia Encyclopedia, Sixth Edition. 2008. Encyclopedia.com. Web. *www.encyclopedia.com/topic/Hillel.aspx*

Hirsch, Emil G. 'Passover', JewishEncyclopedia.com (see Gottheil, above). Web. *www.jewishencyclopedia.com/articles/11933-passover*

Historical Boys' Clothing. 'Ancient Hebrew History', 14 Dec 2009. Web. *www.histclo.com/chron/ancient/heb/heb-hist.html*

Hoehner, Harold W. Chronological Aspects of the Life of Christ, © 1977 by The Zondervan Corporation (13 Mar 1978). Print. (Also available as an eBook published 19/7/2010.)

Holding, James Patrick. 'On women anointing Jesus in the Gospels', TEKTON Education and Apologetics Ministry. J.P. Holding, n.d. Web. *www.tektonics.org/af/femanoint.html*

Holroyd, Edmond W. Holroyd III (Ph.D.). 'Bible Coins – Half Skekel', Genuine Coins of the Bible Period. Colorado Christian University, n.d. Web. *www.ccu.edu/biblicalcoins/Bag21a.htm* NLA; see *www.edholroyd.info/BiblicalCoins*

Huie, Bryan T. Here a Little, There a Little, (Isaiah 28) Web. *www.herealittletherealittle.net/index.cfm?page_name=...*
- 'Jesus' Real Birthday', ...*Jesus-Birthday*
- 'Fallen Angels and Demons', ...*Demons*
- 'Was the "Last Supper" the Passover Meal?', ...*Last-Supper-Passover-Meal*
- 'Sons of God', ...*Genesis-6-Sons-of-God*

Hultgren, Arland J. 'The Good Samaritan', The Parables of Jesus: A Commentary, Copyright © 2000 William B Eerdmans Publishing Co. Print.

Hunt, Michael. 'The Wedding at Cana: The First Sign', The Gospel According to John, ©1998 Agape Bible Study. Web. *www.agapebiblestudy.com/John_Gospel/Chapter%202.htm*

Israel, Ministry of Foreign Affairs. 'Jerusalem – The Upper City during the Second Temple Period'. Israel MoFA, 20 Nov 2000, © 2008. Web. *www.mfa.gov.il/MFA/History/Early+History+-+Archaeology/Jerusalem+-+The+Upper+City+during+the+Second+Templ.htm*

Jamieson, Robert; A.R. Fausset, & David Brown. 'Ch.29, Nu 29:1-40. The Offering at the Feast of Trumpets' (v.39), Commentary Critical and Explanatory on the Whole Bible. 1871. Web eBook accessed 15/10/2010 at *www.ccel.org/ccel/jamieson/jfb.x.iv.xxix.html*

Jensen, Morten Horning. 'Herod Antipas in Galilee: The Literary and Archaeological Sources on the Reign of Herod Antipas and Its Socio-economic Impact on Galilee (Wissenschaftliche Untersuchungen Zum Neuen Testament 2.Reihe)' Mohr Siebeck (30 Dec 2006). Print.

John, J. and Walley, Chris. 'The Life', A Portrait of Jesus. Milton Keynes, Authentic Media, reprinted 2007 (2). Print.

Josephus, Flavius. 'Antiquities of the Jews' and 'War of the Jews'. Translated by William Whiston. Bible Study Tools, n.d. Web eBook accessed 10/12/2010.
- *www.biblestudytools.com/history/flavius-josephus/antiquities-jews*
- *www.biblestudytools.com/history/flavius-josephus/war-of-the-jews*

Kjeilen, Tore. 'The Nile', LookLex Encyclopaedia. Tore Kjeilen, n.d. Web. *www.lexicorient.com/e.o/nile.htm*

Knight, Christopher & Butler, Alan. 'Who Built the Moon?'. Watkins, 31.12.2006. Print. Web: *www.whobuiltthemoon.com*

Liddell; Scott; & Jones. Greek-English Lexicon, Ed 9. Oxford: Clarendon Press, 1940. Print.

MacArthur, John. 'Twelve Ordinary Men'. Thomas Nelson, 2002. Print. (p.135 quoted by Rev. Norman Harris. 'Nathanael Bartholomew' Temple Baptist Church, NC, 2/8/2009. Web. *www.tbcdurham.org/n/nathanael_bartholomew-0.html* NLA

MacCulloch, Diarmuid. 'A History of Christianity'. London: Penguin, 2010. Print.

Ministry of Justice. 'Compendium of reoffending statistics and analysis'. Ministry of Justice Statistics bulletin, 04 Nov 2010. Web. *www.gov.uk/government/publications/compendium-of-reoffending-statistics-and-analysis-2010*

Morris, Leon. The Gospel According To John. London: Marshall, Morgan & Scott. Copyright © 1971 William B. Eerdmans Publishing Co. Print.

Natural History Museum. 'Where did the Moon come from?'. Web. *www.nhm.ac.uk/nature-online/space/planets-solar-system/moon/origins*

Pixner, Bargil. 'Jerusalem's Essene Gateway – Where the Community Lived in Jesus' Time'. Web. *www.centuryone.org/essene.html*

Poyner-Levison, Alan (Dr). 'Born Again: A Jewish Concept', Beit Shalom Ministries, n.d. Web. *www.beitshalom.co.uk/files/Download/Born%20Again.pdf*

Rich, Tracey R., Judaism 101. Tracey R. Rich, n.d. Web. *www.jewfaq.org/...*
- 'Bar Mitzvah...', *...barmitz.htm*
- Ha-Motzi, 'Shabbat ... Ritual', *...prayer/shabbat.htm*
- Kiddush, 'Sukkot Blessings', *...prayer/sukkot.htm*
- Tefillin, 'Signs and Symbols', *...signs.htm*

Robertson, A. T. (1863-1934). Acts 12:12. 'Word Pictures in the New Testament – Acts', Christian Classics Ethereal Library. CCEL, n.d. Web. *www.ccel.org/ccel/robertson_at/wp_acts*

Scheifler, Michael. 'What Year was Jesus Born?', Bible Light. Michael Scheifler, n.d. Web. *www.biblelight.net/year.htm*

Schlenker, Bob. 'The Testimony of Gethsemane', The Open Scroll. Bob Schlenker, n.d. Web. *www.theopenscroll.com/gethsem.htm*

'Shammai.' The Columbia Encyclopedia, Sixth Edition. 2008. Encyclopedia.com. Web. *www.encyclopedia.com/topic/Shammai.aspx*

Silva, Moises. 'Mark, Gospel of', Encyclopaedia of the Bible. 2. London: Marshall Pickering, 1990. Print.

Smith, Barry D. (Prof.) 'The Jerusalem Temple and the New Testament', Religious Studies 2033, The New Testament and its Context. Crandall University, last updated 16 Mar 2010. Web. *www.mycrandall.ca/courses/ntintro/jerusaltempl4.htm*

Smith, Gordon. 'Harmony of the New Testament' and 'New Testament Story Outlined In Maps', Christian Classics Ethereal Library. Gordon Smith, n.d. Web.
- *www.ccel.org/bible/phillips/JBPHarmony.htm*
- *www.ccel.org/bible/phillips/CN091MAPS.htm*

Smith, Graeme. 'Was the Tomb Empty?' Monarch Books / Lion Hudson, 2014. Print.

Smith, Mahlon H. 'Tiberius', IHO. © Mahlon H. Smith. Web. *www.virtualreligion.net/iho/tiberius.html*

Smith, Lee. 'Uncleanness and Authority', Matthew 8:5-13. Lee Smith, n.d. Web. *www.arlev.co.uk/matt019.htm*

Smith, William (Dr). 'Gadarenes, Girgesenes, Gerasenes', Smiths Bible Dictionary. Smiths; 1901. Web. *www.bible-history.com/smiths/G/ Gadarenes,+Girgesenes,+Gerasenes*

Stott, John. 'Sermon on the Mount' ('13 Studies...') John Stott, 1987. Scripture Union, 1989. Print.

ThinkIsrael.com. Web. 'Judean Desert': *www.thinkisrael.com/Tourism_Euk/ Tourist%20Information/Discover%20Israel/Destinations/Pages/The%20Judean%20Desert.aspx?NR MODE=Unpublished*

Thompson, John A. 'Trades and Occupations – Tax Collector', Encyclopaedia of the Bible. 2. London: Marshall Pickering, 1990. Print.

Unger, Merrill (Ed. R.K. Harrison). 'The New Unger's Bible Dictionary.' Moody Press, 2006. Print.

Wassell, Charlie. 'The New Testament – John – Nicodemus', Abound-in-Faith, n.d. Web.
- *www.abound-in-faith.com/New%20Testament/John/ john%20chapter%203%20Nicodemus.htm* NLA
- *www.abound-in-faith.com/intro.htm* NLA

Wikipedia. Wikipedia, The Free Encyclopedia. Web. *en.wikipedia.org/wiki/…*

- 'Book of Leviticus', …*Book_of_Leviticus*
- 'Leprosy', …*Leprosy*
- 'Pool of Bethesda', …*Pool_of_Bethesda*
- 'Mount Gerizim', …*Mount_Gerizim*
- 'Spider', …*Spider*

Wilson, Dr Ralph F. JesusWalk® Publications. Web.

- 'Anointing by a Sinful Woman', *www.jesuswalk.com/lessons/7_36-50.htm*
- 'Confronting Demons at Capernaum', *www.jesuswalk.com/lessons/4_31-37.htm*

Wilthew, John. 'Jesus The Life Changer'. Series: Jesus in John's Gospel. County Church, 2004. Web. *www.countychurch.co.uk/articles/05_jesus_the_word.doc*

Bible References

The following index lists references for the four Gospels (plus Genesis) in order. Thus it is hoped that you may find the section in the book that corresponds to any particular passage in Scripture.

JOHN

1

2

3

4

5

6

7

8

9

10

11

12

13

14

15

16

17

18